Whispers from the Stone Age

How Knowing About Nature

and Humanity Help Can You

Be

Happier

by

David M. Gardner

Mountain Peak Publishing LLC

Published in the United States by:
Mountain Peak Publishing LLC
22 Pine St.   Suite 101
Tupper Lake, NY 12986

First printing November 2006

Cover Idea: David M. Gardner   Cover Art and Design: **Terry Lombard**
Cover Photographs: **Richard Mooney**   Author Photo: by Author

This book is dedicated to my loving parents

Lloyd and Mary Alice Gardner

and also to the memory and caring legacy of

Carl Sagan

Acknowledgments:

Many friends and family assisted with all the myriad details in producing this book, from proofreading and editing, to just believing in me. I want to thank you all, and especially:

Lloyd Gardner, Steve & Susanne Savard, Jim, Diana, & Lisa Savard, Jenda Cotton, Terry Lombard, Richard Mooney, Annie Cascanett-Roth, Jim Landry, Bill Landry, Sean Cotton, Tim Fink, Kyle & Anna Zolner, Mike & Jordy Fleischut, Eric & Sandy Berger, Keith & Peg Johanson, Lesley Waters, Elizabeth Johnson Juppe, Kinney Stires, Robert Carrano, Cheryl Snyder, Dr. Robert Chuckrow, Peter Tigh, Bob Erickson, Mike Leisner, André Pilette, Dan Johnston and all of the brothers at the ΤΕΦ fraternity

Many thanks to the gracious and talented **Dan Bern**

The official website for **whispersfromthestoneage.com** was designed by: **Curtis L. Hostetter**

As a teacher, I know the feeling of accomplishment that I've felt when former students of mine returned years later with sincere thanks and praise for the way I taught them. I feel the same way about my own High School teachers. They helped to make me a better teacher, a better writer, and a better person. I know what it means to be a social educated human.

Helen Worth – Senior A.P. English
Roger York – Chemistry, Physics
Ronald C. Longbothum – Biology
James Black – Physical Science
Robert Alderfer – New York History
David Dunbar – Music
Barb Wintermantel – Trig, Calculus
Barbara Phillips – Algebra, Geometry
Michael McCann – Regents History
Carolyn Hannon – English
Linda Monsell – Latin
Monica Deland – English
Ray Deland – Earth Science
Mary Ann Christopher – Creative Writing
John Herriman – French
James Piatt – 6th grade Science

On the banks of Allegany,
With its waves of blue,
Stands our noble Portville Central
Glorious to view.

Lift the chorus, speed it onward
Loud her praises tell,
Hail to thee, our Alma mater
Hail, oh, hail Portville.

I saw East Africa, and thought, a few million years ago we humans took our first steps there, our brains grew and changed, the old parts began to be guided by the new parts, and this made us human, with compassion, and foresight, and reason.

– Carl Sagan
from the 13th and last episode of *Cosmos*
Who Speaks for Earth?

I was born with music inside me. Music was one of my parts. Like my ribs, my kidneys, my liver, my heart. Like my blood. It was a force already within me when I arrived on the scene. It was a necessity for me—like food or water.

– Ray Charles

It is always best with me when I have the chisel in my hand.

– Michelangelo

Contents

Prologue

Everybody has desires, I certainly do—stop for a moment and think about what you like. While you can't think about 'everything', give it a shot, consider everything you like. What's your favorite food? What colors do you like? Music? Clothes? Cars? TV programs? Shampoo? Is this list endless? Well, probably not, but it can seem that way, especially when "what you like" becomes more intangible. What is it about your friends that you like? What art do you like? In a very large sense, this book is about desires, both yours and mine. Above I asked about the things you like, I could certainly also generate a long list by asking, "Well, what is it that you *don't* like?" Frankly, we have a lot of opinions about a great many things—from the whiteness of our teeth to the job that the president is doing. Things you like, things you don't like. You can determine for yourself what is good, and what is not-so-good. This book is a humble attempt to explore what it is that really makes us tick (just wait 'til you get to the chapter on sex!), both the psychology and the physiology of what it means to be human. While this sounds rather clinical, this book was prompted by a much more important and personal question—*Why is it so hard for me, and everyone around me, to be happy?*

So often we sabotage ourselves, and I started to think 'why'. Why do we cry? Why do we yell and scream at times? Why do we dislike what we dislike? Basically, I wanted answers about myself. What I discovered was the story of humanity, a story that most of us don't really know. Once you know more about humanity and the natural world that shaped us, you have a new appreciation of who you are. Things about yourself and others that have puzzled you are made more clear. Your desires are a big part of who you are, and while we quibble over the fine details (crunchy over smooth, boxer-briefs over boxers AND briefs), I believe that there are core desires that everyone on the planet shares. To love and be loved, to have good times and experiences with friends and family, to eat delicious food and drink clean water, to explore the sensations of sex.

We desire to be happy and all that entails, but there are people who are missing many of the things I mentioned. They don't love or are not loved. They go hungry or have a diet that is bland. They drink water that is compromised. They don't know the physical pleasures of intimate touching or sexual congress. Instead of happiness, they have misery. Most of us are not that bad off in comparison, but our lives are still filled with struggle and unhappiness, I know mine was, and I wanted to know why—maybe you are like me in this regard. *"Most men live lives of quiet desperation."* Why? Why? Why? This 3-letter word is the pure essence of humanity, and when we are children we drive our parents crazy with it: *Why is the sky blue? Why do I have to go to bed when I want to stay up? Why do I have to eat my green beans?* But when we get older, we graduate from school and get caught up in our adult world, we think that we are done learning, we're done asking 'why'. Don't abandon your brain, it's there to help you—unfortunately if you aren't paying close attention your human brain will lead you into lots of unpleasant predicaments. It's time to step up and assume more control, to take the road less traveled. The path is a little harder, but you don't have to blaze it, just follow the markers... I sincerely hope that you enjoy your journey.

David Gardner
May 5, 2005

Helen Keller's words:

She brought me my hat, and I knew I was going out into the warm sunshine. This thought, if a wordless sensation may be called a thought, made me hop and skip with pleasure.

We walked down the path to the well-house, attracted by the fragrance of the honeysuckle with which it was covered. Someone was drawing water and my teacher placed my hand under the spout. As the cool stream gushed over my hand she spelled into the other the word *water*, first slowly, then rapidly. I stood still, my whole attention fixed upon the motion of her fingers. Suddenly I felt a misty consciousness as of something forgotten—a thrill of returning thought; and somehow the mystery of language was revealed to me. I knew then that W-A-T-E-R meant that wonderful cool something that was flowing over my hand. That living word awakened my soul, gave it light, hope, joy, set it free! There were barriers still, it is true, but barriers that in time could be swept away.

I left the well-house eager to learn. Everything had a name, and each name gave birth to a new thought. As we returned into the house, every object which I touched seemed to quiver with life. That was because I saw everything with the strange, new sight that had come to me.

A good place to start

Helen Keller, through the power of language and writing, speaks to us now in a way and a voice that is uniquely human. Words give thought power, and writing magnifies it, shares it, records it for the ages. Her words have touched me, especially now since I am on my own quest for knowledge and enlightenment. I do not attempt to know the depths of isolation that Miss Keller experienced before her miracle moment, but I do revel in her joy of discovery and her sense of amazement and awe. When I first heard her story I was in grade-school, and it affected me in the ways that it should have. I felt compassion at young Helen's plight and joy upon her awakening and transformation—but it wasn't until recently that I read *her* words. Oh, I knew her story, but words we write are more personal, more real.

With words the barriers are down for Helen, and a woman with limited vocal talents manages to speak loud and clear inside my head. It's a type of magic, this synaptic dance. Thought pictures cascade across my brain when I read about her time at the well-house—it can't be helped, you see I happen to know what honeysuckle blossoms look like and smell like, their memory is recorded inside my head. Her written words conjure images and childhood smells of my own treks through nature. Even a deaf-mute girl speaks volumes when she wants to. It's the wonder of writing, one that *you* can relate to—*you're* reading my words right now dear friend, just as I was once reading hers. *Now I get to be in your head instead, a trick of learned language passed down to us both, though I promise to speak in a pitch as amenable as conscience dictates. It takes two to tango after all, writer and reader in their gentle reciprocating waltz of words—I'll lead, you'll follow, and we'll both smile as I try to perform this mental tryst. My success depends upon your trust, and watching for the dip, I love a good dip....*

For Helen, when you have next to nothing *(to include seeing, hearing, and language)*, learning about a vast and wonderful universe that has always been there—a fingertip's reach away and secretly hidden—must be mind blowing. And when the dust settles from that first explosion of discovery, the smiling and wonder can truly begin in earnest. Now you look at your life and your world in a new way. One discovery leads to another, and another. The ecstasy of discovery is a joy that we humans know intimately. This can be achieved with one word, *W-A-T-E-R* for Helen, but you and I who speak and hear will need many words.

I set out to learn a lot about nature, a real quest that began when I was nine, and in the journey I learned much about myself—that quest continues today. Now I can't teach you how to be yourself, but I can show you how nature has produced us, has shaped us, and is an integral portion of us from our tiniest parts to our biggest ideas. In essence, this is a story about you; it is your history and it is vast and encompasses a wonderful universe that has always been there, but hidden.

Will your mind be blown? I certainly hope so, there is actually a pleasurable response in your brain when you discover new things—we've all experienced it, almost like a little mental orgasm *(the big physical type of orgasm produces a pleasurable response in the brain as well)*. Oh dear, it appears as though I've already set the bar quite high, comparing the reading of this book to the pleasures of sex. Language and learning can be like that, stimulating, just in different ways. And besides, as recent trends indicate, sex sells; I wonder why? < *smile* > How you think and what you think is really who you are, and we think about sex, a lot. There is a reason for this. As it turns out, there are reasons for a lot of things we think and do and this book will just start to scratch the surface; your story is long and intricate, dare I say 'sexy', but entertaining and ultimately illuminating. So, time to pull back the curtain, and if possible help you to see nature, yourself, and all humanity with a strange, new sight.

Beauty, Grandeur, and...?

The words we use, including those you are reading right now, are limited. However, they are the best we have at the moment for communicating to each other our thoughts and intentions. They can be more emotive and more precise, more informative than body language. The words we use can be beautiful or ugly, warm or intimidating, but believe me when I say that even though words are many things, they are also limited. For example, let's look at the Grand Canyon.

Have you ever been? I, unfortunately, have not, but I am looking forward to my first visit. You see, I've seen pictures, I've seen slides. I've seen video footage taken from a helicopter swooping over the rim and into the pit. The images flickering across my wide screen TV looked most impressive. Words come to mind, easy words to describe what I see. These words are _'Beauty'_ and _'Grandeur'_. They certainly do the job, don't they? Can you think of better, more descriptive words yourself? You might be able to, but if you did, I say, "Okay hot shot—do it again." Go ahead, see if you can top yourself, think of an even _better_ word than before, then do it again, and again. How long will it take until you are out of words? And even if you have come up with better words, don't those words pale in comparison to the actual beauty and grandeur that is the Grand Canyon?

They are only words—look at what lies before you; there is mystery and awe and a timelessness to the Canyon. There is the blue sky touching the dark earth, there is the jagged edge of the cliff, a rictus of colored layers—some horizontal, some bizarrely twisted. There is the inexorable grinding of the mighty Colorado River, pulled down to the sea by gravity's siren call.

These are pretty good words I think, but soon they'll mean something different to me. I've written them without experiencing the Canyon, without seeing it with my own eyes, without breathing in the air and witnessing a vista that seems insanely wide. After I see it for myself I will read these words again. And then, with the images and memories and emotions within my brain I will reinterpret those words. I believe then that I will find my words completely inadequate to describe the true Grand Canyon. And yet words are all I have.

Picture if you will Helen Keller standing near the edge of the viewing platform that overlooks the scenic glory of the Canyon. It is sunset and it is beautiful, and you can see it, the beauty and grandeur, but she can't. How does this thought affect you? How would you feel standing next to Helen—privileged that you've been given two working eyes that see but sad that you cannot convey the majesty before you? *What can you possibly say to Helen, in her language of letters and words, that will be accurate enough, that will be telling enough?* But you can't leave her just standing there—to say absolutely nothing would be mean, but to say anything would also bring attention to her blindness, her inability to fully experience one of nature's wonders. You are inspired, you try, you use the words that you know and she knows, and you find them limited. And yet words are all you have.

Sometimes I feel like Helen Keller: I've been taught to read, I've smelled home-made blackberry pie bubbling in the oven, I've felt a summer shower soak my clothes, I've dreamed of flying. But there is so much more to the world than my childhood home. Helen discovered that. She was joyous in her discovery of the hidden world when she learned language, but how did she feel when she found out about the Grand Canyon? Someone had to tell her of its famous existence, it's part of every child's education—but as we've discovered today our limited words make this a really difficult job, one that's never truly accurate. How did Helen feel upon finding out about this little tidbit of visual beauty that she can 'hear' tales about, or read about, but never truly experience? Before the words came along her world was extremely limited. After the words were learned it opened up her horizons. But the Grand Canyon shows us that words can only take you so far—sometimes not that far at all when up against the wondrous. And words were all she had.

And what about me? Here I am trying to put my thoughts into words, trying to convey what I see is the beauty and grandeur of human life, how we are connected socially, organically and physically to each other and our environment. I have to choose the words you are reading, and I agonize over their choice at times. Could it be said differently? Would better words work here? Are more words needed? So, at times, I feel hamstrung, disabled by our language's limitations. And yet words are all I have, and so I am going to use them, as limited as they may be, in the most beautiful and entertaining a way that I can. If my words seem poetic at times, that's not a freak flaw, it is inspired. Thoughts turn into words, and words have structure and sound, rhythm and rhyme. I feel as though the music of the universe reverberates inside my soul, and I try to turn this cosmic music into words—not the other way around, and that is, at its best, challenging.

There is a lot of good and helpful information in these pages, but if you look closer you'll also see a symphony of written cadence and textured sounds, and what good is a beautiful concerto if no one is there to hear it? This may be a twisted artistic bend on the old '...if a tree falls in the forest...' bit, but I invoke a writer's license. I may bend, or even break, a few literary rules, but my goal goes beyond proper grammar; I wish to commune with you mentally, and musically. *My time with you is fleeting but durable; nature resonates and ripples appear in the world—one ripple gets a book printed for the trouble of thought in the language of the thinker, a telepathic sculpture of structure and theme. A gift that keeps on giving, perhaps even past my mortal time on this wandering and spinning planet.*

So I thank you for reading these words of mine, though it has been difficult choosing them, it has also been a lot of fun. Life can be that way too sometimes, difficult yet fun, as I am discovering—like a rafting trip down the Canyon perhaps, but I wouldn't really know about that, not yet anyway. Well, I better keep writing. If the river keeps its current, then why can't I? These words aren't going to choose themselves after all. That takes human thought. You're human too, right? Good, because words are all we have.

Sometimes I have my doubts of words altogether, and I ask myself what is the place of them. They are worse than nothing unless they do something; unless they amount to deeds, as in ultimatums or battle-cries. They must be flat and final like the show-down in poker, from which there is no appeal. My definition of poetry (if I were forced to give one) would be this: words that become deeds.

— Robert Frost

What's hidden

There is so much that I want to share with you through this book that I've opted to undertake a more conversational style of writing rather than a rigid and dry dissertation of theory and speculation. _(Rigid? Hardly, I want these words to flow, to move, to grab you by the cerebellum.)_ I love words, their sound and their structure—their power and potential. I also love science, and I love people—not necessarily in that order mind you. But my enthusiasm for all of these, and more, should show through my words; they're all I have at the moment as I try to communicate my thoughts more clearly. And what joy for me to get to combine many of my loves into one; this book is a dream come true—_thank you thank you thank you!_

I assure you that everything in these pages reflect my ultimate goal—to help the reader know more about their history and themselves, hopefully in an entertaining way. I want you to find a method to your madness, to uncover a power and a world that is hidden to many of us. You possess a duality of nature to include _who you are_ and _how you got here._ Tough topics to say the least, but stay brave and be enlightened; don't shy from the truth, embrace it for it shall set you free. Once you know _who you are_ and _how you got here_, then planning the next step, _going where you want_, is a lot easier and joyous—I'm living proof.

With such goals and a canvas as broad as the whole of human knowledge, I can safely say that my matters of discussion are divided into one of two main disciplines _(again the Duality)._ First, there is the physical universe that we inhabit. The part we care most deeply and selfishly about is composed of mass and energy and behaves according to certain known and regular rules. It produced the very atoms that make up you, I, the air we breathe, the food we eat—verily everything on the planet, including the planet itself. Everything large is really made of everything small, and the truly small *(Atoms)* are really a mysterious dance of energy fields that masquerade as solid matter.

E=mc² is the famous mass-energy equivalence formula after all; experiments show that when you throw a baseball, for example, something somewhat 'magical' happens—since **you added energy by throwing it,** *the ball somehow* **GAINS mass.** *Why? It's because of that 'equal sign' in the formula. The 'c²' refers to the speed of light, and that is a constant that doesn't change. But if ONE side of the equation goes up, 'E' for Energy, you 'threw' the ball after all, the OTHER side* **has** *to go up too, and nature only allows one thing to change on that side of the equal sign, the 'm', the* **mass.** *This begs the question—if mass can change so easily, just by throwing, then what really is mass? We have mass too, what does that say about us when we walk faster or drive faster or fly faster? Does our mass change magically too? What are* **WE** *really made of? Thank you Mr. Einstein, I think. You're equation is simple, the implications are not. Hmmm... Mass-Energy, Mass is Energy, Energy is Mass, more Duality to ponder...*

Your physical body is not what you think it is. You are not really solid, nothing is; it's all an illusion of perception, what our limited senses relay to us. There is an invisible hidden world not only just past your fingertips, but **IN** your fingertips as well... Some of you may have learned the facts of physics in school, some or all of this may be new to you, regardless, it is a wild ride just getting from the origins of the universe, the Big Bang, to a planet that could support life some seven or so billion years later. And then we humans come along a few billion years after that to tease the secrets out of the Cosmos.

This leads me to the second major theme discussed throughout this book—human behavior *(the Cosmos isn't all we tease).* More difficult to measure than mass or energy to be sure, there are still patterns that repeat and an assured logic applies—rhyme and reason if you will, born from our behavior.   Frankly, a person like yourself wants certain things today, that is, some things hold a higher importance in our lives than others. *What do you value? Why do you value it?* A lot of who we are was not established behind the wheel of a car, or by tapping on the keys of a computer, or from shopping for food in the supermarket. The world today is crazy and complicated and almost mystical when compared to a time before cities, before agriculture, before government and law. But the tool that we use to get about in this increasingly complex world is nothing more or less than our wonderful adaptable human brain; your happiness begins and ends with it.

I've named this book **Whispers from the Stone Age** for a reason, one that applies to you. You laugh, you cry, you love, you hate, you think, you eat, you sleep—there is a world that runs deeper than technology, and that world runs right through you. *How different are you really when compared to Stone Age humans? Are you superior? Why do you think so?* Our standard-of-living and technology may be superior, but those have been handed to you as a birthright, the way a newborn in a Lord's castle will inherit all that wealth and privilege without really working for it or earning it. A modern-day Paris Hilton and her sister, Nicky, come to mind... *And what view do we have of those privileged few?* We resent them outwardly, but secretly many of us would wish to change places with that heir to wealth. We want what we consider to be 'the easy life'—and for good reason, few pine for 'a hard life' of toil and little reward.

And what of that privileged aristocrat? That smug, overbearing, and conceited individual may actually think that they *are* better than the common man, that they themselves have risen above the masses even though it was not they, but a direct recent descendant, who 'moved and shaked' the world in order to produce the family's riches of grandeur.

Be careful how you judge them, the pompous rich, for while you have not been given money and land as a birthright, you use and benefit from a science and technology that you, personally, did not earn. Do you use roads, cars, bridges, tunnels, TV's, computers, phones, clothing, sneakers, medicine, contacts or eyeglasses? I'm not saying that someone should *give* you a pair of sneakers, but which is easier: you making a pair of sneakers from scratch yourself, or you doing some sort of labor to earn money to buy the sneakers?

This is the beauty of money, it's nothing more than a powerful flexible **modern** human tool; it can turn relatively unskilled labor into something else, something that does take skilled labor. It doesn't take much skill to pump gas in New Jersey *(State Law: no self-service gas stations; this creates jobs, supports the local economy, and gas is still about 20 cents cheaper per gallon than in New York...)*, but that attendant can take his or her earnings and buy a motorcycle; it's a beautiful symbiosis, this ability to trade— your labor and effort are turned into other 'things'. Don't be fooled though, the 'tool' of money is modern, a recent gift handed down to you, but your physical brain is not.

"Money doesn't buy happiness, but it sure 'rents' a good time!" If I only had enough money, I would be happier... This sounds like a lot of us, because most of us understand that money represents freedom, it represents wider choices. Sure I would like to buy a brand new C6 Corvette, but with my bank account I really don't have that option, instead I'm forced to buy a used 'econo-box' of a car. Will you be happy driving around an underpowered 4-cylinder 'shopping cart'? Well, that really depends on you. Who else decides the value of things? Consider the words of another blind person—it seems that when we are forced to

undergo hardship, like losing a bodily sense or two, it helps to put a perspective on the world.

> **I'm not into the money thing. You can only sleep in one bed at a time. You can only eat one meal at a time, or be in one car at a time. So I don't have to have millions of dollars to be happy. All I need are clothes on my back, a decent meal, and a little loving when I feel like it. That's the bottom line.**
>
> – Ray Charles

Do you really care that much about what your family, friends, and neighbors think of your car? When is enough money, enough money? Do Corvette owners drool over even more sporty and powerful machines? *(A point not lost to writer/director Cameron Crowe. In the opening scenes of his movie, **Vanilla Sky**, you see Tom Cruise zipping around on the empty streets of Manhattan in his Porsche. Only this is a dream sequence. After he wakes up, he gets into his tricked-out Mustang for real and drives to work...)* If you have unlimited wants without realizing your limitations, then you will always lust after things that you cannot afford. This may make you very unhappy in general and resentful of those who have a lot of cash on hand, especially if the cash was 'given' to a person. *"They inherited that wealth! They don't appreciate it, they didn't have to work for it!"* But don't forget what you've been given—your inheritance. It's easy to be a pompous aristocrat, easier than most know; they just don't recognize the true value of the wealth that surrounds them. Do you? Value is a funny thing—it changes with perspective, as you learn more. Keep reading.

If you can make the conscious decision that you are happy with what you have, then you will be. There are reasons, ones that marketers know well, as to why you want more. They push our buttons with words and advertising to tap into that human need to always want more, to compete, to prove to the world how valuable or important we are. We are manipulated *(this word comes from the Latin 'manus'— 'hand', and translates literally 'to shape with the hand')*, and the really, really good manipulators get you to do things without you even noticing. They convince you that it was *your* idea, not theirs, to hand over thousands of dollars in order to drive away with your shiny new Corvette. *(Boy, you look great in that car. I bet this is something that you've wanted for a very long time, mmmm, love that smell... How does it feel to you? Snug? Like a warm embrace? — A good salesman will sell you the feeling, the emotion, not the car. Why? Because of course you want it, **that** cannot be denied! Emotions are not rational, they just 'are', and your emotions can be manipulated with words and images and smells, without you even realizing it. They can use your brain against you.)*

Adults behave like little kids at times. P.T. Barnum, the late-nineteenth-century circus genius and salesman, has a famous quote: *"There's a sucker born every minute."* (Barnum may not have actually said this word-for-word, but he is often credited with it, and when asked about its origins the perennial salesman and consummate hoaxer did not deny it...) To this day we use the term *'Sucker!'* or *'that sucked'* to indicate someone or something that is inferior. Where did that use of the word come from? What does 'sucking', or the 'drawing in', have to do with inferiority? I believe that P.T. Barnum was making reference to a baby who was rather recently 'born' into this cold, hard, complex world, one who 'suckles' at the breast. A baby, this cute little breast-sucker, is pretty naïve about the world; a baby is easily taken advantage of. Ever play hide-n-seek with a little kid? You, the adult, can fool them pretty easily, yes? Barnum felt the same way about people; you may be an adult, but you are foolish and immature in the ways of the world, like a baby—*fools and their money are soon parted.*

There's a sucker born every minute refers to the fact that humans will always behave that way, predictably, a never ending stream of foolish rubes to replace those that were already 'used'.

Barnum saw humanity as stupid sheep to be fleeced, babes in the wood, and he was the smiling wolf with the hand in our pockets. You can trick adults into thinking they are purchasing something of value *(caveat emptor—more Latin, 'let the buyer beware')* because people want value, they want more, it's part of who we are. We don't want to think of ourselves as babies when we're all 'grown up'— though we most likely are babes in so many ways, new and wide-eyed about the world outside our hometowns.

We behave in a conditioned, unthinking, knee-jerk reacting way—often naïvely and often predictably. For lack of a better term, we behave like 'animals', not that there's anything wrong with that, we *are* animals after all, and all animals need and want things to survive, to be content. We think it's normal to want things we can't have right now, and while I say that you should have goals, you should have aspirations that you reach for and drive you upward, focusing on what you *don't* have compared to what you already *do* have is not a very reassuring and happy thought. We always want more for some strange reason. Again, enough never seems enough... *Why don't you have all these things that you want? Well, it's because of you—you haven't earned it, and you don't have the skills and talents to trade for the vast luxuries you want. You aren't lucky enough to have the money just given to you—dollar and a lousy lotto dream, right? The Lottery Commission—Barnum would be proud, they sell the dream, only a dollar folks, step right up, somebody's gonna have their dreams come true tonight, maybe, and it might as well be you... (Sucker!)*

These types of thoughts, while intrinsically true, tend to make a person miserable. Do you know someone, perhaps yourself, who complains a lot? These people are not satisfied, they are frustrated by other people and the world around them *(believe me, frustration will find you before you find it)*. And why are they telling you *(or why are you telling them)* how awful things are, how wrongly you were treated? Because we are social animals, we care a great deal about what other people think; we value this for a reason. We needed it, at one time, for our very survival.

When we complain this is really a defense mechanism for unhappiness. *"Don't you see how I was wronged? I was right in this situation, don't you agree?"* This person is trying, in their misguided way, to be happier, to deflect inadequacy and insecurity. *(French folks crossed the street when they saw Vincent Van Gogh approaching; he was very depressed, belligerent, and argumentative at times. His brother Theo wrote of Vincent:* ***"It is a pity he is his own enemy. He makes life hard, not only for others, but for himself."****)* People want the world to be fair, they expect to be treated with kindness and appreciation. Many of us put too much emphasis on other people and the external world outside our heads, we believe that what happens to us determines our happiness—where do I sit in the social standing? But if you have this philosophy in life, then you have relinquished control—you are helpless to change the world, so your misery is justified. *It's not just me, it's them too...*

Being a victim is seductive on many levels. But consider the alternative, my alternative. I cannot control the world, I can only control how I react and what I think. I decide what is important, what is valuable to me, not the world. Though I am influenced by it, I decide what to think about things and people and myself. I may not have total control of my brain, there are still secret agendas within my genetics, but all it really takes is a change in thinking, a change in values, in order to exercise more control, in order to be happier.

Let's try again to put this in perspective. Your current lot in life may not seem very luxurious right now, but look again, think about it in a new way. Albert Einstein said that 'everything is relative', meaning the value something has depends on how you look at it. *Right now, is that parked car moving? Relative to the ground it sits upon, it is stationary, but relative to the sun, it is moving quite fast in a complicated oval-like orbit. Which is true, moving or non-moving? They both are true, depending on your perspective.* Your happiness is governed by the same basic principle. For example, we take today's common 'luxuries of living' for granted. A modest family living in a modest apartment with carpeting, indoor plumbing, a television and a microwave oven, maybe even a computer, would be 'richer' than the most powerful king from a few hundred years ago—kings didn't have those things I just mentioned. Kings used chamber pots then. Kings wore animal skins to keep warm. When kings became ill the Royal Doctors would apply the Royal Leeches, lovely. *Would you like to trade places? Makes you appreciate antibiotics a little, eh? Medicine is another inherited gift for you, like money, from modern science.*

Still, there were the kings who also laughed, who cried, who loved, hated, thought, ate and slept—sound familiar? It's that crazy world below technology again, go ahead, try to not laugh, not cry, not love, not hate, not eat or sleep; good luck with that. The King and I have a lot in common with you. We all have a tendency to compare our current lot in life with the current society and culture *(money is called 'currency' because after some time it won't be valued the same, it won't be 'current')*, but it's easier to appreciate where you are now if you understand the standard of living your ancestors enjoyed; they had to live too, and without microwaves.

Heck, widespread use of tableware didn't happen until the famously fashionable French King Louis XIV decreed it to be so, for safety's sake rather than etiquette. Before the King spoke up we all carried our normal eating utensils, pointy knives, with us everywhere we went, including to dinner parties. Wine, guests armed with sharp knives, human pride—mix well and serve at room temperature; a recipe with rounded tableware is much more civilized, and safer, yes? All Hail the Enlightened King.

Today we still carry knives, and guns, in our pockets. And when I read in the paper or hear on the news of someone being stabbed or shot to death, I wonder, did the killer plan to do that, or was there some sort of emotional outburst that precipitated it? Our animal emotions can cloud our judgment in ways that work against our logical and rational needs *(you 'need' to stay out of jail; people forget that when they are really, really angry and there's a gun in their hand. Guns don't kill people, people don't kill people either, it's people WITH guns that kill people...)*, and that includes either pulling the trigger in anger or buying a Corvette out of mental euphoria. For example, if a person kills another person with a gun, how often would you hear that person say a week later, *"I'm glad I shot him, he deserved to die! If he wasn't dead, I'd shoot him again!"* Not often I would venture, but if someone did I would say, be careful Mr. Shooter, if you hold life that cheaply, perhaps someone else with a gun will feel the same way about you one day.

Don't fall into the trap of judging yourself solely by what society says is valuable and important; society is fickle in many ways. Achieving happiness and well-being is not society's job, it is yours, and you are on your own for a lot of it—with maybe some help from the family secrets, a head start so to speak, if you are lucky. If parents do not achieve this blissful state of grace though, how can they pass on the clues and winning strategies to their children? We see so many people struggle and fail to attain what they want from life, should we even try? What should we do?

We don't give up. My answer is to take a step backward, not in the terms of society or technology, but in the way we think about ourselves and our desires, our values. There are lessons that we can learn from the Stone Age that will help us in our quest, subjects that smug aristocrats and many modern humans could stand to learn. Included in the lesson-plan of a fulfilled life are assignments in humility, appreciation, love, and the need for struggle and discovery. Our Stone Age ancestors, who are only a few generations removed from us, had these things. They also had a hard, short life that revolved around hunger and disease.

Modern economics can change a culture, can lower the incidence of hunger and disease, but at what cost? Is it possible to have the luxuries of modern life *and* the humility, appreciation, love and learning struggle that Stone Age humans had in such abundance? The answer is a resounding '*yes*', and thanks to our Stone Age ancestors you already possess the tools to make it happen. You have a more important type of birthright, one more valuable than gold or land, but only if you can recognize it. You see, it's been hidden from a lot of us.

What is hidden from you lies beyond a deaf-mute's trip to the well-house and the wonders of a Grand Canyon—the spin of galaxies plays out in the splashes of water that spill between your fingers and the Canyon walls.

What is
        hidden

You look at a spider – spinning its beautiful but
delicate web and you think to yourself, how
                        amazing
Here is this little
                'being' with a little
                                body
eight legs and a tiny head,
and look at her go – building a near invisible snare
to take advantage of passing insects.
The spider seems
                oblivious to the
                                grandness of
her
        handiwork
She
keeps on working even as you
                                stand a few feet away
watching in
                awe
She
goes on about her business producing this little
piece of magic, the
                        secret of the trick
being passed
down and down and down her family line
until it gets to her. She has
                        real talents and abilities,
though they aren't recognizable as such to her tiny
arachnid
                brain
She is a miracle of nature and she doesn't even
know it. Within the patterns her potential is
                                hidden
She
        is a lot like
                you

"In a world where..."

It seemed like any other day. She woke up hungry, as you would expect a growing 3-year-old to be, but her mother took care to feed her shortly after she heard her moving around. Now it was mid-morning, and the sun shone down on them as they both walked through the forest, hand in hand, smiling as they went. They were not alone, other mothers and children were walking along the path to the riverbank too, their excited chatter bounced off the trees as the motley crew meandered slowly downhill.

The familial merriment though, the simple joy of life, was suddenly cut short. Mothers are attuned to danger, and it only took a warning motion and shout from a single overprotective *Mom* for everyone to stop what they were doing. The other mothers felt the oddness too and became scared, a stiffening that sent silent fear passing from parent to child by way of body language. They stood there like statues with senses straining—but there were no birds, no normal forest sounds. Even with their previously carefree and noisy journey, there should be at least a little activity in the woods. And now, now that they were still and quiet, listening and looking intently in all directions, everyone knew, even the little ones; *something was wrong*.

The feeling of dread grew and swept over them, and it only took one of the mothers grabbing her child in a move to return back up the path to start a stampede. Soon the silence was forgotten as they all ran back in a mad terror, toward the safest place they knew. Their fears were justified—before they reached their homes the sky had already started to darken in a way that none of them had ever experienced. It had begun—and by the time it ended they would all be dead. The mothers, the fathers, the children—they would all be gone forever.

Scenes like this one would be replayed the world over, with families struggling to survive only to find themselves killed off, some murdered by desperate men looking to save their own skin, but most dying of starvation as chaos reigns and food cannot be found. Life has become a luxury; even the men who murder, pillage, and rape are living on borrowed time. Soon they will turn on each other as resources and food become more and more scarce day by dismal day—humans on Earth seem to be fighting a losing battle as those still alive struggle, fight, and then die.

Eventually, the massive killing and dying come to an end, but when the dust settles, a census, if it could have been organized, reveals just how deadly this disaster was. There are between 1,000 and 2,000 people left on the planet, the entire planet! Now the hell that a few barely survived is transformed into a forced march through a barren Garden of Eden. The world gets knocked back to a relatively few 'Adams' and 'Eves', but they have to start over, what choice do they have? They made it this far. They are all that's left to repopulate and restart. *Things are going to be different this time...*

The above story sounds like a Hollywood movie, doesn't it? I love sitting in a darkened theatre, munching on popcorn, watching the coming attractions of next season's blockbuster hopeful. A lot of times those previews begin with a narrator's deep voice saying, *"In a world where..."*, and then they go on to describe just how different things could be in this manufactured movie-screen world, choreographed of course to the staccato rhythm of explosions, sound bites, and sexual cues. *(Clint Eastwood stands tall and asks some ne'er-do-well to 'make his day' while squinting down the barrel of a .44 Magnum revolver, and I'm thinking, hey, isn't that the most powerful handgun in the world...?)* Every few summers it seems extraterrestrials invade with the intent of killing us all. Or perhaps our doom comes this time thanks to chemical warfare from unscrupulous scientists, or maybe the Ebola virus and its cousins will rear their ugly heads—regardless of the threat, we are always dramatically saved by our cinematic heroes and heroines at the last moment, Huzzah!!

What? What's that? What if there wasn't a happy ending? Yeah, right! Sure, who wants to lay down good money to get bummed out at the movies... But wait, you might be onto something here... no happy ending... Okay, how's this, there's this guy, he's got vision, real talent see, but he also has this fatal flaw. He rejects the Hollywood stereotype and wants to make this masterpiece of cinematic excellence, but it had to have an unhappy, un-Hollywood ending. No one would touch the project; his rejection continues as his wife even leaves him. He lives out of his car for a while, but he still believes in himself, he still believes in his dream. He perseveres, he makes his own luck, and his idea gets into the head of someone with the power and clout to get the movie made. It happens, it all happens, unhappy ending included—and America loves it! The art is amazing, it takes 'Best Picture'—he has succeeded!! He has defeated Hollywood, has shown them the error of their ways. The reporters, the cameras; it's a spectacle. Oh, but get this, later, after the parties and the praise, he is alone, staring at the golden statue in his hands... That's when it hits him. He has become the stereotypical Hollywood success story, but his art is all about pain. Now that he's here, his pain, his art, can no longer be the same; it's over, and Hollywood ended up cashing in on his ideas, sucking him in by buying him out. Hollywood has destroyed his art, all in its automatic-smiling happy-ending way. "Happy ending indeed—" he says to no one. He sets down the statue and walks over to the desk and opens a drawer. "I'll give them a happy ending..." He pulls out a revolver and checks the chambers... Want to find out what he does next? It's not what you think, but then that's what makes a good Hollywood movie, the one that twists and keeps on twisting. To find out more, or to inquire about movie rights, please contact David Gardner, or his agent. Let's do lunch — and now... our Feature Presentation!   *(Cue the musical crescendo)*

    Yes, that little tale I described that started out talking about almost all humans being wiped off this planet sounds like a Hollywood movie—but it isn't. It sounds like it might be a dim glimpse perhaps into mankind's distant future or not-so-distant future, that dark apocalypse yet to come. It is not these things either. Yes, that little story I told sounds a lot like fiction, a disaster where almost everybody on the planet dies. How scary and over-the-top does a story-line have to be to get your attention? And just like a good Hollywood movie, it needs an awesome twist at the end, the big pay-off. And here comes the twist. It is not fiction; not only is this story true, but also, it has already happened. It is human history, and it is a big part of who you are and how you got here.

    Modern humans, you and I, almost went extinct; the evidence is in our DNA. Part of our story is written there, has always been written there, in code, and only now do we know how to read it. Our genes tell us that apparently we were doing quite well as a species. We, meaning us and our direct genetic hominid ancestors *(you know, the family line, with chromosomal secrets being passed down and down and down until they get to you)*, had been around for almost 5 million years, outlasting and out-competing our cousins along the way, our bodies and brains becoming ever more adapted to our survival in the wild, in the natural world.

    Our general success and improved diet led to an increased growth in numbers—it spurred the planetary population to swell to a high of around 100,000 humans as we gradually became smarter and larger. Then, around 74,000 years ago, the volcanic island chain of Indonesia shook with ultra-violence, as it is wont to do periodically. A super-volcano, called **Toba**, erupted with a fury that was greater than the 1883 Krakatoan eruption, greater than the earthquake that generated the 2004 tsunami, greater than any natural disaster to have happened in several million years actually *(a 1978 study says that Toba was the largest eruption in the last two million years. Geologic evidence indicates the eruption produced a caldera-crater 18 x 60 miles wide and an ash-cloud that may have risen 50 to 70 km into the atmosphere. The cloud contained 2,800 cubic km of ash; this amount could have covered almost ½ of the continental U.S. In comparison, the 1980 Mt. St. Helens ash-cloud measured only 1 cubic km. Some Toba ash deposits measure 1800 ft/600 m thick, over a quarter mile deep, that's a lot of ash!)*—and we were there as a people to bear witness to it, to suffer globally from it.

We experienced the eruption intimately as it killed about 99% of us and extremely affected the 1% or so that remained. It's ironic that the intense heat of explosion led to the global cooling and drying of Africa that changed us as a species and forged us into who we are today. Ultimately, this brief cataclysmic time period made us great, but in the short term it didn't seem that way. Growth and pain often coexist—the *'crucible of travail'* being far from pleasant for us then; death was the norm.

Evidence of the eruption lies buried within the Earth's geology and within your own genetics. The ash produced by the super-massive eruption would enter the atmosphere and circle the globe. The skies would darken as sunlight, precious life-giving sunlight, would be bounced off the microscopic ash particles and back into space, their heat and energy lost forever *(planetary reflection of light energy is called the 'albedo effect' [al-BEE-doe])*. The ash and sulfur dioxide gas in the volcanic plume is very plentiful and very light—they are spread by global winds until the toxic cloud encircles the Earth, covering it in a ghostly but deadly shroud. *(Sulfur dioxide mixes with water in the atmosphere to form tiny, shiny, mirror-like spheres, also good reflectors of energy.)* It doesn't take long for things to start getting colder and drier, and colder and drier still. One by one plants die, animals die, humans die.

If you were located thousands of miles away, in Africa, would the change have been sudden or gradual? No one really knows for sure, the physical evidence points toward gradual, but all we know for certain are the end results, not the rates. The ash would eventually fall from the sky, most likely after years and multiple trips around the globe, and collect on the bottom of the Indian Ocean, and other places, in a thick geologic layer of evidence to the eruption's ferocity. By using DNA mutation analysis we can also see what it did to us as a species, how it almost killed us off. How lucky you are that you weren't there at the time—your odds of surviving would have been poor, only around 'one' in a hundred, the same as everybody else fighting and struggling to become the 'one'. And then, when the volcanic dust finally settled, the thousand or so humans left alive could start over, and they did. That one thousand or so would eventually become the six billion of us that are walking around today, and while this story does sound like Hollywood fiction, again, it is not.

Who we are, everyone on the planet today, stems downward in a direct line to those survivors, to a bottleneck in human history. It is my story and it is your story, and it is only a part of the epic, but it is such an important and critical part. That volcanic explosion produced the Modern Human you see today. It produced 'us' in all our glory and shortcomings, honing the strengths of an earlier and different time; some of these 'past strengths' might be considered design flaws in our current present, in many ways today we are like fish out of water *(but don't realize it—humans, however, want more than to 'just breathe', they want to be happy, too)*. Regardless, we had little choice in the matter then—we would not be here to argue this point without the eruption. And now we have to play the cards that are dealt to us—I say it is better to play with knowledge and skill, wouldn't you? What if I told you that part of the deck is stacked? You better shuffle and pay attention, you cold lose your shirt, or life, if you're not careful. There are some hidden wild cards too...

What would the world and the human landscape be like if we were never globally challenged as a species? Newton and Einstein, you and I, would never have been born—the world would have changed. You, personally, are lucky that that explosion tried to rip apart our species. You, personally, are lucky that your grandparents met when they did in order to produce your parents. You, personally, are lucky that your parents met when they did in order to produce you. You, personally, are very, very lucky indeed. I've heard it said that sometimes *"It is better to be lucky than be good"*—this is one of those times. Congratulations, you just made it to 'the new world', you are the ultimate lottery winner, now what are you going to do? Intelligent life, the ultimate winnings... Boy, I could sure go for a donut right now... jelly filled...

How much longer would it have taken us to develop language, clothing, and mathematics without the eruption? Ever since I heard about this defining 'choke point' moment in human history and how its effect was recorded within the language of human DNA mutations, I've been fascinated. I could see logically that a large part of human behavior and success today is directly attributable to that near extinction. That event shaped us, molded us, and ultimately changed our species overall for the better, at least in a creative-intelligent sense. Eventually I would learn of even more tantalizing bits of the human saga from the time of the eruption *(~70,000 years ago)* until the time of agriculture *(~15,000 years ago)*. It was during these years that Stone Age humans, our direct ancestors, would conquer the globe, and they did it all as hunter/gatherers without the aid of agriculture.

How do you conquer the world without growing food? The answer, and the evidence, makes me smile. Who I am, the basic pattern that plays out producing my life, was laid long before I was conceived. I was born a Stone Age man, genetically identical to those 'primitives', but I've taken what some believe is the next step in human evolution. I understand myself better, and I've developed my ability to shape reality and my life with more confidence; in other words, 'I' am in control now. The environment today *(societal as well as natural)* and my genetic programming can try to push me around, but I am wise to their game. I can play by their hidden rules and win. I can be happy in the face of adversity because while the environment and my initial programming, the DNA, doesn't change quickly, how and what I think, can. I have the advantage because I found an advantage—and then I learned how to use this to my advantage over time, and soon you will too. *(Confused? It's all about the thinking...)*

I have a great history and legacy, and now it's time to use it to my benefit, to include having a lot of fun along the way. I wouldn't be alive or be able to make this great leap if not for that ancient Indonesian eruption, and for that I am extremely thankful. We are all here because we are lucky, regardless of whatever skills and intelligence we might possess. And it wasn't the first time that the planet or solar system rolled the cosmic dice to determine not only our survival but also our very existence—the Indonesian eruption was just one of the more recent, and it came at the perfect time. We were ready then as a species to be challenged. After the pain would come the healing. There is an old saying that I really like, *"That which does not kill us makes us stronger."* – Friedrich Nietzsche   We weren't killed as a species and we emerged better than ever. Years later I came across another ideology that has stuck with me and reflects the same sentiment. It came from a man named Conrad Hilton (yes, that Hilton) after he successfully built some hotels; he built them out of wood. I'll paraphrase his philosophy: *You need good wood to build with, but the best lumber doesn't really grow with ease, if the wind is strong, then so are the trees.* You can rise above adversity; we did it as a species, and those lessons remain buried deep inside you, hidden until you tap them. You think you have it tough? You don't really know what tough is. It's all relative. Get ready. The wind blows sometimes—you can't stop it. But you can learn to harness it.

Welcome to the Dark Side–watch your step

We try to avoid struggle, as life is harder and less happy under those conditions, and who wants to encourage more hardship? However, when you endure hardship and survive, you are stronger. To grow strong you need to be challenged. Negative aspects of your life can be turned around to your advantage, _(there's that word again)_ if you let them. All it takes is a bit of brain gymnastics to cause a change in your thinking; something technically called a 'paradigm shift' _[PAIR-uh-dime]_. Consider the hands-off alternative of naïveté—you can do nothing and watch mutely as negatives turn against you, rob you of your happiness, or you can learn to accept negatives, analyze them logically and turn them around. A change in thinking can really pay off. You get to understand your flaws and see them repeated in others. They are too blind to see it, but your eyes, and mind, are open.

The United States government is the 'brain' of this country, which, as you probably know, is not perfect and sometimes seems a scary place. Politicians operate under a carefully constructed and written code of laws that are also not perfect, but our Founding Fathers understood, at least partially, the folly of men. Our governing laws remain under scrutiny and at times they are revised or eliminated. Changing the law happens when you change the words that are written. Now it's true that we have the Supreme Court to interpret sometimes what the wording means, but the fact that they are written down gives them power, it gives them tangibility even though they represent ideas.

You operate _your_ life under carefully constructed laws as well, only your laws are a bit more intangible; they are the thoughts, beliefs and morals that reside inside your head. _Have you ever written down what you believe to be_ *right and then analyze why you believe what you do? Have you ever? What are your 'Personal Laws'—the Laws of 'insert-your-name-here'? Careful, don't break your own laws...* Chances are you haven't because there doesn't seem much reward in it at first, most likely for two reasons, possibly three if you're honest with yourself—and that's easier said than done.

One: You don't see the value in it. You know what you know, and frankly you don't have to write down something you already know, right? Two: Who has time? My life is busy after all. And three: Fear. If things change, I could be worse off. It's more comfortable to *not* challenge what I already think is secure, what I've already learned. Writing them down gives them power, perhaps too much power, because what happens if they are wrong? Do I have to amend my own personal constitution?

What do you value? You have to make decisions, you have to decide what is important. And this is a job you cannot avoid, all animals do it and you're an animal too—we make judgment calls all the time. We need to because it is a part of who we are, some wrong decisions can kill you after all. *(I'm not that drunk, I'm okay to drive...)* However, in our heads we are judges without the benefit of written law. Oh, we have guides to help us along our journey—we have the gentle and good precepts of religion and the words of the Koran, the Bible, the Buddha and the Torah to light our way. True, they are written words, but they are not enough. Those good words do not remain pristine and perfect on their paper, they go inside our head where they have to be analyzed and remembered in an organic, unwritten way that connects those words and puts them in conjunction with everything else you've learned—and that is a lot, much of which could be inaccurate or unhealthy. Perhaps the gentle words get twisted, perhaps they are flavored by your childhood or the types of parents, or lack of parents, that you had.

A good example of this is Adolph Hitler. From what you know and what you've learned about him to date, what do you see? A madman? An incarnate of pure evil? As awful as Hitler turned out, what do you know about how his internal values were formed? Did you know that he had a lot of help getting all twisted? He didn't do the job by himself. All most of us ever see is the surface, and that includes when we look at ourselves as well as at Hitler; but if you look a little deeper, if you use that wonderful brain of yours to detach yourself and look at information in a more logical, analytical, dare I say 'human' way, then you gain more insight.

Our developed frontal lobes allow us to do this better than every other animal on the planet—humans are emotional, but they are also rational and logical, if they want to be. You just have to value that more, even at times when it is painful. You decide the value of everything, but you've also been influenced, many times without even knowing it: by your parents, by your society, by your genetics. There is a Dark Side to being human. We think it's hidden, but it really isn't. It's there for all to see—you need only to look for it.

The United States military wanted to use Hitler's behavior against him somehow, to gain an advantage from the man himself. About two-and-a-half years before he committed suicide at the end of the war, they did an interesting and unique thing, a thing never before attempted with a world leader. They created a psychological profile of Adolph Hitler. Police departments of today know the value of trying to get inside a killer's mind to uncover who they are, where they are, and what they are going to do next. It's about habit and prediction, in a word, behavior, but there had to be a first, and it was Adolph Hitler. And while a profile doesn't always bear fruit, sometimes with hindsight we find it eerily accurate and tremendously helpful. Why? Because behavior in all organisms, from hummingbirds to Hitler, has patterns. There is cause and effect to all things—there are connections that may be hidden, but we are intelligent enough, and persistent enough, to uncover them. Science is about details, it is about information. Seek and you shall find.

The military and police have a very specific mission: to win. And you don't have to be fair either. I am just beginning to understand that old adage, *"All is fair in love and war"*. In battle, it's okay to have an advantage, because you want to win, and your enemy is not going to fight fair. Those among you who have played the Parker Bros. board war-game *Risk* know what I am talking about. There is risk in attacking the enemy, you can be defeated after all, but the risk is a lot less if you have twenty times the armies. Is it fair that a country with a huge army can invade and take over a neighboring country with a small army? *(Iraq invades Kuwait, U.S.S.R. vs. Afghanistan, The U.S. Army vs. The Cherokee Nation)* No it isn't fair, but that's the way real war, natural selection, and the board game Risk, operate. Concentrate your forces and overwhelm your enemy to achieve victory with minimal losses, hence our mass landing in French Normandy on D-Day, which worked. *(We tricked the Germans into thinking we were landing at closer Calais—they sent troops there instead.)* It is a sound warfare practice, even though it's not technically fair to the enemy, but we're talking about 'kill or be killed' here. *(Gentlemanly ethics give way to winning at minimal cost— proper British Redcoats also didn't like the fact that 'uncivilized' American Minute-Men fired their muskets from behind the cover of trees instead of the middle of a meadow. War is hell.)*

Even before that European invasion could be conceived, the U.S. military was trying to gain an advantage against Hitler. They wanted to know how he would react if the tide of war changed, because it would when America entered the fray; how would he *behave* if he started to lose?

Could we use his own weaknesses against him? To do this, 'Wild Bill' Donavon *(who ran the OSS, a WWII forerunner to today's CIA)* brought in an expert on behavioral psychology.

The expert himself, a civilian *(Walter C. Langer)*, did not see the value in doing this, but the military felt otherwise. Know your enemy completely is their credo. This could include knowing how an enemy developed the values that they hold, what makes 'a man tick' so to speak. Toward this effort approximately five months were spent in tracking down as much information about Hitler's youth as possible.

The relatively young theory of Dr. Sigmund Freud's, that an individual's personality is formed in their early years, was applied to Adolph Hitler. This was difficult to do at first because Hitler the Dictator and megalomaniac had done a very good job of eradicating almost all records of his youth. All psychologists had to go on at first were Hitler's published writings and speeches, and these sources were poor in explaining the details of how he was raised. Then researchers hit upon the proverbial goldmine.

When Adolph was a young boy, his family, like most families, had a family doctor. They needed that doctor a lot; Adolph's older three brothers had died as young boys and Adolph himself was rather sickly and weak. Ironically, the man who prescribed medicine that may have kept young Adolph alive was a Jew, Dr. Eduard Bloch. This family doctor, who saw the open and intimate details of the Hitler household, left Austria when Germany annexed it in 1938. Imagine the psychological researchers' incredible fortune to find out that Hitler's boyhood doctor was living in The Bronx.

And what a treasure trove of information he turned out to be. After the interviews with this man a new picture of Adolph Hitler emerged. Yes, it was already known that his older brothers had died, and yes, it was already known that Adolph's father, often drunk and belligerent, had also died when he was a teen—death surrounded the boy—but very much about his mother remained a mystery. That all changed. Here is, paraphrased of course, what the researchers discovered.

Adolph was *adored* by his mother. This is not surprising given the fact that she had already lost three sons to illness. Here was her Adolph, her only son, still alive. In response, he retuned his mother's intense affection to the point that it was also extreme and unhealthy. With a domineering and belligerent father in the picture, a classic Oedipal Complex, as described by Freud, would be cultivated. Adolph despised his father and loved his mother. *(An important point in Ira Levin's Nazi cloning thriller, **The Boys from Brazil**.)*

His mother also exerted an overt and extreme cleanliness in their household. The doctor described 'housecalls' he made *(Mrs. Hitler suffered from breast cancer, Dr. Bloch would arrive and administer daily injections)* where he was amazed at the absolute lack of dirt anywhere—no dust, no fingerprint smudges, everything as pristine as could possibly be; it was unnerving. This may be as a result of the earlier sons' deaths—*to be clean is to ward off further sickness.* It may also have been a compulsive behavior, one that extended to cleanliness of the body, to include the genitals *(something that we know today could produce an 'anal retentive' personality).*

Adolph Hitler, as an adult, is deathly afraid of the venereal disease syphilis and mentions it often in his prison-penned manifesto, **Mein Kampf** *(My Struggle or My Sorrow).* This also reinforces the idea of a mother with an abnormal and unhealthy need to be clean; she was molding her son, infusing him with her fears. Today this might be labeled as obsessive-compulsive disorder, or **OCD** for short. *(Actor Tony Shalhoub has gained fame, and television Emmys®, playing the fictional 'defective detective' Adrian Monk, a modern day Sherlock Holmes with this mental* *disease. From a non-fictional standpoint, director Martin Scorsese depicts a young Howard Hughes being bathed and warned by a germ-worried mother in his movie,* **The Aviator.** *Most people have heard that Hughes was a bit 'kooky' concerning personal hygiene, now you know why. It was his mother, his role model in life, who greatly influenced him.)* In addition it was later speculated from interviews of aides and hotel staff that Hitler's 'alone time' with women, to include his main mistress Ava Braun, was spent in sexual activities that did not culminate in sexual intercourse. Hitler's fear of syphilis, and 'uncleanliness', could easily have driven him to this paranoid state *(being 'disinterested in physical sex', or being 'asexual', is also a result seen sometimes in anal retentive individuals—sex is dirty and forbidden).*

His mother may have seen young Adolph, as sickly as he was, as a gift from God, chosen by God to live for some higher purpose—to do great things. She filled his mind with her grand thoughts. The boy could grow to be a man who would see himself as the most important leader on Earth, able to lord over it all. God Himself *(I doubt Hitler's God was a woman)*, after all, had chosen him and the Aryan Race, to do it.

When Hitler's mother died, the doctor reports an outpouring of grief—the depths of despair the likes of which he has never witnessed. Her love for her sickly boy was consuming and unconditional; adoration is not a strong enough term for what she felt for Adolph, and he pined for her and her emotional support. Hitler would pursue that same complete fawning from the German people—*Hail Hitler!* And the German people gave what Adolph Hitler craved, the love and devotion that his dead mother could no longer supply.

Because his mother viewed him with the eyes of perfection and destined greatness, it was hard for Hitler to see flaws in himself. His refusal to believe that he possessed flaws is called denial. Problems in his life must come from an external source, not from within. It was an easy thing for him, and a lot of a disaffected and economically destitute Germans, to project their problems onto the Jews, the Gypsies, the homosexuals—anyone not seen as pure, as God's chosen. The cleanliness of Hitler's childhood, force-fed by his mother, would manifest itself as a cleansing of the human population. This vision of perfection and dominance would incite and rally the German people around him, fueling his need for love and acceptance.

The psychological report went on to make some bold predictions based on this information. If things turned badly for the German effort, Hitler, the lover of limelight, would make fewer public appearances. He would not be able to endure the criticism and doubt of his people, both of which would increase when the Germans started losing. This dissatisfaction would also spread to the German military, precluding a possible assassination attempt. With uncanny accuracy both of these predicted behaviors occurred. _(Incidentally, when Hitler survived the bomb placed in his private bunker, The Wolf's Lair, this reinforced the idea that he was invincible, protected by God—a divine acceptance provided an overruling of any human rejection of him, his ideas, or his leadership.)_

In his mind he cannot see anything other than an image first supplied by his mother—someone who was always right, someone who always deserved love and devotion. It was also fatally predicted that when the war's conclusion came, Hitler would allow Germany to burn to the ground before he committed suicide. Defeat, to include capture and humiliation, would ruin his version of reality. In the end, the German people let him down by losing the war; let Germany burn as a punishment for those who lost faith—the 'Great Dictator' thought they deserved it.

Adolph Hitler was a boy who did not learn to handle rejection thanks to an overprotective, possibly mentally ill mother. As an adult, the unhealthy and extreme positive self-image of himself would lead to denial and projection, and global anguish. In a sense, the boy never grew up, never accepted his flaws. Later, when he came into power, any rejection of him deserved to be met with death. In the end the world, and his people, rejected him, and for a person who cannot handle rejection or personal imperfection, his own death was the only way he could escape. Hitler took cyanide and then shot himself—even the double method of his suicide was extreme.

So, why speak of the horrors of Hitler? Surely you and I have no real connection to that monster. But there are connections, ones that we don't really want to look at, the ones that expose our own flaws. But here is your chance to do what Hitler could not, to face them and diffuse them. You don't have to succeed at another person's peril, although that is easier at times.

Public schools are rather new to the human species. Thomas Jefferson thought it was a very good idea to educate the citizens of tomorrow, how else would they be able to elect qualified representatives in this 'new representative democracy'? The Federation of the Five Iroquois *[EAR-uh-kwoy]* Nations might have something to say about the 'newness' of our form of government in North America, but Jefferson helped pen the Declaration of Independence and the Constitution; he wrote down the words so he gets credit, not the Iroquois. They got something else besides credit and good wishes. They got the Dark Side of human behavior. The Mohawk were fierce and fashionable, and smarter and happier than most of us give them credit for, but all we saw at first was how different they were. We were better than them with our gunpowder and written word, with our golden coins and blackened hearts. Sounds vicious and cruel, doesn't it?

Surely we are more civilized today—that time of musketry and savagery was so long ago. Let's take a stroll down the hallways of today's modern public school. I know them intimately because I was a student in those halls at one time, creating my own life out of adolescent chaos like a lot of you, but I've also walked them as a teacher who can witness and see kids behaving badly with a clarity earned through age and experience. The halls can be a vicious place, just like New York's Mohawk Valley of yesteryear.

There is no written law of the hallway and classroom. Oh, there are the school dress codes and behavior initiatives *(Fighting on school property earns an automatic 3 day in-school suspension for the first offense, for the second...)*, but I am talking about the business of life, of social circles, of humanity; and it can be cold and cruel.

A 'new' girl walks down the hall. She comes from another part of the country so her accent sounds funny, and she dresses differently—*and her hair, what's up with that hair? Can you believe it, here is what I heard about her...* And the whispers start. The new girl can hear them, and soon the snickering gets louder, soon they want her to hear them talking about her, they want to see her cringe in fear. There are no written social laws in the school *(or the work-place, or the community—though school is the more cruel, kids are in more control than you'd like)*, there is only the unwritten law of the group, you are either in or you are out, and if you are out, then you are not one of us.

The group leaders sense this as an opportunity; they pick on the outsiders, verbally chastising them within their clique. The followers in the group sense this as an opportunity to get inside the good graces of their leaders; they join in on the ridicule, the put-downs, and soon also the stares and name-calling. And what can our victim do? They are small and relatively defenseless, here a whole population is after them.

They start to feel depressed as they become everyone's popular victim, doomed, without recourse *(like the Jews, the gypsies, the sexually deviant)*. What should they do? Go to the principal and say, *"They're picking on me!"* And if something is said to those offending Alpha Males and Alpha Females about their poor social behavior, they can't really be punished as they've broken no written laws, and as a result when the cruel students return to the halls the snickerings will increase, not decrease. They've really gotten under the skin of the new girl now—the principal's lecture to them has proved it!

There is no law forbidding the cruelty of bullies, and people with power tend to use it, not deny it. Do the easy thing. Single out those different individuals and make sure they know that they are inferior. Establish and maintain dominance. It's the easiest thing in the world to be mean, to single out the different, to ridicule and revel in the delight of another's discomfort. In essence, there are a lot of little Hitlers running around our schools. Hitler's evil is not the exception in this world—it is everywhere, he didn't do the job alone. It seeps in and controls us because its power, the social power of the group, is so intoxicating, it is so invasive, it's such a big part of who we are and how we got here.

Maybe there is some individual in the clique who knows that what they are doing to the new girl is wrong, but he can't speak up now. He is part of the dominant group, if he speaks out in the new girl's favor then *he* will be the one who is ridiculed, *he* will soon be cold and lonely on the outside looking in, an outcast standing where the new girl is now. No, acceptance in the group demands that you be mean, even evil in your thoughts and actions at times. It's okay for her to be laughed at, but it's not okay for him to be the pun. This is an extremely selfish way to view your world; it's very un-loving, un-accepting, un-dignified. It's very *Hitler-esque*, don't you think?

The Dark Side is there for a reason—social survival. We are still Stone Age savages and behave that way even today, driven to ensure our own survival at the expense of others. This is easy to do, especially when the others are considered outsiders. *What's that? Not everyone behaves in this manner?* Sure, there are the Little Darlings that attend classes, but don't forget the Little Demons, and the Demons are going to rule the school; they like power, they flaunt it and use it. The Demons are going to have the Darlings for lunch. Just like Hitler and his 'in-crowd', you know, the prettier, the smarter, the more athletic Aryans. *(The 'Church' is known for promoting acts of kindness, but they didn't really challenge the fascists—the Angels apparently feared the Demons...)*

I once taught at a very large public school with over 600 students in each graduating class. Thousands of students had to pass through the 'student' lunchroom in shifts around noontime during the school day. My classroom was at the far end of the building, and I ate my lunch (from a brown paper bag) in the small teachers' lounge located there. It wasn't until a few months after I first started this job that I happened to be strolling by the cafeteria shortly after the students had finished their 'eating', though what I saw made me stop and stare.

The lunch tables were glorified picnic tables, made of metal above with attached benches on the side that fold up and also sturdy wheels below to ease maneuverability. Well, the maneuvering would have been easy, if not for the piles of food and garbage on the floor. And when I say piles, I mean piles. I watched as the custodians wheeled the tables carefully out of the way. Then they got out the snow shovels, yes I said 'snow' shovels, and started 'shoveling' the food and garbage to one side of the room. I couldn't believe it. The place looked like a disaster. I stepped up to one of the workers with a confused look on my face.

"Did something special happen in here? Where did all this mess come from?" I was thinking *food fight*.

The custodian looked at me and just shook his head. "Nope, we do this everyday. This is normal. It's the only thing we use these shovels for." The shovels were quite disgusting by this time.

Now high school children could be appreciative, they could be considerate, they could be nice, they could take all of their uneaten food and garbage on their tray to the trash cans when they're finished eating. Really, how hard would it be to do these things? Apparently very hard. Apparently it's much easier to be mean, to be cruel, to laugh as you dump the remains of your lunch on the floor. Someone else will clean it, they're paid to clean up after me. And besides, everyone else is doing it, look at the mounds of garbage already there? The Dark Side of humanity is that it's easy to be mean, it's easy to be cruel, it's easy to be part of an anonymous in-crowd. Hitler lives in the lunchroom, too.

There is no law against being cruel in the school. Selfishness and cruelty combine to form a powerbase, one that intoxicates, one that comes from our Stone Age ancestors, one that needs to be addressed with thinking, real human thinking. This callousness toward others, toward outsiders was needed before, during the time of the eruption thousands of years ago, but is it so needed now? What our students really need is a paradigm shift, to do the right thing instead of the powerful and popular thing. But that could open an individual up to social pain, because not everyone is going to be 'on board' with this plan. "It's better to keep the status quo..." they'll conclude. I can say with confidence that 'Social Cruelty' *(the modern term for 'Bullying')* will never go away in public schools.

The Dark Side will be preserved because it is who we are, it is our normal behavioral condition, and has been so for thousands and thousands of years. If we were in the in-crowd, would we follow our natural tendencies for social *acceptance* from our leaders and friends at the expense of others, or would we strive for social *excellence* and stand up for what's right and good? *(I recently heard from a single mom about her 'above average intelligence' pre-school-age* daughter. *Other children started picking on the girl at daycare because she was smarter, so she started to act dumber on purpose, to be better accepted by the group—her observant mom noticed this and took action, she taught her daughter otherwise. It starts young. Why pick on a little girl because she was smarter? It's not the fact that she was 'smarter' that the offending kids glommed onto, it was that she was 'different', that's all it takes.)* No, the paradigm shift that sounds so nice will not happen any time soon, there is too much social risk for groups of children and adults alike, too much fear, too much social standing to lose. The paradigm shift has to happen within you, the individual—it's going to take a lot of time for the human race to learn *not* to be cruel, more time than you have right now I'm afraid—World Peace is an unattainable pipe-dream, we're too hung up on our Stone Age differences. Right now we can only fix one person at a time. *(But we can print a lot of books and reach a lot of people, you know, to speed up the process... Tell your friends! Go to **whispersfromthestoneage.com**)* You can't control the Dark Side of humanity, but you can make a change within yourself. You can do the right thing, if you decide to, if you find that more valuable.

What is it you value? Why do you value it? Be honest with yourself, have you ever ostracized? Do you like to ridicule a person or a race? Do you tell ethnic jokes or laugh at ethnic jokes? Why do you do it? Is the Dark Side hiding within you, too? Don't be surprised if it is. Recognition of your flaws is not something you should shy away from, though most of us, given the chance, would find them easier to ignore, just like Hitler did. If only he could have seen how weak he really was. Looking in the mirror is hard when you don't like what you see, but a change in thinking can help with that. There is hope, we can evolve rather than devolve. When you look honestly and sincerely at your own Dark Side, and you do have one, then light and logic are shed upon it.

It's high time for more illumination in your life. See the reason that people, even you, can be cruel and selfish. Don't be shy, understand why it's there—that's your new paradigm shift acting out, your change in thinking. Shine a bright light of focus and human thought on how you behave and how others behave. Society has classes, it has layers. They exist because we perpetuate them. And they're strong, these layers, rock solid—but even solid rock is washed away; a river cuts its canyon exposing the layers, the history, the hidden structure. This book is like the river, giving off energy to change, and you are a pebble washed free from the bedrock of societal dogma. You tumble along, on an adventure, bumping into the sides and other pebbles along the way. Where will you come to rest? Will you come to rest? How long is this river anyway?

Darwin needed to get out more

or

Why size does matter...

How do we know so much of our dramatic story? Well, as I've alluded to, evidence in our DNA was the first clue that a human disaster of global proportion occurred. I will discuss a little of what we know about DNA in this book, both generically and specifically, but the reader is encouraged to find out more if they are truly interested. A well-written and entertaining source of genetic information is the 1992 book and National Best Seller, **Shadows of Forgotten Ancestors,** by Carl Sagan and Ann Druyan. They do their usual excellent job of explaining one of the most complex life processes without the use of muddling mathematics. You don't need to calculate the 'standard deviation' to appreciate what goes on inside your cells.

Charles Darwin could have used the science of genetics in the worst way to defend his ideas. He, like everybody else, was clueless that the genes, DNA, passed information from parent to child. *(Living at the same time as Darwin was **Gregor Mendel**, 'the Father of Modern Genetics'. Gregor was an Austrian monk who became a priest, but before he was either of these he was a gardener first. One day he wondered about the variety of peas growing in his monastery's garden. Some peas were 'born' wrinkled, some smooth. Why?)* At first Darwin didn't know what drove evolution, he just knew that there was all this variation, these 'differences' between individuals as well as between separate species. What Darwin stumbled upon was a crime scene; he had to piece together what happened after the fact.

He had no idea that genes were passed along via sex prompting variety. Would he have been shocked to find that one of the smoking guns of diversity could be found inside his own pants? As a scientist who studied biology, probably not.

While genetic material provides the blueprint for life, the main mover and shaker in the world of evolution is the environment. Organisms from bacteria to trees to leeches to humans all have to exist in the environment, in 'nature' if you will. They have to be born, take in energy, excrete waste, mature, reproduce and then die. Yes, death is one of the successful parts of evolution; the previous older generation has to get out of the way of the next newer generation. *(The female Black Widow spider is known for devouring the smaller male of the species after they have sex. When most of us hear this tale our minds conjure up the image of the larger female spider with her intimidating and tell-tale red hourglass marking pouncing on the hapless 'father of her future brood' immediately after sex and eating him alive. In reality, it's a lot more mundane than that. After sex the male spider just 'hangs around' and waits for his mate to get hungry; this usually takes a while. Eventually she does and then dines on her 'husband'. Males feel the need to wait around and 'get eaten' not because they are smart or stupid, but because the ones that do provide an extra nutritional boost for their babies, babies that will find it easier to survive with a healthy and well-fed mother around to produce and protect them. Newly born males will inherit the silent message 'when it comes time to mate, be sure to wait...' from their father—just one part of this spider species' winning strategy. Fathers that wimped out and didn't get eaten produce less numerous and less viable spiderlings. As it turns out, there are many species of spider that also practice this patricide, it's just that with a name like 'the Black Widow spider' you're bound to get noticed for it...)* Resources are finite, and if nothing died, then all the food would be eaten up so that everyone starves—eternal life is not a recipe for a species' success, there is a constant recycling going on. To complicate matters, the environment that the organisms find themselves in doesn't remain the same forever. It can change suddenly or gradually, and if you can't adapt to whatever changes occur, you are going to perish.

This is one of the reasons why organisms that reproduce asexually, meaning a 'parent' producing identical *clones* of itself without the need for a sexual partner, are extremely susceptible to the pressures of a changing environment—they usually become extinct. Why? All the clones apparently had the right sort of identical physical characteristics to be alive and happy before the change occurred—*would they be so lucky after a drastic change?* A different (changed) environment means different physical characteristics are going to be needed. Sexual reproduction between a male and a female mixes up the genes and produces offspring that are similar, but not identical, to the parents. With sex you end up with a lot of variety, and variety is important when the environment changes. Variety helps to ensure survival. Because there are so many different types of individuals around, a few will luckily possess *(hopefully)* the characteristics to survive and succeed in the 'new changed environment'.

The dinosaurs didn't make it when the world changed rather suddenly about 65 million years ago. Some organisms did survive that time though: the shark, turtle and crocodile have all been around for over 100 million years and remain mostly unchanged since then *(according to the fossil record their physical design has been superior regardless of the changing conditions)*; on the other paw *(hand)* the mammals who also survived that time period went through quite a bit of change that continues to this day. *(At the time of the dinosaurs your warm-blooded ancestor could have fit in the palm of a hand, we were tiny* *insectivores then. Read dinosaur expert Robert Bakker's novel of this time period, **Raptor Red**, for more fun insights).* Of all the different species that ever existed on this planet, over 99% are now extinct. The name of nature's game is Change or Die. Are you in? *(You are so 'in' and don't even know it. Time to skew the house advantage with outside information.)*

Small mammals morph over time into separate species, some into primates. Primates evolve into humans, and we humans, smart as we are, are still not safe from the molding forces and planet that spawned us. Consider a volcano that spews enough dust and ash into the atmosphere to change the climate, the environment, of the entire Earth. Not every human survives. However, a small one percent possesses what's needed, thanks to glorious sex with its ensuing variety, and they make it under extreme hardship. In essence, the changing environment acts as a filter, weeding out the inferior *(the sick, the weak, the stupid, the unlucky)* and elevating the superior *(the healthy, the strong, the clever, the lucky).*

Some academic circles refer to this as 'the survival of the fittest'. *(Most people are unaware that this term came not from Darwin, but from the English philosopher and social scientist Herbert Spencer [1820 -1903])* Again, it's all about the environment; if environments don't change, then there is no need for the organism to adapt to that change. This was the main thrust behind Charles Darwin's seminal work, ***The Origin of Species.*** Darwin was looking for the mechanism that caused 'speciation', meaning you could see similarities between certain organisms though they were different: lions vs. tigers for example, or a rainbow trout vs. a largemouth bass. How and why did they change? Darwin never did figure out the 'how'—that would come later with the discovery of DNA, chromosomes, and the field of genetics, but he did figure out the 'why'. It was the environment.

Evidence supporting Darwin's theories, as many of us have learned in school, came from studying the physical characteristics of organisms, both plant and animal, found on the isolated Galápagos Islands *[guh-LAP-uh-gus* or *guh-LAP-uh-gose—named after the Spanish word for 'tortoise'; galápago]* in the Pacific Ocean 600 miles off the coast of Ecuador. These are very special islands for a couple of reasons. First, there is a bunch of them, not just one or two. Second, of all the plant and animal species found there, none are native to the islands—they are all invaders. Third, the animals depend on the Galapagosian (or Galápagan) plants for food, but not all of the plants are found on all of the islands, setting up separate and different conditions, or environments. What Darwin fell upon was an isolated series of experiments in nature (islands) that had been running unmolested by man or major predators for millions of years. *(The volcanic islands are 'young', about 5 million years old. Trust me, that's young for an island. Hawaii's volcanic activity started over 65 million years ago.)*

Darwin delighted in studying and cataloging much of the flora and fauna of the islands, many of which seemed quite exotic and could be found nowhere else. It must have been a most wondrous five weeks *(19 days actually 'on shore')*, that's all the time he had to do his work. *(He loved to get off the boat—young Chuck Darwin tended to up-chuck his dinner; he suffered from violent bouts of sea-sickness. His planned '2 year journey' would also stretch into a '5 year jaunt' around the Earth.)* Marvel at the famous giant land tortoises and the unique swimming marine iguanas. Smile when you learn about the blue-footed booby, a type of wild bird with a carefree attitude and a fashionable set of feet. Exotic though they are, Darwin's ideas were later crystallized when he focused his attention on a rather common type of bird also found on the Galápagos, the simple finch. *(Many people who hear this tale assume that Darwin knew that he was looking at finches. He did not. He actually thought that they were something else. But when he returned to England with some specimens, the famous English ornithologist of the day John Gould informed him that he had discovered many new species of finch. That started Darwin thinking...)*

Their ubiquity on the main continents is what made them valuable to Darwin in the end. A lot was already known about finches, so it was a rather simple thing to begin measuring the physical characteristics of the island birds; there were thirteen different varieties of them to study and catalog, and then they could be compared against ones common to the continents.

What Charles Darwin discovered about these birds and how their bodies could change over time, even short periods of time, led him to unravel 'the origin of species'. *(What's the big deal about '13 different types' of finches? The big deal is that 13 different types of finches didn't originally reach the Galápagos, only* **one** *did. This one type of finch, originally from mainland South America, would spread out and change into 13 other, never before seen types of finches on the various islands—a process called evolutionary radiation.)* How did he do this by looking at birds? Well, once he got back to dry land *(never to return to sea)*, he noticed how English pigeon breeders could actively select for certain traits and produce, through the hand of man *(manipulation)*, a variety of pigeon types. *(Why did Charles love birds so? Because his mother did, she bred pigeons when he was a boy. Mothers mold their sons, just ask Hitler.)* Darwin could well see that if human intervention selected for physical characteristics, perhaps nature itself did the same.

Evidence of just this type of natural selection was shown upon further study of the thirteen different Galapagosian finches. He saw that the birds there had a variety of beak types. The birds would feed on the local Galapagosian insect life and plant life, seeds for example, but the plants and their seeds were subject to the changing weather. Is it going to be a wet growing season or a dry growing season this year? Will the plants produce a lot of seeds or only a few seeds? *(There is a very special finch, unique to the Galápagos, that eats neither seeds nor insects. The 'Vampire Finch' has evolved to exploit another, larger, species of bird, the 'booby'. The tiny Vampires peck at vulnerable spots until blood starts to flow—this is their dinner. Booby chicks and booby eggs also fall prey to these small but vicious, specialized predators. And you thought mosquitoes were bad, imagine if they were the size of birds...)*

Darwin discovered that as the environment changed on an island, or even between isolated islands, a specific shape of the finches' beaks would be 'selected for' depending on the availability of food—sometimes short beaks are better than longer ones, sometimes vice-versa. When certain birds were more adaptable to the conditions, they dominated, but Darwin's data showed that when the environmental conditions changed, so did the beak shape. He could then use the power of logic to see that if organisms here are affected by changing environments over time, then all species, including our own, are subject to the same molding forces everywhere—they are just more complex because the rest of the world is not isolated on an island. *(If you think about it, the Earth is like a lonely island isolated in the sea of space.)* With time, and nature has a lot of time, the many different environments found around the planet *(ocean, land, cold, hot)* produce the entire variety of life we see both today *(fish, fowl, Inuit, python)* and in the past *(trilobite, pterosaur, wooly mammoth, sabre-toothed tiger)*.

The past leads us to the present, and soon the fossil record, and later DNA analysis, would provide even more evidence for Mr. Darwin's wonderful observation and insight. *(In 1861, two years after publishing 'Origin', an important fossil named **Archaeopteryx** [are-key-OP-ter-iks] was uncovered in a layer of limestone in Germany—the first* *of only nine such fossils ever found. This 'early bird' had feathery wings, but also dinosaur-like teeth and claws. Physical features also indicated that the 'bird' lived in a tropical environment. Apparently Germany's climate used to be a lot warmer.)* He had solved one of the biggest mysteries facing a logical thinking species—why is life everywhere similar in some regards *(born, take in energy, excrete waste, mature, reproduce, die)* but so very different in others *(shape, number of legs, color, size, etc.)*?

Charles Darwin was a devout Christian. How many people know that before his legendary journey aboard **The Beagle**, he was studying to be a religious minister? Charles' father, and his father's father, were both English physicians. Young Charles Darwin started out studying medicine, to continue the family trade, but he grew bored with medicine and instead transferred to Cambridge University where he began to prepare for the ministry. But Charles also loved 'bugs'; as a student he was an excellent collector of beetles. *(Returning home from his journey to wondrous foreign lands, he also brought back beetles as well as finches. Darwin had 'Beetlemania' bad, he had preserved in alcohol over 1,500 different species of beetles. Beetles, by the way, are the most 'successfully diverse' type of organism on the Earth; 75% of all species are insects, and of them, the lowly beetle reigns supreme. Line up every living animal on this planet, and one out of every five will be a beetle. Gene Simmons may have his Kiss Army, but John, Paul, George and Ringo recruited an even larger six-legged squadron...)*

Besides animal and plant specimens, Darwin also returned with personal notes; he had over 3,000 pages of his hand-written scientific thoughts. *(Go ahead, sharpen those pencils, you try to write 3,000 pages...)* Because of his religious beliefs, it would take Charles Darwin over 20 years to publish his findings (in 1859). Many people think that 'Evolution' was a notion that Darwin just 'came up with' one day... It's not that simple. It would take 20 years to condense those thoughts, those 3,000 pages of old notes and also many new notes, into an ironclad argument supported by example after example of physical evidence.

Charles was tortured by his thoughts and their conclusion, by talking about the ascension of Man via a changing environment, but what he saw and what his brain pieced together through simple logic could not be denied. **Evolution is a logical idea that derived from a very religious man, one who studied closely the intimate details of nature's variety.** We are also a part of nature, and when nature changes, we also change. We eventually get to where we are standing right now. *(As a boy he once found a fossilized rhinoceros tooth in an English cave while digging around. The popular view said that the dead rhino's body was transported by water from the tropics to England during the time of Noah's flood. Darwin thought otherwise. He imagined that a long time ago the English environment was a lot warmer. This rhino once lived here, indigenous to Dover. Things had changed over time and England's rhino was no more.)* And standing right behind you, hidden in the very fabric of your genetic code, is an unbroken chain of winners in the global casino of a changing environment. Your father, and your father's father, and his father and so on; and your mother, and your mother's mother, and her mother and so on—they were all sexy enough, smart enough and lucky enough to survive, at the very least, long enough to have children. What does this all have to do with the Big Boom of an Indonesian super-volcano? The Big Boom would lead to *The Origin of Species*, both literally and figuratively, for us.

Who survived the cataclysm? What did that one percent have that the rest of primitive humanity did not? It is just speculation, but let's look at the evidence and use human logic to set the scene. Before the eruption there were approximately 100,000 modern humans running around, looking very much like us but obviously behaving very primitively. There is no evidence of clothing or art or truly creative endeavors before this point. Enter the explosion and massive climate shift.

When the dust settles about a thousand people remain—what are they like? Well, part of the success of many primates, including Man and the Great Apes, is our ability to work together as a group, socially, for the benefit of all. We work best as a team and when we have a strong team leader. Your group can't be too large, how would you feed all those mouths? *(The upper limit of Stone Age groups peaked out around 30 total individuals.)* It also can't be too small, there is a lot of work to be done—not every hunting trip is successful, especially when the drought gets worse every year and game animals have all but disappeared.

With fewer resources around, one would have to be the most clever in the hunt, the most adaptive and alert in the forest while looking for possible food and supply materials. If you did have some food stored up, you might have to protect what little you have against starving and violent marauders, perhaps the marauders win. They are clever too, maybe stronger as well. Go ahead, try and stop me from taking what you have, I'm hungry.

We almost went extinct, but a few talented, violent, and lucky individuals made it and passed their genetic heritage on to us—like a healthy momma finch passing on her superior beak. Some interesting artifacts have been unearthed that date to a relative time just shortly after the eruption. Here's a part that I enjoy, the physical evidence.

Humans started carving simple geometric designs into at least one chunk of relatively soft rock called Red Ochre *[OH-ker]*. Over the following millennia, Stone Age humans would continue to use Red Ochre as part of important social ceremonies, including burial. This carving shows thought, skill, control, and geometric symbolism. This piece of colored rock was carved by a person only a few generations removed from the Big Boom, someone who inherited more creativity, more intelligence, more fear of strangers and the supernatural perhaps—all the instincts and skills of the people who struggled to survive the great extermination were passed down through sex; the creativity and wit that were needed to survive were still there, but now the world had changed again.

The game animals were coming back in abundance. Food was more plentiful, and because you are so good at catching and killing and gathering and building simple stone tools, you have free time, time to think, time to create. Time to scratch geometric designs into a nifty chunk of soft colored rock perhaps. And that's not all. Small seashells with tiny holes hand-drilled through them have also been traced back to this time period. *Do you like jewelry? What does the wearing of jewelry represent? Why do people want it? Jewelry has symbolized wealth for a long time—why are we so mesmerized by these pretty bits?*

We know the answers to these questions, but there had to be a time before jewelry, before true creativity, and a time after. There was also a time before clothing, and a time after; we know this by studying the genetic code of the Human *'Body'* Louse—it didn't evolve away from the Human *'Head'* Louse until 'clothes' had been invented to shelter and protect them as well as us; the lice adapted to a new environment, clothed humans. So when did clothing appear? The lice's DNA says *after* the eruption, not before.

It appears that the boundary between the periods of human non-creativity and true creativity is the Indonesian explosion; it actually refined the human species, forced it to be smarter and creative in order to survive. Then nature would take that newly enhanced human species, that surviving top one percent, and start all over again, relatively fresh, only this time we moved forward a lot faster. More ornate jewelry, better clothing, better tools, a better diet, a better language, a consuming desire to explore and exploit the land next door—India to Australia, Mongolia to the Americas. Stone Age humans were on their way to conquering the world. *(And all of it by adapting to each changing environment through the use of our brains and our skills in hunting and gathering—also in living socially together, by helping each other, by accepting insiders and avoiding outsiders.)*

The eruption 'kick started' the modern human species by killing most of us off. The creativity and wanderlust that filtered through would peck away at the hidden structure of nature, first on a small scale *(three more full moons until the mammoth return...)*, but they would eventually be applied on a large scale to help unravel the workings of the universe. In its way, the eruption would produce language, and books, and Charles Darwin, and me, and you.

Knowing about the explosion makes me smile, it helps me to realize how lucky I am, how very lucky we all are, even to be here. Big Boom and we exist, no Big Boom and where's your concentrated creativity now? We needed the *environment* to change to force *us* to change, to forge our species into something better than it was *(bad things can happen personally to you too, but even bad things can make you a better person, can cause you to change for the better),* and it wasn't the first time. It's happened several times on this planet, to our species and to others. And then, just as evolution usually does, it takes characteristics and traits that were useful and successful in one time period and environment, and starts to use them in others, only in a slightly different, more efficient and effective way—usually that is, some forms still go extinct. *(Dinosaurs walked the planet for over 150 million years. Humans have only been here for around 5 million years—yet we're the more adaptable, we're the survivors of drastic environmental change many times over. It's brains over brawn. You can adapt even today—conquer your fears, it's scary but humans are used to it, we succeeded in spite of fear and danger. You can too, it's built into you.)*

Eventually, in this time of plenty, the surviving species come out of hiding to engorge themselves on food at first, and then they feast on each other later in a sexual frenzy. Without glorious sex, genetic variation, and a changing environment, none of this would be possible—it's only natural to get your groove on. *(According to 'timing' I was conceived two weeks after my parents got married. What was the occasion? Friends of theirs in 1965 got married two weeks after they did. Let's just say that my parents had a good time at the wedding reception, and later they apparently had an even 'better' time on their own... To this day I still thank Sam and Patty Smith for getting married when they did—I wouldn't be here if they didn't. In some things, like human conception, timing is critical.)*

The act of producing offspring comes as a necessary secondary effect to the pleasures of sex, we do it because it feels good. Stone Age children weren't even an afterthought; babies grew thanks to supernatural magic, not from copulation. Sex feels good for a reason—we've chosen it to be that way over time, a *filter of pleasure; only the sexy survive.* And don't let anyone tell you that 'size' doesn't matter; inch for inch and pound for pound, the human male has the largest penis of any primate its size. This doesn't just happen by itself, there are reasons we look and behave the way we do. Remember, 'form follows function'—if human women didn't care about penis size, and the ensuing pleasure contained therein, then there would be no reason for human men to change and follow suit. *(Most male mammals have a permanent 'bone' in their penis to make sex an easy thing to accomplish. My semi-retired father has a friend who still hunts and traps wild mink, the tiny weasel-like mammal known for its sleek and soft coat. He sells the pelts, but he does keep at least one thing for his amusement. At social gatherings he sometimes pulls out a small, white, bleached bone from his pocket and challenges onlookers to guess what it is. When they can't he smiles and tells them the truth. "It's a 'mink dink'..." Of course human males don't have this ready-made rigid internal luxury, we need to be 'aroused'.)*

Women have altered the sexual environment and men have adapted to that change—again, there are no written laws here, only the law of sheer animal magnetism, ladies just know what they want. You go girl! *(As I heard Desmond Morris, the famed British Zoologist/Humanist, once say with his dry-but-warm English inflection, "Man is the sexiest ape alive..." Be sure to read his witty and entertaining non-fiction books,* **The Naked Ape** *and* **The Human Zoo**.*)* In contrast, the mighty male mountain gorilla, in human scale, would sport a penis measuring a paltry one-to-two inches long *(~4 cm)*, and that's when erect *(reportedly, I've never seen one personally)*; apparently orgasmic bliss ranks pretty low on a lady gorilla's list of priorities, pity for her, doesn't she know what she's missing? The gorilla doesn't have the big brain to change her way of thinking the way you can, to stand up for what she desires— aren't you glad that you aren't a gorilla?

The size of a male's testicles also indicates another battle for sexual dominance. A silent war has been waged for millennia, with troops numbering in the millions per cubic centimeter. Spermatozoa leap forward into battle; some go for the gold, hunting for the egg, while others proceed on search-and-destroy missions, looking for the enemy. And when they find foreign sperm *(some ladies do get around, it's why male sperm has developed these attacking attributes—sex is fun for everyone, but in the end there can be only one winner)* they'll unleash a dual attack designed both physically and chemically to incapacitate and immobilize the microscopic squatters.

Extra-promiscuous primates need to produce lots of sperm, hundreds of millions, billions, per day, to ensure genetic success above and beyond the deposits of other like-minded males, a massive frontal assault on the fallopian beachhead to overwhelm an enemy already entrenched if you will—the brazenly horny chimpanzee wins this *battle of the balls*, they have the largest *'cojones'*, or *'huevos'*. *(Chimps are some of the 'fastest copulators' on the planet—non-Alpha males have a lot of quick 'stealth sex' when the leader isn't looking. Sometimes a ready-made bone in your penis comes in handy, no need for Viagara®...)* Mountain gorillas, with a huge dominant Silverback keeping the peace, are quite monogamous and sport the tiniest testicular package. *(Tiny balls and penis? 'Great' Ape indeed...)* The human male's testicles rest squarely in the middle; sometimes we're monogamous, sometimes we aren't. Place an order today, now you can double your pleasure with only half of that pesky promiscuity. *(Caution: your results may vary)* Do your own research, if you dare; it can be amusing and humbling. As an excited anthropologist might utter, *the evidence is in the bones...*

Why bring all this up? Because sex is everywhere, it's a big part of who you are and how you got here. The drive to reproduce has to be strong in everything that's alive today, from bacteria to blue whales, from algae to Al Gore—did you see him kiss his wife on TV? We are a social species, and it's good to 'fit in'. When Al Gore was running for president he needed to improve his image—he was considered a bit 'wooden' and dull. No one really thought of Al Gore as a 'ladies man'. That kiss, in my opinion, was not spontaneous—not much in a presidential campaign is. It is too easy to say something wrong or do something offensive.

The kiss was planned, and in the end it succeeded in doing at least part of what it was intended to do. Al Gore was human after all, people talked and talked about it. I'm writing about it here in this book—and all this talk over what? A kiss. *(We 'learned to kiss' as 'kids', Stone Age parents had no pre-packaged baby-food in those days, just what was killed or gathered. They had to chew up the food and pass it lips-to-lips to their children who were born toothless. Your lips are super-sensitive for a reason, humans had to eat to live—kissing came later.)* In the end it wasn't enough to turn around Al's image completely. People remember that closely fought election with a nearly-evenly-split Florida finally giving the nod to George W. Bush in his first presidential bid. **What people don't remember is that Florida's election results would have been a non-issue if Al Gore could have won his own state, Tennessee, in the election.** *(The last time a major presidential candidate didn't carry his own state: George McGovern in 1972 vs. Richard Nixon, but that electoral race wasn't very close.)* In hindsight, he not only needed to work on his national image, but one that appealed to voters in his own state.

People are primitive, and politicians play social mind games to appeal to your own basic needs, and we need sex. Vote for me, I'm the sexy candidate. Former President William Jefferson Clinton, while far from perfect, was considered very sexy, and therefore very popular, at least during his own election campaigns. *(But 'Slick Willie' is also a man, one with manly desires. He succumbed while in Office, and the ensuing sex scandal kept him from actively campaigning for his fellow Democrat, and friend, Al Gore. Again, that election was so close—if you're upset with George W. Bush's current job, think how the Democratic Party could have cruised to power if the former President would have unleashed his 'campaigning charisma' instead. Al should have had a little more help from the Party's top man, but power, whether political or sexual, is intoxicating— sometimes it's hard to focus on the greater good of the Party when your hormones are screaming at you. Why is it that we cringe inwardly when we think of the President, or our parents, naked and excitedly groping in the dark? It's what WE like after all...)*

So, sex is everywhere. It has to be. We are surrounded by it. Even if you are chaste and asexual, you are here because of sex, and you still think about sex. All sex begins in the brain; we think about it a lot, we can't help it. And with that animal brain we can also 'substitute' one thing for another in our heads, we can focus in on just a part of the physical body for our pleasure—this doesn't just happen with humans either, it also happens with other animals. The brain and our behavior can be modified, different things can turn us on.

Most of us are familiar with Russian scientist Ivan Pavlov and his conditioning experiments with dogs. Dogs love food—there is a common expression, to 'wolf down' a meal. *(Dogs and wolves are still closely related genetically, they can still mate and produce viable offspring—technically, they are the same species though they look externally different.)* When dogs are shown their food, their mouths start to salivate—and why? Because saliva is a part of digestion—in your mouth saliva begins to break down the food chemically. *(Teeth break up the food mechanically, exposing more surface area, so that saliva can do its job better.)* In the wild you'll die if you don't eat, it's good to have strong, sharp teeth and plenty of saliva to get the job done quickly before the food's all gone. The dogs can't help drooling, it's part of being a wolf and a dog. You show me a home-made blackberry pie and I'll drool too! *(I'll also howl with delight!)*

So Pavlov wanted to see if he, with his big human brain, could alter the dogs' usual behavior by creating a 'substitution' for pleasure. Normally, if you ring a bell in a dog's presence not much will happen. The bell doesn't mean anything significant to the dog, it is a neutral stimulus—but that can change. Ivan would ring the bell right at the dogs' dinner time, eventually they came to associate the ringing of the bell with food. The food makes them salivate, and soon the bell did too. Pavlov would ring the bell but produce no food, and yet the dogs started to drool all over themselves.

Behavioral substitution has taken place—all because of a curious human mind.

Humans can become conditioned too. As I mentioned earlier, some of us focus our sexual attention on certain parts of the body—both men and women do it, we all have certain preferences. Short, tall, skinny, fat, curvy, not-so-curvy, light hair, dark hair, red hair, no hair—the list is a long one. *(I know the real reason why 'blondes have more fun', but that's for another book.)* Why we focus this way is not just a human trait, it's an animal trait, and it can produce some interesting variations.

Take the bird world for example. If you see two Mallard ducks slowly swimming by in your local pond, look closely. Your eye might spy both a male and a female paddling along—you'll know by looking at the colors of the feathers. One duck will have a bright-green feathered head perhaps, including another colored band around the neck. The other will be a rather dull brown, with no colored feathers on top of the head, just a few on the wing. Which of these two birds is the male and which is the female—and why are they different?

When you look at humans, it's the ladies who usually get all decked out in colorful clothing more so than the men—'a slave to fashion' is a term normally associated with women. But in the bird world, the tablecloths have been turned. Our bright-green colorfully headed duck is the proud preening male and his rather dull counterpart is the female. Female Mallard ducks like green heads—why? Because their mothers did—and their mothers before them, and their mother's before that—it's a part of being a duck. Green heads are sexy, they are healthy. *Quack Quack, I wanna mate with you! Swim that sexy head over my way Big Boy... There is a theory that feathers evolved from lizard scales through mutation and were at first advantageous for their colors, for sex purposes, not for flight. A running raptor's double forearm strike mimics the wing-motion of a bird in flight. There's a good chance this is not a coincidence—you have to run around with feathers before you can use them for flying. To us, primitive flightless birds with colorful plumage running around may seem silly, but to the opposite sex of the day, colored feathers are sexually attractive, they still are.*

And not just ducks do this feather trick, one of the most famous examples, and one that now should make more sense after my discussion of ducks, is the peacock—*Yowza!* Now that's some feather trick! Many of us have seen pictures or been to the zoo where these exotic birds spread their tails and expose a *HUGE* and colorful display—their tails measure much, much larger than a regular birdy body. This is the extroverted male of the species. Look around at the zoo and you might see the female half of the species, the *peahen*.

The peahen is like the female Mallard. She is a dull brown with no large colorful tail at all. Let's just say that few would rush down to the zoo to see its brand new 'peahen' exhibit—we like the exotic, and apparently the peahen does too. It's been discovered recently what really turns a peahen on, what is it about that strutting male peacock's tail that is so alluring? *It's the sexy 'eyespots' Big Boy...*

The 'eyespots' are those dark colored areas, sometimes a beautiful iridescent purple, on the male's tailfeathers—the bigger the tail, the more eyespots can 'grow' and be exposed, and to a peahen a 'bigger tail', meaning more eyespots, is better *(symmetry of the spots has also been discovered as having an influence)*. How do we know this? Well, curious scientists, a lot like Pavlov I imagine, took a 'less well endowed' peacock with a less than average number of eyespots and 'painted' a few more fake ones on. The peahens of the experiment liked the newly changed peacock better than before, a LOT better. Their peahen brains didn't really care if the spots were real or not, basically because a peahen has never seen fake eyespots before, her brain automatically assumes — *"Eyespots? Oh, they're real..."*

Does a large tail and more eyespots mean more sexual pleasure for the female? I would say no, the large male tail serves another interesting feature; it makes the entire species stronger and more successful, thanks to the peahens choosing them of course. It's a team effort.

Here's a fictional/historical portrait on how it quite possibly worked. At one point in time there were no 'large tails' in the peacock world. There was 'normal' variation among the birds I imagine. Just like some people are 6 feet tall, and others are only 5 feet 8 inches tall, some birds had a slightly bigger tail, and some slightly smaller. Let's say that there were two groups of peahens, ones that liked the small tail, and another that liked the large tail.

All the peahens get to mate with their choices, and the offspring produced will have similar characteristics of the parents—meaning female chicks produced from peahens that liked small tails will ALSO like small tails, the genes and preferences get passed along—and the peahens with a penchant for 'above average' tails would pass that predisposition along to their daughters as well, lucky girls. *(Ever hear the one about how women often are attracted to a man that reminds them of dear old Dad—why? Well, her mother was attracted to a man like her father(!) when she was your age... Genetics makes us similar, though not identical, to our parents.)* Now there are two spreading populations of peacocks, the ones with the growing tails, and the ones with the same old small tails.

Sex is only part of the story, the other part is survival in the wild. Let's face it, the only way you are going to have sex is if you stay alive long enough in the environment to get past puberty. So who survives in the wild? Small tailed peacocks or big tailed peacocks? Both are hunted by tigers, and other predators, that live in the jungles and forests of

Southeast Asia. Carrying around a big, heavy, conspicuous tail is not the best way to stay alive in the jungle. You would think that when a tiger has to chase down a tasty peacock for that morning's meal, the slower, heavier bird dragging his big tail behind will be easier to catch and eat than the smaller tailed counterpart. But not all the big tailed peacocks get caught, some are even bigger and faster, so they escape.

They live to mate another day; the peahens that like big tails, now they have *really* big tailed peacocks to tickle their visual fancy, oh those eyespots! So sexy! Their offspring go through the same filtering process until it produces a bird with a huge tail and huge muscles in order to escape from predators while dragging that cumbersome thing around like some sexy ball and chain.

What of the peahens who liked small tails? Well, their offspring continued on that way, without really changing, without needing to get bigger and stronger. Eventually the tigers got the message—big tail means big and strong and fast, too easy to escape. That bigger tail at first slowed the peacocks down, until their bodies and muscles changed to accommodate it through selection. Now the birds that used to be slower, they are faster and smarter than ever—they had to be in order to survive. The tigers, I assume, started to dine on their slower relatives, the small tailed peacocks. Soon, all that remained were the peacocks with the 'Mardi Gras' flair. *Here, let me show-off for you ladies. Check out all of MY eyespots, see how big and strong I am? Perhaps the muscle-men of California's Venice Beach know of what I speak... Which came first, purple eyespots or primped pectorals?*

The peahens and peacocks got bigger and stronger not from a change in their physical environment, like a climate change, but from a change in their *social* environment. A volcano can 'change the rules' so to speak, well so to can horny peahens with a penchant for colored feathers. In essence, peahens made it harder for peacocks to survive in the wild—there was a new filter in place. *I wanna have sex so I have to have this big tail, but then I have to be bigger and stronger and faster and smarter because I have this big tail...* Small tailed birds got filtered out. This is natural selection of a sexual nature, and we do it too, without even really thinking. It's part of being an animal, and we behave like animals for a reason, everything for a reason. *(University of Newcastle professor **Marion Petrie** has done many varied experiments involving social 'peafowl'. Prof. Petrie tried removing spots at first, cutting out as many as 20 eyespots from proud males' tails. Females would 'check out' the competing males, and over 90% of the time they chose the one with the most spots available to them.)*

So, the peahens' kinky fetish for selecting big tails over small ones actually led to the species becoming more successful. Similar to human women selecting men with larger penises—there's a reason things are the way they are. You might be saying to yourself, *Oh, you can't really compare something nonsexual like a peacock's eyespots to something very sexual such as a man's genitals—humans are a lot smarter than birds.* Yes we are, but we still operate under the same types of animal instincts and emotions. We also can substitute a non-sexual part of the body, like a colored head or tail feathers or a set of spiky antlers, and turn it into a sexual mating cue or ritual. Case in point: Chinese foot binding.

For many centuries there has been a custom that has been practiced throughout China—the binding of a young girl's feet tightly when they are young. This is a painful procedure that lasts for years. The feet are constantly squeezed, the desired result being as tiny a foot as possible. And if you have never seen the result of this custom, I can assure you the end product does not resemble what most of the Western world would call attractive.

Eventually, social pressure from the Western world would shame a 'backwards China' into changing, into condemning a practice that was once common and popular. Accepting the custom at first, and condemning the custom later, both happened because of the same reason, the need for social humans to fit into human society—*What will the neighbors think?* It's just that the neighborhood got a lot larger in the twentieth century for China, *and your neighbors are casting a critical eye toward your barbaric customs, they find you 'different'. They are laughing at you, teasing you, no law against it...*

The bound foot does remain smaller than normal, it's hard to grow when you're being squeezed, but it does not resemble a little miniature foot—you know, normal in all regards, just smaller. No, what follows next smacks of physical torture, one endured for years—the toes, usually the four smaller ones, get pushed back and under the foot. Try this on for size, take off your shoes and then 'curl your toes' under your foot. Imagine having them wrapped this way for so many years that you couldn't 'uncurl' them even if you wanted to. The girl's foot actually ends up looking like a misshapen stump. You have to turn her foot over in order to see her malformed, stunted little toes.

Sometimes bones in the foot were broken purposefully in order to facilitate the perfect shape, that of the 'golden lotus' or 'golden lily'—a tiny malformed foot that measured just three inches long *(size does matter)*. In addition to being rather grotesque in appearance, there was also the health danger of the filth that gathered next to the skin; gangrenous wounds could form and fester. The toenails don't stop growing and sometimes slowly pierced the flesh of the foot; a more severe and deadly type of ingrown nail would ensue. *(Many girls supposedly did not survive the procedure, I've even heard of data describing a mortality rate as high as 10% among those undergoing the 'practice'—*

though accurate figures are hard to come by as older records of this 'now shameful' procedure have since disappeared.)

If they survive the initial ordeal these girls then have special tiny shoes made for them, some with little high-heels, which they squeeze their 'stump' into, toes curled under of course—when they walk it is actually on their 'toe-knuckles'. Like I mentioned, this practice has been going on for centuries, almost a thousand years, and was outlawed in China only a few decades ago, since 1911. Some women defied the law at first and continued to bind their daughters' feet—why? Because it was still attractive to some men in that social culture like it had been for centuries. And the ladies do like attracting the attention of the men-folk and vice-versa. *(Beverley Jackson researched over seven years and traveled to China before writing her book, **Splendid Slippers: A Thousand Years of an Erotic Tradition**— she claims that women were still binding the feet of their daughters in isolated areas as late as 1959. Old social habits die hard. Ms. Jackson reportedly owns over 170 pairs of the tiny, delicately hand embroidered shoes in her personal collection.)*

And why do the men like the results of this painful and seemingly barbaric practice? I wondered about this for many years because I couldn't really see how this 'feet turned into stumps' was physically attractive—and then I learned the reason why, and now it fits nicely in this book about human behavior; it fits like a foot-stump squeezed into a specially made shoe. It's just like the Black Widow spider, or the Mallard, or the peacock—their story is our story too. We are pushed and pulled by our environment and society, and our bodies and behavior become modified over time. Chinese foot binding is an extreme example of human nature, but it's not that far removed from what happens to all sorts of other living things—from peacocks to rhinoceros beetles to a rutting twelve-point stag. *(Nice horns, Big Boy!)*   Here's the story as I have come to understand it.

A long, long time ago in a Chinese empire far, far away, there lived an Emperor. Now being an Emperor is nice in a lot of ways, you get pretty much everything you want the way you like it. This Emperor, however, behaved a little like a quirky peahen—this Emperor liked 'different' girls, ones with small feet *(and the smaller, the better)*. Not feet that were bound mind you, that hadn't started yet. No, this individual man, who happened to be an Emperor, had a foot fetish. Like a peahen who swoons over big tails, this man's heart would race at the sight of tiny toes.

The Emperor of China, a living God, manipulates the ultimate royal 'in crowd' by his sheer will and presence. *"If it's good enough for our esteemed leader, who is descended from heaven..."* Soon, palace officials start to fancy women with small feet in order to curry the Emperor's favor and delight. Then the aristocracy follow suit, and soon small feet become fashionable. Then it trickles down to the common peasant whose life is hard and there are children to feed. *Hmmm... if my daughter had smaller feet she would be more attractive to men and to the Mother-In-Law who makes the marrying decision, I could marry her into a higher social circle making my own social standing even better, there's money to be made...* So naturally small feet gave way to un-naturally bound feet, and if small is good, *then smaller is better...*

The Emperor would die (well, even Emperors don't get 'everything' their way), but his legacy and kinky desire would live on, and on, and on... for a thousand years. Eventually this would lead to the 'stumps' of the twentieth century. Millions of Chinese women and men have all fed into this practice for centuries, all because of one man, who happened to be a social leader *and* a foot fetishist, in conjunction with our human desire to fit into the social group.

And in America, we don't have the foot binding problem *(though 'foot worship' still ranks as the number one sexual fetish even here—the foot is normally hidden, get it? It must be sexy if it's hidden... Value is perceived)*, but we do have another social heritage that has stemmed down the same way, from royalty and aristocracy to everyone else. I'm talking about dogs. Think how many *millions* of households have dogs. And why? I mean, dogs are great and friendly quite often, and we have put them to work on the farm or in the field at times, but such a prevalence of dogs, millions of them? *(150,000 wolves live in the wilderness, but there are 50 million domestic dogs in the U.S. alone.)*

Well, for us it started a couple of hundred years ago in Europe. *(The Pharaohs also raised dogs for entertainment, but we tend to covet our 'current' royal figures.)* You had to be rich to afford a dog, especially a purebred dog, and in the beginning it was just a curiosity among the leisurely wealthy. But the common man caught on, just like the peasants of China. If I get a dog, even though I am a commoner, what I am saying to my social group is, *look at me—I'm doing so well that I can feed my family and have the luxury of this dog...*

Eventually though this changed, from a dog being a status symbol, to a dog being a friendly part of the family, one that loves you unconditionally, also a personal social benefit—statistically people with pets are healthier and live longer, we so need that social connection, even if it comes from our domesticated animals. And common people can breed dogs, and bind feet, relatively easily. We are so caught up in the social construct of society, we forget how desperately we want to fit in, how desperately we need to appear in a positive light to everyone else.

"...but my best friend down the street, her family has a dog—can we get a dog, please?" Everybody else is doing it, where have we heard that one before? Or how about this

one, a man walks along a busy sidewalk next to a city street, he stops walking, and looks up intently... He is looking at nothing in particular, but yet other people stop and stare upwards as well, wondering what he is looking at. Why do we care? Because we are programmed to care—to slow down and look at the car wreck as you drive by in the opposite lane. *What did that person do?* We are so connected to each other, even strangers, that we can get all twisted-up if we're not careful.

Ivan Pavlov's dogs learned to appreciate a neutral stimulus, the bell—now it stood for something. China didn't used to be a nation of bizarre foot fetishists, but men learned to appreciate a stumpy foot, they can be as conditioned as a hungry dog, I say even more so.

Foot binding in China began its rise a lot like dog ownership did in the Western world; it became a status symbol, one that reeked of wealth. Here is why. A woman with tiny stumps for feet is considered attractive because the group thinks so, but this woman cannot walk normally, cannot work and do a lot of things that normal 'big footed' girls do. A severely foot-bound woman might need servants to help her get around, even carry her perhaps—she certainly lives a life of leisure (paid for by childhood and adult pain). If you were a Chinese man in the heyday of foot binding culture, then having a woman, a wife or concubine, with these tiny feet became a luxury status. *I'm so rich and successful look at me, I can afford to have this woman—she is like a rare and expensive flower that needs special care...* It was the 'ancient' Chinese male equivalent of having a flashy sportscar in the driveway, or an expensive Italian suit, or a diamond encrusted watch—*look at what I have, see what I can afford...* A sentiment not lost in Pearl S. Buck's acclaimed story of Chinese society, **The Good Earth**.

We are so concerned about what our neighbors think. And while this does drive us a bit crazy these days, we needed this social-focus-aspect of our personality in order to survive in a harsher time. Well, part of this book's purpose is to break the *chains of society's* hold on your happiness. Stop thinking and acting like an animal, look around you, it's everywhere. Start thinking and acting like a human. But that is difficult to do at times because of who we are and where we come from—while the group can be cold, hard and cruel, we yearn for its embrace. We want to rise up that social ladder, to be accepted, to be recognized, to be powerful.

In the dying days of disco, there was a new fashion wave that engulfed America. Jordache® Jeans. *For that 'Jordache' look...* What the heck was the Jordache look? It was apparently tight blue jeans with fancy stitching on the back pockets. And they were more expensive, and everybody knew it—and you had to have them—it was a brilliant marketing ploy.

Those jeans were all about sex and social standing. A shrewd marketing professional exploited these basic needs to get extra money, double even, for the minimal cost *(pennies)* of some fancy stitching on a back pocket. It taps into the social core of who we are, getting the group's attention. Something that successful doesn't go unnoticed, enter *Sergio Valente®* jeans. These were 'designer' jeans too, with fancy back pocket stitching as well—*who the heck was Sergio Valente?*

It didn't matter, they cost more, but the advertising was everywhere, becoming a staple in American society. And there were also the *Izod Lacoste®* polo shirts, with a little alligator sewn in the corner and a collar that you could turn up just so—it was so preppy *(short for the more expensive private 'preparatory school' fashion)*, so 80's— shirts that rich kids could afford and wear to set themselves socially apart, but soon they could be seen in the halls of public schools as well. *Jordache, Sergio, Izod*—exotic names and expensive to wear, hey, who are you trying to impress?

(Everybody silly—look at my diamond ring, look at my Rolex watch, look at what I can afford...)

We buy into the group mentality, we can't help it, it's how we got here. We buy clothing to wear, we buy a purebred dog, we buy a concubine with tiny malformed feet—we do it all to get noticed. What do you do to get noticed? What 'little' things do you pay attention to otherwise others might get wise to your social ineptitude? What are your preferences? Why are your preferences the way they are? *Ever think about: Fashion? Footwear? Underwear? Cologne or Perfume? Eyeglasses or Contacts? Sunglasses? Hair style? Facial hair style? Cosmetics? Toothpaste? Antiperspirant? Shampoo? Nail length? Nail color? Watch? Jewelry?*

This may seem like a human litany, but it isn't. It's just another manifestation of the group and how we want to look; young and healthy and hip, we need to fit in and be accepted—humans didn't invent social society and group living, but we've adopted it with a vengeance. We'd like to think of ourselves as so human, when the genetic and behavioral facts show that so much of us is not. We behave like reactive animals for a reason, a deep one that we forget or ignore or are uninitiated to. Start thinking and acting like a human? That's harder than you know—the animal and the human are intertwined. You are both of these things at the same time, it is your dual nature.

Werewolves may be fiction, but this clever story can be an allegory for human nature—what lies beneath your skin, what animal lusts carouse across your brain? Why are they there? And why do they rule your world—can you exercise power over them or are you helpless to deny their dominance? Can human thought take you there—expose the beast and make your world more serene? Only now, like never before, can that happen. Consider the famous but troubled impressionist Vincent Van Gogh, who may have genetically inherited his depression and possible epilepsy from his mother.   Vincent was once jailed because of his public emotional outbursts, but concerned friends and a local doctor thought otherwise; they had him transferred from the prison to a hospital where he eventually regained his sanity.   Van Gogh was amazed at his own recovery and the mysterious biology of the brain.   He wrote:

> **I knew well enough that one could fracture one's legs and arms and recover afterwards, but I did not know that you could fracture the brain in your head and recover from that, too.**

For most of human history we didn't really know a whole bunch about reality, so much was guesswork and superstition.   But now the curtain that's always been there has been pulled back a bit so that we can peek.   We get to see ourselves like no one else ever has—it's hard, but a human can achieve serenity, if they can learn to think like a human. But that's where you're headed—see where you've been coming from for clues to lead you forward.

The reason it's hard to think like a Human

It's very simple really, the reason why it is so hard to think like a human is that you are mostly non-human to begin with. Humanity, in all its supposed unique glory, is a creative and lucky flash-in-the-pan bolstered by layer upon layer of proven non-human success stories. *(There is no gene structure that is unique to humans. ALL of our genes have been borrowed from other species.)* The biggest and most important one of all is DNA itself; in its very structure is the basis for all life as we know it.

DNA, or **D**eoxyribo**N**ucleic *[dee-AHK-see-RYE-bo-new-CLAY-ick]* **A**cid, is a replicating organic molecule; it's a living microscopic machine. Sometimes referred to as 'the blueprint of life', it spells out in a four letter code the instructions to make you, or a butterfly, or an oak tree. Yes, even oak trees have DNA. It's also carried in their seed, the acorn. If it was fertilized properly by another oak tree and buried by an industrious but forgetful squirrel, then a new tree, complete with its own unique DNA, could be born. *The kids grow up so fast these days...*

Most of your DNA is not human DNA. You share it with cousins found far and wide. This shared heritage runs deeper than you think, and connects you to others and to nature in a way that you may have never pondered. Get ready to understand what no non-human animal has ever been able to see, the real mystery of life.

We are going to play a game. A mental exercise that can be backed up with hard data and real DNA analysis, but we are just having some fun here, so go ahead, pick a person, any person... *(similar to 'pick a card, any card...')* It could be your neighbor, or it could be former heavyweight boxing champion of the world, Muhammad Ali—whoever it may be, let's look at the genes, the genetic information that describes 'you' and 'them' in detail.

When you compare *your* DNA to *theirs* prepare to be surprised—you'll find them almost wholly identical. There are tiny differences of course, and these can be used as 'fingerprint' identifiers, unique personal forensic evidence used to pinpoint a suspect at a crime scene for example. Most people understand that genetic material can be analyzed minutely for differences, but what I'm talking about here is analyzing DNA for what is *the same*, what is identical, and that is very, very close to 100%. Why? Why is the vast majority of it identical? There is a reason that your DNA is almost the same as every person alive on Earth, you are related to all of them.

Go back in time—your father, your father's father, your father's father's father... Your mother, your mother's mother... Do the same with your other subject, they had a mother too, they had a father... There is a reason your DNA is so similar, mostly identical—you had a common ancestor somewhere. Do you have to go back 5,000 years to find them? *25,000* years? *74,000* years? Look at me, I am related to you, too. Our DNA is nearly identical as well, and now you know why. Somewhere down your family line and somewhere down mine—they merge. We are related.

Our closest genetic non-human cousins are the chimpanzee *(including the 'bonobo' [buh-NO-bo], a chimp subset who often walk on two legs and, like humans, have sex face to face)*, then the gorilla, and then the orangutan. It's been widely bandied about that the chimpanzee boasts something on the order of a 98.4% identical DNA match when compared to humans. *(Chimpanzees are actually closer genetically to humans than they are to Gorillas.)* Most people are unaware that there is an even closer link between our two species.

The 98.4% figure most folks reference relates to the *entire* DNA strand, but most of the strand is inactive, it is 'junk' DNA. Only certain small percentages are actually at work, the 'active' genes. They are what really determine who and what you are. If you look at the 'active' genes between chimps and humans, you'll find an even greater correspondence—over 99% identical. Why are they so close? Because we are all related—you, me, Muhammad Ali, and that chimpanzee swinging from tree to tree.

Keep on playing our game though. Look at gorillas. Less identical yes, but most of it, our DNA, is the same. Common ancestor there. Look at a dog, any dog—purebred, mutt, timber-wolf, it doesn't matter. Look at that dog's DNA, look at your own. Would you be surprised to learn that we have **90% identical genetic material**? I was. There is a common ancestor once again, though we have to go back millions of years, instead of thousands, to meet them. Still, there is a *good* reason for the genetic similarity. It's one reason how we know that whales and dolphins came from land animals; whales used to look a lot like wolves millions of years ago—the genes don't lie, the similarity is too easy to measure.

And what of our friend the oak tree, or a blade of grass? Do they have DNA similar to our own, are we related to them as well? *What is your logic telling you?* With your mind, go back in time, and the link is always there, the genetic information is so similar for a reason. Every living thing on the planet, even everything that has ever lived and then died, from Einstein to Tyrannosaurs, is related to you. All life on this planet is connected somewhere in the past, your brethren extend far and wide. And dare I say it, even Kevin Bacon is connected to all life everywhere if you go back far enough.

It sounds like science fiction, but it is science fact. DNA is an intricate and long, very long, molecule. Spelling things out in a simple four letter alphabet takes quite a few letters when the instructions get complex, and yet every living thing uses that same four lettered code, and a lot of that code is identical... For a reason that you now know, it all gets passed along, from them to everybody else—and it gets passed to you, and me, too.

So what animal is the oldest? Who is 'The Originator', the one with similarity but the fewest bits identical to our own, the one farthest down the line but still connected to you by a common ancestor? In the multi-cellular world (we could go back to single cells, but we won't, at least not yet) it is the lowly sponge. The form and function of the sponge is seen in most living creatures today, including us.

Life advanced well past the single cell stage *(thanks to sex and DNA mutation and a changing environment to filter and stimulate the dominant traits—if one cell is good, then many are better)* when the cells wrapped around and formed themselves into a tube. Cells on the inside were protected and became specialized. Water, with dissolved nutrients, was drawn down through the tube. The specialized cells protected there soon excelled at filtering out the 'goodies', the food from the environment that just happened to float by outside. This sponge looks like a passive plant anchored to the seabed, but it is actually a primitive animal, and it is feeding successfully.

Its body forms a mouth, through which nutrients are passed down into the tube—where they are then worked over and absorbed en masse. The sponge takes what its body needs; soon the waste products are ejected out. Scientists didn't know that the sponges were feeding this way, actively pumping water down through their mouths, until they did experiments with dye in the liquid environment—they could trace the movement of the colored water through the sponges' bodies.

We have a mouth, and a digestive track, and an anus. What are we but a tube, a fancy one with appendages? We don't have to stay attached to the seabed pumping near anemic water through our mouths though. No, we *go to* the food, we _walk_ to the McDonald's with our legs and use our hands to shove fries and burgers down our _tubes_, oops—I mean _throats_... We use our specialized teeth at the entrance _(the mouth)_ of our feeding tubes and slippery secreted saliva to start the breakup of nutrient rich material, food, so that specialized cells further down the tube, in the protected stomach and intestine, can better work over the rendered remains. We are all tubes, our DNA builds us that way for a reason, it's a very successful form; tubes of the world, unite!

Yes, between you, me, and the sponge, we all have a common ancestor; think of all the other creatures that also have a mouth, a digestive 'tube', and an anus—just like you. The squid, the eagle, the cockroach. Humans are not that unique in form and function from the vast majority of the multi-cellular life crawling, walking, flying, floating or swimming by on this planet. It's hard to think like a human because most of you 'isn't' human at all. Most of you 'is' what came before, when the world was different, simpler in a lot of ways.

One of the lessons that I promised you would be one of appreciation. Many of us don't appreciate or fully understand our bodily functions, but we need them to survive, and they are so like what so many other billions and billions of life-forms _(ah, those crazy relatives...)_ are doing right this moment. They are eating, they are digesting, they are mating, and some, very few, are resting and thinking their thoughts.

It's hard to think like a human, because humans are not that far removed from everything else. But you can transition and step up, by first understanding and embracing your base nature, stepping up by stepping down so to speak. The true mystery of life does not lie with humanity and its logic, mathematics and digital technology—the mystery and awe belong with the replicating nature of life itself. There was a time when there was no life on this planet, just raw materials, the chemical elements and ooze. And then there was a time after, when those same chemicals came together out of nature in a four lettered code that worked, at least well enough to get the ball rolling and keep it rolling.

The pattern started to replicate itself, sometimes with changes, mistakes, mutations if you will. From these simple beginnings every living thing with DNA can be traced. And it is this trial-and-error method of the environment toying with mistakes that helps us to read the story. The mistakes, these mutations, are identifiable and measurable in their style, function, and frequency—they are the markers that we can read like a book, they show our level of relation with every living thing. DNA is the story of life, the story of life's journey as it changed through evolution, and it's not over—today we worry about viruses and bacteria that will mutate beyond our chemical poisons' ability to kill them off. It's never over here on battlefield Earth, at least not until the sun starts to die (in a far-off future).

Life taking hold and advancing was not an easy journey, it is one filled with a mystery that we may never understand fully, but we can see the results around us and in us, the beautiful 'works-in-progress'. Leonardo Da Vinci was once a baby, but he grew to paint masterpieces. He started unskilled but learned along the way, learned quite well how to paint with the materials around him. With our microscopes and analysis techniques we can look upon the fabric of nature and see a masterpiece painted with simple chemicals as pigments, see the DNA unleashed upon a sheltered but changing world.

We see the end results of nature, so far, and its patterns are intricate and measurable—they contain information and stories, a history is hidden inside the helix. You've glimpsed some of that epic just now. Again, we've only scratched the surface; there is so much more exciting science in this field to explore. (*Check out geneticist and* anthropologist Spencer Wells' 2002 book, **The Journey of Man: A Genetic Odyssey,** *for a wild ride through the human genome.)* I hope to expose readers to the wonders they themselves are a part of. You may take your DNA for granted, but not me. Every cell of my being reminds me of my connection with the Cosmos. My problems don't seem so large when compared to the cosmic beauty of nature and the singular grandeur of existence. It's hard to be angry or depressed for too long when there is so much more to smile about. You're alive—that's amazing. And you're human. That's even more amazing.

You're allowed to understand, you've been given logic and learning to guide your way. You have so much potential, unrealized potential, that is becoming more real with every paragraph. Don't hide from yourself, think about yourself—learn to like what you see, embrace the mystery that is you. *Does that sound goofy and corny to you dear reader? Whose voice is telling you that? Is the voice that pressures you always right? Who gets to define awe and mystery for you?*

And you, my friend, you are literally filled with DNA, a vast self-cloning collection that screams your genetic heritage at every bodily turn, and that's okay, that's who you are. You were once a microscopic cell, a single cell with one, count 'em, one, complete set of DNA—my, look how you've grown. *How did you get so big? What's your secret? What's that? Oh, you gathered nutrients into your mouth or body (via placenta), broke them down, and then brought the basic parts together to build copy after copy after copy of the DNA...*

That sounds like a lot of work, and it is—it's a good thing that your cells do it all automatically. Take good care of your body, will you—you literally are what you eat—what else would you be? You turn food and drink into you, that's what your body does, it breaks them down to build you up, taking what it needs and discarding the rest. *(You go from microscopic to gargantuan, from one cell you become trillions, a vast collection all connected together—over 80,000 miles of neurons, more than 600 muscles, 206 bones...)* And when your body doesn't get enough food and drink, it lets you know, in various ways; pain usually gets our attention, motivating us in the short term, pain is there to protect us. We will die eventually without sustenance—*we are tied to this planet at the molecular level*: we need air to breathe, water to drink, food to eat. And we are not alone in these needs.

Our wild and woolly basic nature is part of who we are. We think that because we have language and technology we are separated from the beasts. But it is not that simple—we are still mostly beast ourselves, it is our frontal lobes that allow us to leap above and study nature and ourselves like no other. Know that the basic guttural world of the beast is always looming; its call is seductive and familiar. A wild boar will happily root around the forest floor, looking for tasty tidbits. You push a shopping cart around the supermarket floor, down one aisle and up the other, looking for tasty tidbits. Your body and brain rooting through the marketplace were developed in a much different environment than they find themselves in today, the one of the wild boar, a Stone Age one. The one without supermarkets and the World Wide Web.

We forget that we are fooled by our current surroundings, our current 'present'; we put ourselves on a pedestal. We try to be lofty in our self-image, in our thoughts and in our actions, but look about you. Look at others, look at yourself—how are we behaving? *What are the things we are thinking about? What are the things we value? How many of us seem to be at peace with ourselves, with others, with the world around us?*

From our chemistry we can easily see that we are not that far removed from the wild, we have a hidden biological animal base that belongs to us, and we to it. But this 'detrimental connection' can be overcome—the tool to get the job done is the brain, our adaptable Stone Age brain that has already done so much. It's up to the task. Plus, you are not alone, you have some help.

We learn and pass on knowledge, thanks to language, which is nothing more than code. Language is a way to record information. The person may die, but the words, the information, lives on. *This sounds an awful lot like DNA, doesn't it?* Our ancestors are dead, yet their genetic code lives on in chimpanzee and human genes generations and years later; information is coded, then passed on. Changes are introduced, some improvements get inserted, sometimes advancements flow. This book is like that. I write some; then I reread what I've written, add stuff, delete things, always trying to improve the original. Leo Tolstoy was constantly sending in revisions to his epic, **War and Peace,** even while it was being printed; he was never satisfied, always improving the language, the code *(this was before personal typewriters, Tolstoy's poor wife, Sonya, performed the duty of 'rewriting'; it's been estimated that she hand-copied most of the mega-novel at least six times, some say eight)*—an eccentric man, or one just modeling his own successful DNA?

Language is the new DNA, the new advancement, the new storehouse of human knowledge and achievement—it is an instruction booklet, literally. *(Want to build a backyard deck or an atomic bomb? You can do either with the right instructions. Want to build a man or a mouse? The same philosophy applies.)* When the records are lost, as when the great library at Alexandria was destroyed centuries ago, the human race's progress is sent reeling. We need our words, our code, to guide us; they last longer than we do, just like the DNA. *(I argue that the most popular and used word in the world today is 'okay'. It is an American word, not an English word, and because of the exporting of American culture and currency around the planet, 'okay' has become an oft-used word in everyday vernacular in all kinds of languages the world over. Its meaning is universal—'yes, I agree'. Is this okay? I think so. But what the vast majority of people don't know, Americans included, is the origin of this super-popular word. Take I-90 from Albany to Boston, and you'll pass over Kinderhook Creek near the border. An American President came from a small town south of there, Kinderhook, NY, and when Martin Van Buren was in politics he was known by a certain nickname, 'Old Kinderhook'. Sometimes legislative bills pass the Senate and House and reach the Oval Office, where they would then need the Eighth President's signature to officially turn them into law. When it was MVB's turn, so the story goes, he would put his 'O.K.' on it personally and literally; this was his signature. 'O.K. = Yes, I agree, this bill should be a Law')*

It turns out that Archimedes did indeed invent integral calculus almost two thousand years before it was fully developed by Sir Isaac Newton—but the words and information he wrote were lost when the parchment broke down. Where would we be scientifically today if those words had been saved? *(Aeschylus, one of the great Greek Tragedians circa 500 B.C., is believed to have written over 90 plays; only six have survived to modern day, and a seventh,* **Achilles**, *is only fragmentary. On a more modern 'note' (1800's), genius pianist Franz Liszt supposedly penned an instructional manual on his piano technique—his musical thoughts and insight are now lost to us.)*

We are much better at recording the words now—oral history gives way to books and compact discs and computers. Words have gone digital, information is coded electronically in an alphabet of silicon bits and bytes. *ON* or *OFF*—the digital two letter alphabet is even simpler than the genetic four letter one of DNA, but we can manipulate and experiment so readily with our electronic code because we made it. We toy with our simple invented code like gods, we proceed at a pace that far outstrips nature's—we make the digital mutations and apply them on purpose, they are guided by logic rather than randomness. Digital information processing is evolving at an accelerated rate. We know how to multiply.

We learn from nature and improve some procedures to benefit our lives. Gordon Moore, co-founder of electronics giant Intel, inadvertently coined what became known as 'Moore's Law' when he described, in a 1965 edition of Electronics Magazine, how the rate at which the number of transistors, or "number of components per integrated circuit", on a micro-chip should double every two years for the next ten years. People claim that he said 'double every 18 months', but he denies it. Interestingly, Moore's Law has continued to hold true, with computers evolving into faster and faster digital processors every two years at the doubling pace far past the original 10-year-trend he foresaw, it's still happening today, 40 years and counting... Gordon Moore was just being observant, and see how successful he turned out to be. You can be observant, too. You're allowed.

Our coded language is a simple thing compared to the storing and editing of video images—why do we love photography so? There is a reason—language mimics the written recording of DNA, photography and videography mimic visual recording of information in the brain. Vision is the processing of external Electro-Magnetic energy from the environment, you know, light, to help you get around, find food, find the opposite sex... You need information about your environment. Image may not be everything, but it sure goes a long part of the way. A large portion of our brains is devoted to sight—there is a lot to know, plus maybe you might see some danger ahead. _(More on this in Chapter 13, the 'Hollywood' chapter.)_

Computers are amazing, but they pale in comparison to the three-pound processor made by nature and time that rests between your ears. But you can't build a computer without knowing the basics. And you can't achieve true peace and understanding in your life without seeing your base nature—you can see from whence you came, you understand your origins and how they might influence you to your current detriment or happiness. All of your questions will not be answered in your search, maybe they cannot be answered at this time or at any time, but now you can see why and how some daily life-pressures get inflated. We assign importance in our lives. But life itself is really special all on its own—we forget that at times. We forget the value that we possess. I'm here to remind you.

Education is the key to appreciation, and you can learn via language *(a.k.a. this book and other ways)* some interesting things. You can go to a school or a library or the Internet to learn, learn, learn—all through the code of language and maybe some imagery. Consider your sources carefully though, we assume validity so easily, we want to believe that we are being treated fairly and with honesty, remember? Not everything written or shown may be true, including this book, though I sincerely try—you are charged with researching more on your own, like I did, find out the true answers to your questions for yourself. What you uncover might excite you; it inspired me to become a teacher and to write this book.

Learn about language, learn about human behavior, learn about animal behavior and genetics and science and nature. All of these topics are really about you—do you see? It's hard to think like a human because we are so much more than just that part. The human part is your salvation though, your ticket to happiness, but you must understand that it is a promising young sapling in a forest of mature, and somewhat more belligerent, primitive oaks. Reading this book is like taking a chainsaw and thinning out the snags—let in some light. Time to grow. See the past connections. Feel the future possibilities. Know what sunshine is and how it helps you grow.

Understanding your base nature, where you ultimately come from *(your bits and pieces even at the tiniest levels)*, serves two purposes. The first is humility. Be humble when pondering the time and cosmic machinery that worked and hewed until you had taken form. A lot had to happen to produce you, much of which you do not know, though you can learn. The calcium in your bones, the iron in your blood, the oxygen in your cells—they were all formed inside the hearts of stars, stars that later exploded to scatter their seeds, all the bits that would eventually make you, into the cold Cosmos. They would come together again, these pieces, under gravity—they would reform into a sun, a planet, even 'you' over time. Your DNA built you according to instructions, but the parts had to come from somewhere. They came from stars. More on this later, you're going to like it—this bizarre tango of gravity and heat will become a dance of dreams, a crucible of creation.

It's humbling, true, this view of nature and of your place in it. Your story indeed goes back to a time before the planet Earth was even formed. The second purpose of understanding your base nature is the opposite of humility—it is pride. Pride of accomplishment, pride of enlightenment, pride of discovery. Sure you behave like a reactive animal, but so does everybody else—and now you know why. You can also see it in your fellow Man and Woman, they may be oblivious to their nature and heritage, but you aren't. You can sense their frustration, how they are pushed and pulled by sex, by friends and family, by society, by their genetics, by advertising. You see so much more now, the chemical workings underlying the behavior. It makes you powerful, this knowledge; there is pride in knowing.

Helen Keller took great pride in tapping into the hidden world around her, you hear it in her words, and you too can experience this same joy of discovery. You can look back through time and see history, your history; you have an amazing mind and imagination. And where did these powers of yours come from and why? They didn't just appear. It's all about food and survival and sex in a much harsher climate, but the side-rewards of self-knowledge include happiness. Take pride in being a survivor. Take pride in inheriting not only a great brain but also a culture with language and electronic technology. You are lucky in your life and poised at the moment. You are ready to make the leap, and knowing your past can help to guide your future.

Be both humble and proud—the opposite sides of a personal spectrum. Be a savage and a sophisticate. Be both matter and energy. You've come such a long way to get here, and the future has so many directions. Arm yourself with knowledge—choose happiness.

The Social Circle–pressures and pleasures await

Like the pride and humility of knowledge, the aspects of social society have their own dual nature, their Jekyll and Hyde sides. In some very basic ways social structure and behavior work to your advantage—and in others, not so much.

There are plenty of successful but anti-social creatures out there. You know the murderous tale of the Black Widow spider, but then there is also the very successful solitary sea turtle, relatively unchanged after 100 million years of planetary upheavals. She comes up out of the ocean alone, laboriously, to lay her eggs in the sand. She covers them up and then returns to the water, never to see her offspring or have social contact with them again.

Hmmm... maybe the turtle is not such a good example of non-social behavior after all. I now recall about how those turtles hatch... The babies come scrambling out of the sand and make a mad flopping dash for the relative safety of the ocean waves only to be scooped up by hovering hungry birds or a lucky predatory crab. Many young turtles are eaten, true, but many also make it to the water—their birth numbers are fine-tuned through evolution to make up for those lost to predators. But what most people don't know is what happens *inside* the 'egg mound' *before* the mad dash.

All of the eggs don't hatch at once. The turtles, driven by their unseen genetics, wait when they are born. They wait and listen for the movements and sounds of their brothers and sisters. Only when there are enough alive in the dirt does the mad dash begin. What of those foolish young turtles without this genetic leaning? What if they just get up and leave too early or too late compared to their brood-mates? They will most likely be eaten. There is safety in numbers—*flocks of birds, herds of sheep, and schools of fish show the real success of mob mentality*—newly hatched turtles who wait do so with everybody else, they conform, and there is real safety in conforming to the group. When you all go together the predators will be confused, they won't know which one to choose *(this is also the secret to the zebra's black and white stripes, they're not for hiding amidst the grasses, the prey will blur together when they run as one)*—more will survive to the sea that way and pass on the trend, the genetic command to conform, a natural selection that takes advantage of social behavior. *What about the human species? Sound familiar?*

So while the sea turtle is relatively anti-social in the wild, it does rely on a very real social aspect for its individual survival at the beginning of life; the initial moments after birth depend upon it. True, this social behavior is not recognized as such by tiny turtle brains, but it is ingrained nonetheless. Social activity has its advantages, it is instinctual for a reason.

There is the anti-social success though of the salmon and other fish that lay and fertilize their eggs and then swim away. There are the lizards, the snakes, the insects, many of whom are born ready-made to take the world on in their own way, trusting to luck and the law of large numbers to survive rather than love and nurturing. You are descended from social creatures however, and if you look closely at social creatures, the ones that live and work in a collective group, you'll see some interesting features.

First off is intelligence, especially in social mammals. Who's who in the rankings of intelligence on this planet? *('intelligence' being loosely defined however you want to define it—I'm partial to finding food and solving problems.)* I offer the following list of pretty smart critters: humans, apes, dogs, dolphins, killer whales. These creatures, including humans, can all be trained, can all be ostracized from their group. They are also all hunters. You need a big brain to be a hunter, and by ingesting meat into your diet, why, that protein in turn fuels better muscles and a better brain. *(The predatory spider may be tiny, but I'll bet an arachnid's brain outweighs the fly's.)*

In the above list I've made a mistake, I offer now the more accurate choice of 'wolf' to be substituted for 'dog'—wolves are still the hunting predator more so than their domesticated cousins. Wolves' brains are bigger, up to 30% when compared to their housebound counterparts. *(Snouts are longer too, teeth are sharper, muscles are denser, ears don't droop...)* So much of their lives are in turmoil; it's tough being a wolf. They have to be smart, and they have to rely on the group in order to survive.

Ever hear of the saying 'it's a dog's life'—meaning the pampered, carefree, happy existence that a dog enjoys? Your life should be so cared for and happy—isn't your life more like a wolf's life? It's a fierce world out there, with plenty of competition; don't take anything for granted. *(work work work—struggle struggle struggle)* Provide a good shelter for your pack, bring home nutritious food to the pups, go out and do it again the next day.

Are you and the wolf so different? I don't think so—if you look at what you consider the 'smartest' critters on the planet, from army ants to elephants, they will have some kind of social nature. Our command in life is simple, the same command given to all life; survive, take in food, reproduce. Every living being is driven to do these things, some just do them better than others. Social creatures, like mammals, work together and care for each other—they survive to continue this emotional trend until a being is produced that loves and hates with such ferocity that none can stand in their path. Humans are passionate, the most passionate perhaps—and that didn't just happen, right? Our social connections started early, well before the arrival of humanity's Stone Age.

Mammals take their name from the 'mammary glands' found in a female's breasts—caring mothers make and feed milk to their babies; even dolphins nurse. *(Blue whale babies suck up 150 gallons of milk a day for the first five months of life. I think that nature screwed up—wouldn't having the male half ALSO with working breasts benefit the mammals? Twice the number of functioning nipples seems like a more successful approach to me, but I don't make the rules, I just work here...)* This sets up a strong protective social and emotional bond from the beginning of life, and even this isn't the true beginning if you consider the womb. Mammal babies are closely nurtured in a warm and protected environs, giving their brains time to develop physically into the social hunting and judging powerhouses that they are bred to be.

Parents who care raise children who live long enough to continue the trend—love, and emotions, are evolutional. That doesn't make them bad, it's just that you need to know that humans don't have the market cornered on powerful feelings. When it comes to cubs, beware the bear that cares. Love is powerful, wonderful, and helpful at times. Helpful if you're a cub, not so helpful if you are the lost hiker stumbling upon the momma grizzly bear's lair—it's relative. Still, it's good to understand this part of your psyche. We are not alone, we are connected. It's a rough and tumble world out there, we need each other. *(From recent brain chemistry studies, we have discovered that the emotion of 'love' releases chemicals that stimulate cranial pleasure centers in ways similar to the drug cocaine. It appears that Robert Palmer was right when he sang of being '**Addicted to Love**'; let's face it, we act differently, sometimes 'crazily', when hooked on drugs or love. And then when either leaves us we experience the pain of withdrawal... Just ask Romeo and Juliet...)*

In a social group, you have to rely on others to help with finding food, either hunting or gathering. You see, the group takes care of their own. Sure, we could all venture out and fend for ourselves, and when you are a panda bear who dines mostly on bamboo that might seem like a good idea. *(Pandas aren't that social, even with their own babies—a mother with twins will often let one of her cubs die. It looks to me like a species that's suffering the consequences of their anti-social actions.)* But when you are after meat, with all of that protein and promise of easy energy, then a group ambush makes more sense than a single attacker going it alone—your aim is to kill and take another creature and ingest it, this is a challenge, most creatures prefer to stay alive instead of being eaten. Challenging yes, but the nutritional rewards from a kill are superior, they power an organic revolution in brain development the way coal and water-power fueled the Industrial Revolution, energy powers growth in many forms.

There are resources to be tapped out there, and group living with its common goals gets a lot accomplished. With a group you become more than what you are individually, a synergistic effect seen in nature quite often, even at the cellular level. *With a group you become a 'limb' of a much larger animal, one with multiple moving parts. You are now no longer an individual, you are just one 'claw' of an amplified being as wide as the meadow on which you hunt.*

This new hunting formation, this 'pseudo mega-animal', is a complex thing, it takes complex brains connected in similar intent to make it work—a network of minds and purpose, driven by hunger. Stone Age humans, killer whales, wolves—the individuals need to know where they are in the hunt and in the social hierarchy—what's their status, who are they above? Who are they below? Where is the leader now? What's expected of me? Am I allowed to mate? Who am I socially allowed to mate with? *(Only one wolf, the Alpha Male, does ANY mating in the pack, with the Alpha Female of his choice; it's good to be the king... In dolphin and killer whale societies though it is often a Female that rules the roost... By the way, female dolphins are NOT monogamous, only 3% of mammal species are, and male dolphins in the wild are quite vicious toward each other. Don't think friendly 'Flipper', think ferocious 'Orca'—killer whales are actually dolphins, not whales.)*

There is complexity in the pack; there has to be organization, decisions have to be made. Your body is like a pack too, with individual cells, individual organs—yet all of them coordinate their efforts toward mutual benefit, sometimes not even aware that they and their neighbors are doing it. And we, the individuals in our social human groups, come together and work like these cells *(brain and blood cells, skin and bone—let's all work together)*, we are mimicking nature here—cells can live alone, like pandas, but look who's going extinct? The pandas or us? *(There are only 1,000 Great Pandas left in the wild. 1,000 on the planet, sound familiar?)*

There is safety in numbers, there is an advantage and an increase in intelligence when you are part of a social group. We are just doing on a large scale what is going on in our bodies successfully at a small scale. Patterns that succeed tend to repeat. I said, patterns that succeed tend to repeat... As an individual, an *organism*, we are collection of 'organs' and cells. As a *'group of people'*, especially as a hunting group, we behave as one larger more successful organism, with the individuals playing the roles of specialized organs and cells. *(Sure, we're bankers and bakers, doctors and truck drivers now, smaller parts of a bigger societal whole, but we were something similar in Stone Age days. A larger, fluidic, super-organism has evolved that coordinates, that sweeps through the forest, the jungle, the plain, the ocean, any environment it encounters— looking for prey, looking for food. See what we've been turned into, and all because it's advantageous.)*

Some creatures take advantage of this aspect of nature without the benefit of large individual brains. There are the army ants of Central and South Americas—some ants will use their bodies to form a 'living bridge' to cover a gap so that others may march over them. There are the honey-bees with specialized jobs within the hive—the famous figure-eight bee 'waggle dance' is a type of clever code *(fly in this angular direction relative to the sun for this distance...)* to tell her sisters where a particularly healthy bunch of flowers heavy with nectar are located. The termites of Africa build huge protective mounds, engineering feats complete with natural air-conditioning chimney effects. These creatures, and others like them, do benefit from social organization, but they are not hunting as a small group—that takes more coordination, more communication. This type of activity requires a much larger brain.

And we have that much larger brain, as do the other social hunting predators on this planet. That is the benefit of living in a social hunting group, a larger more complex brain that ensues from this complex lifestyle. And dietarily speaking, more meat means an even bigger brain and an even better chance of survival. Your bodily tissues are best built from a rich source of protein—including your powerful brain.

Many hundreds of thousands of years ago, more than one early hominid roamed the African landscape in the struggle for survival. By hominid I mean a proto-human, someone more than a chimpanzee but less than a modern human. These hominid groups could either be a direct step or a side branch on our evolutionary tree. And these groups lived side-by-side, maybe competing for the same food sources, maybe not. *(The Neanderthal, our genetic 'cave man' cousin, a hominid species separated by 200,000 years of evolution, had left ancient Africa and lived in isolated Europe until about 30,000 years ago. The 'first Europeans', the Neanderthal, had evolved to exploit the cold climate, but the weather started warming, the glacial ice was melting. The thick northern forest was changing into a more open landscape; it was harder for them to hunt. But not for us, we preferred this type of landscape and had invented tools, like throwing-spears, to kill our prey from a distance. The ice retreated and we hungrily moved in. The Neanderthal weren't built for speed or changing conditions, they didn't stand a chance. Your Stone Age ancestors won the day, the Neanderthal are gone forever.)*

A good example of this would be our (possible) direct ancestor, *homo erectus*, when compared with a close cousin, maybe even a precursor, who existed at the same time in Africa *(~1.8 million years ago)*—a hominid species known as *homo habilis*, but whom we affectionately refer to as *handy-man* today because we have found some of his simple tools. *Erectus* over time survived, but *handy-man* did not, why? Both had simple stone tools, but *erectus'* hand axe was much larger and more versatile than *handy-man's*. *Erectus* used his hand tool for many different things and ate many different kinds of meat; his brain size increased with the richer diet.

When *handy-man's* stone tools were analyzed however, some strange scratch-marks helped to form a theory on their demise as a species. *Handy-man* didn't last because of this battle over protein, he didn't get enough to fuel a growth in brain mass; fossil evidence confirmed his smaller brain-case—his hand tool, while it was a good one, was too simple in the long run.

Erectus had a better, more versatile tool, one that was developed because of a diet that was greater in protein to begin with. That protein came more easily because of the hunting/gathering as a social group that produced bigger brains. Better brains mean even better hunting skills and cooperation, and this means even more success in the hunt and more protein, and even bigger brains, and a better tool, and better food... the cycle feeds upon itself and we see *erectus'* brain size swell with his increased hunting prowess—we are the current end results of that struggle over protein. *Erectus'* tool was like a Stone Age

'Leatherman®' multi-tool'—it had many uses, but *handy-man's* stone tool, there were these common strange parallel markings—it appeared that perhaps *handy-man* had a much more specialized use for his tool—what could it be? *(Those of you who watch TV's most popular show,* **CSI: Crime Scene Investigation,** *know all about our ability to analyze tiny scratch marks on a semi-blunt object in order to solve a mystery.)*

In a science experiment attempting to duplicate the markings found on *handy-man's* tool, an interesting coincidence was found. A similar modern hand tool was used to 'hack' into an African termite mound—a challenge as these are made with dirt and termite spit and can be as hard as concrete. The effort resulted in making similar scratch-marks on the modern stone tool when compared to those of ancient origins—the coincidence begs a logical conclusion.

Handy-man used his tool for this one main purpose— to break into termite mounds to get at the tasty insects inside. And termites, like many insects, are a good source of protein, but that amount of insect protein was not enough when compared to *erectus* who appeared to be hunting larger game. *Erectus* had better tools, better social structure, and a better diet. He 'grew' a bigger brain and advanced while *handy-man* did not; perhaps the termites, their main source of protein, were adversely affected by a climate change, and *handy-man* couldn't adapt to a new food source—their tool couldn't help them then. Termites were good eating, but it appears that they weren't good enough. Early hominids needed bigger game than insects to fuel a bigger, even better, problem-solving brain.

Chimpanzees have been credited as 'tool makers' and took a jump up the intelligence tree when evidence was documented of them doing something similar concerning their own jungle termite mounds. Chimps would break off a small living branch using their lips and teeth to strip the smaller off-shoots and leaves leaving a long twig *(basically making a tool from the surrounding natural resources)*. Then the primate would stick the twig into a side-hole of the termite mound.

The termites inside would detect the twig—*an intruder*—and bite it in defense. After a few moments the chimpanzee would remove the twig with some insects still clinging to it—the twig would again be stripped clean as this time the chimp dined on the plump bugs. Then the bare twig, the manufactured tool, would be re-inserted into the hole and the process repeated until the tool maker had a full belly.

Chimpanzees exist because they have not had to struggle for food in the relatively lush jungle with its fruit trees and insect colonies. The chimp may be smart enough to turn a twig into a tool, but that behavior stops there. Those side-holes that the twig goes into, those were made by the insects, not the ape. And the chimpanzee only does this during the limited rainy season.

Handy-man, on the other hand, actually used a tool to break into a termite mound, a more difficult thing to do, and yet *handy-man* is gone and the chimpanzee remains. It was more difficult to find food outside the rain forest, but *erectus* managed well enough in his spartan environment over *handy-man*—his efforts in group living thankfully paid large dividends.

The big brain you and I have now, that's the big bonus. We also still care for each other. Ancient fossil evidence shows individuals with broken limbs, breaks that would preclude finding food in an easy manner. And yet those bones healed; someone was caring for individuals who couldn't fend for themselves. Other animals don't do this, if you break a leg in the wild you are done for. And today we still carry-on in this tradition of care. If you are seriously injured, go to a hospital emergency room. It doesn't matter if you have insurance or not, the professionals there have dedicated themselves to preserving life—they will work to help you, to care for you in your time of need. We would want that same level of care for ourselves were the situation reversed, wouldn't we? We look out for each other, we take care of our own.

So the social circle provides intelligence and caring for our species, and that's a good thing. But the social circle has its other side, the Dark Side that was mentioned before. European colonialists, al-Qaeda terrorists, Ku Klux Klan extremists, Nazi loyalists—they and others like them single out the outsiders for derision, even elimination. It's the underpinnings of evolution acting out, stretching its muscle in the forum of social competition. Groups of people normally dislike those other groups that are different from them—it's the way that humanity, and many species, operate, for their own survival. And it has worked, this fearing of strangers.

Living in a small hunting party group is how we developed—the Stone Age refined how we interact with each other. We feared our neighbors, and for good reason, there is only so much food to go around after all. Survival in the Stone Age was never guaranteed, it was precarious—we lived alongside of the wolves and the sabre-toothed cats, all groups fighting against similar brethren and each other for dominance. And we are still fighting each other today, it's what we're used to (and let's face it, we're good at it, perhaps the best ever at inflicting pain both physically and socially).

We haven't changed psychologically as a species, though we have made inroads on a person-to-person basis. The social circle that produced our brains also nurtured our fears. *How am I going to survive? How can I get more food, more money, more sex? Who do I need to be worried about? What do I need to be worried about?* We have the hardware to ponder these things, and it drives us crazy—there are a lot of things to consider, there are a lot of things to fear out there.

This fear of strangers has grown out of a general fear of the new and different. When we were hunter/gatherers we feared new plants—*could they be poison?* We feared coming onto a new game animal; there was a time when modern man first gazed upon a wooly mammoth lumbering along—*is this new animal dangerous?* There is fear of injury, fear of sickness, fear of death, fear of rejection, of being outcast by the group.

The big brain, coming to be because of the social interactions foisted upon the individual, has the ability to ponder lots of dangers. And it does, because danger is out there, lurking everywhere. It's best to be prepared—the Boy Scouts were only following a natural edict. The big brain that helps us to survive also helps us to worry, it helps us to envision future calamities and spurs us into action to suppress them, to prepare against them. Sure, we can think about what might go right, but more often it was healthier to think about what might go wrong. We, as a species, are a bunch of *worry-warts*. This is an old-fashioned saying for someone who can't relax, someone who is always worrying about something, envisioning the worst-case scenario.

My mother has always been that way, as I assume many mothers are. It's only natural to want to protect our children, it's a drive that comes from genetics. This overwhelming desire to protect the offspring isn't present in all animals, but it is in us; it helps with our survival this caring and protective posture that parents possess. And this caring nature is needed for many, many years. The human species pays a large price for having the big brain that we do—some of us are ignorant to the added hidden costs of this development.

Consider child birth. As a kid myself, I was quite aware of the pain that mothers go through during labor—it's legendary. You hear stories, you read stories, you see actors portraying pregnant women giving birth on TV and in the movies—in comedies, in dramas, in action films—a pregnant woman about to give birth demands that you sit up and take notice. *What's going to happen? There is pain—are there going to be problems? How far apart are the contractions?*

I knew about contractions before I knew about puberty. Giving birth was painful I learned, but necessary. When I was young I actually felt glad that I was born a boy and not a girl so I would not have to experience this pain, it looked excruciating. *(Do you know what an 'Episiotomy' is?)* And then I heard about the other animals. Other animals do not go through the extreme pain that humans go through. Human mothers can die during childbirth a lot more readily than our animal cousins—from the bleeding and the pain *(labor pains last on average about 13 hours for a new mother, and 5 hours each for the future siblings).* Why are we so unlucky this way?

It's our heads. We pay a price for big brains and our social intelligence; we have a big head, literally as well as figuratively. *Our heads changed faster than the rest of our bodies—there's trouble in trying to keep up, a woman's hips can only go so wide and not impede walking, plus that narrow pelvic gap acts as a biological bottleneck.* It takes nine long months, almost the longest of any mammal, for our bodies and brains to grow inside the womb. And grow they do, though it is the protective skull and its precious cargo of brain that needs the most nurturing. The brain would like to stay longer, develop more fully, grow even more—but the body can only stretch so far.

Everything needs to squeeze out through the narrow birth canal, big head and brain included. The bones of the skull surrounding the brain aren't fully fused, and the head sometimes morphs and changes shape, elongates, during the birthing process. There is that 'soft spot' on the top of a baby's head *(the 'fontanel')* for a reason—the skull needs to be malleable, it needs to be formed out of several separate pieces that can shift around under stress. Only after birth into the cold hard world outside the womb do the different parts of the skull finally toughen and fuse together. *(Go ahead—touch your own skull, feel its hardness? It didn't used to be that way. My how you've grown...)*

The 'split' skull prior to birth is not a purely human feature, though we do take it to extremes, it is more of an animal one. When I first started teaching Earth Science ten years ago, I heard of a relatively tiny fossilized skull of a Tyrannosaurus Rex dinosaur *(the 'Cleveland Skull'—it was dug up in Montana, but now resides in the Cleveland Museum of Natural History).* However, there was a problem, it didn't look like a normal T-Rex fossil. It wasn't very large, and at first scientists thought that they had uncovered a juvenile, a baby T-Rex—a very rare find. But upon closer examination it was noted that the bones of the skull had fused significantly together, indicating that the specimen was actually an adult. Scientists had discovered a new type of 'man-sized' T-Rex that roamed an ancient Earth. *(It was subsequently named Nanotyrannus, but there is still lively controversy over this saurian subset—more fossil evidence is needed.)*

Bones, brains, bodies, and DNA—they all tell a story. This may be a new adult miniature species of the giant Tyrannosaur, the fused skull bones certainly indicate it. *(Now why did a miniature T-rex develop in the first place? Fossils are limited in their revelations.)*

We are born, our skulls harden, and we mature. As humans we take the longest of any mammal to reach full adult status—around 18 years *(I've heard that we physically 'peak out' at 25).* Think of how quickly other animals reach adulthood. Puppies and kittens need to be spayed and neutered a year after birth. A pony is born, weak kneed at first, but galloping to garland-wreathed victory at Churchill Downs only two or three years later. Why do humans take so long to develop? It's our brains again. Those big, complex, problem-solving analytical brains between our ears—it takes years and years of observation, of learning, of trial-and-error and social interaction to fine-tune the human existence.

Sometimes this existence is tough. I once had a 14-year-old student in class, a girl who was picked on regularly because she was different, a little slower and larger than her fashion-minded tormentors. Her mother was at her wit's end; these other girls could not be forced to be friends with her daughter, or even to be civilly nice to her. The daughter was sad, she tried harder to befriend her harassers, but desperation is not often seen as attractive. It was a sad story, one a 14-year-old girl or boy goes through from time to time—the quest for social acceptance and the ensuing pain of ridicule and rejection.

And when we ourselves struggle socially it affects the other parts of our lives, our academic performance or our jobs. We don't feel on top of the world when we're criticized or put upon. It takes a long time to grow up, and some of us reach 18 years to find that we have excelled or fallen in the hallways when compared to the classrooms. Boys and Girls play at being Men and Women with no written rules to guide us, just genetics and MTV—growing up could have been a happier time for many of us.

We didn't know we were supposed to be happy in the face of adversity—no one had told us many of the things that you've read about so far in this book. We were naïve, going where the social current and our genetics would lead us. We felt powerless, we felt like children, but little did we know that we were so much more, even then.

We try to empower children by teaching them—as a student and a teacher I've encountered the famous, *"Why do we have to learn this?"* query from bored students learning about the minutia of history or calculus. My response these days as a teacher handles that question easily—we don't know what you are going to need years from now. Even you don't know what you're going to need, you could change your mind in the future and switch interests or careers. Why learn this 'stuff'? Because we have to teach you everything, that way you'll have what you need if you need it, it'll be in your bag of tricks, *be prepared*, remember? Learn it all, you're capable—the problem is however that this takes time and effort, time and effort that we would rather spend elsewhere, perhaps in social pursuits instead of academic ones. *(Einstein often skipped classes to hang out in the local café... His social predilections came back to bite him, he couldn't get a job at first after graduating. In hindsight maybe that wasn't such a bad thing—a teaching job may have gotten in the way of his discoveries. It's all relative with Einstein.)*

So what do they teach us in school? Spelling and Vocabulary (came in handy for me), Math and Science (these too), Art, Music and History (heck, it's all good) to name a few subject areas—and then there's Gym, or *'Physical Education'* to go by its more official moniker. That was another whole type of education, getting picked, or not picked, for teams. Social posturing, bullying—it was, and is, a type of free-for-all with no written rules concerning social etiquette, just a gym teacher to break up any fights that pop-up. The school provides the environment, but we awkwardly have to feel our way alone *(inside our heads)* along the selfish social landscape. Some children bring guns to school to cope with the competitive pressures—can these social pressures be that overwhelming? What do you think? Most of us are familiar with the real-world tragedy at Columbine, but listen in on a fictional conversation between a father and son before a violent outburst in the socially unforgiving **Do The Right Thing** *(some of Spike Lee's Academy Award® nominated script dialog has been edited out; Danny Aiello's performance was also nominated for an acting Oscar®):*

Danny Aiello: **Why you got so much anger in you?**
John Turturro: **Why? I'll tell you why. My friends—they laugh at me. They laugh right in my face...**
Danny Aiello: **...They're not your friends. If they were your friends they wouldn't laugh at you.**

And then there were the school sponsored social activities—the dreaded 'square dance classes' when we were in fourth grade, or the ice cream socials or the high school dances where everyone stared and stood around the edges of the gym floor while the DJ or live band rocked on. No one wanted to be the first one to dance, to look foolish—to be the focus of everybody else. Eventually, a few brave and/or intoxicated girls and guys would throw caution to the wind and gingerly start to shake their booty *(or was it their 'groove thing')*. That was all it usually took, the ice was broken and soon everyone was not afraid of getting down in their fancy designer jeans to some bad 1982 rock and roll music. *I wish they would play a slow song...* You came to the dance for a reason.

It takes a long time to grow up, and even when we 'arrive' at adulthood we have no real enlightenment as to our purpose or pursuit of happiness. We're given a diploma and many warm sentiments instead. *(Good luck, the future is yours!)* And yet here you are, scratching your head in confusion at times—maybe you haven't graduated from school yet, maybe you have, but regardless of where you are in life it's never too late to understand yourself, and others, better. Or, in another way, it's better late than never to see your dual nature.

See the two sides of the social circle—see how it forges us and binds us together, but see also how the negative aspects inflict pain upon its members. *How much does it matter what other people think?* This mental recognition of social manipulation changes the way we are affected by personal and group interactions, it helps deflect the sting of social stigma.

Life isn't perfect, for anybody—but you have an advantage. You can see every social setback on your path as another step along your journey, another step toward total consciousness of your being, your surroundings and your happiness. See many of your problems for what they are, your normal attempt to fit in, to be a part of the group. And that *is* normal, you just don't want the group to get your goat. Let it build you up, not tear you down—take away the tiger's teeth. Do you follow the latest trend or buck it? You decide what suits you. How much do you care? Why do you care?

Nikolai Valuev is the current WBA heavyweight boxing champion of the world. He is the first Russian to ever hold this title, but he is special in other unique ways. Nikolai may be the first champion to be an avid reader of Leo Tolstoy, but at a weight of 328 lbs./149 kg and a height of 7'0", he is also the tallest and heaviest of heavyweights to earn the human male pinnacle of accolades. *(He is also undefeated with the stunning record of 45-0 to include 33 wins by way of knockout.)* His height and strength have served him well as an adult boxer, but imagine him as a kid. Imagine being 6'6" tall in the sixth grade. Imagine the stares you receive from being unable to hide your great size no matter where you went. In a pre-fight interview, Nikolai describes how he has personally dealt with being socially different. This boxer is wiser and happier than many I imagine.

Lots of people, I'm sure, don't see me as an ordinary person, but this really doesn't have an impact on me, because for me the most important thing is how you perceive yourself, not how the world sees you.

It's nice to be chosen, it validates us, it flatters us. But what if we aren't special? The majority of us are not the gifted, beautiful people you see on MTV videos or the Oscars® or the cover of Cosmo, the majority of us are far from super-stardom. But the group calls to us, seducing us, urging us to take notice and to play by the group's rules. To the uneducated and reactive animal nature we possess, it's an easy thing to fall prey, to see where you lie on the social scale and find it far from the top, far from truly satisfying. We spend our lives judging and being judged—we can't help it, it's part of what got us here, the good and not-so-good side of being a social analytical tool maker.

We wage war against prejudice in society—it's not fair to pre-judge a person based on their sex, or skin pigmentation, or age, or hair color, or place of national/local origin, or sexual inclinations, or religion, or weight, or number of missing limbs—the list goes on. But to not pre-judge would go against what it means to be human; you are denying the processing power of the big brain, the one that got us here. To be fair is a modern concept—the Stone Age world lacked fairness, there was no written law. We pre-judge today thanks to who we were; we are not fair, aggression and greed got us here. We will not be able to stop with the prejudice now because that is what your big brain does. It's not thinking 'civilization', it's thinking 'survival' and 'advancement'.

Your Stone Age brain thinks hard. It analyzes things, including social standings and social networks, by comparing what you see or experience against everything else you've learned, seen, or experienced. We hold things up for scrutiny, everything—*Is this new? What do I know about it? Is it similar to something else? Is it dangerous? What have others told me? How does this affect me?* Being able to make quick, sound judgments, or decisions, in the wild is what helped our Stone Age ancestors survive—*judge* everything, *compare* everything, *contrast* everything. *Learn Learn Learn—about everything, then Judge Judge Judge...*

We've inherited that processing power. We do it everyday, especially in the hallways and at the cocktail parties; we can't help ourselves. It's built into us at the genetic level, but we can recognize it and offset its influence if we're savvy enough. We can try to detach ourselves and not fall prey, but as we are finding out, that may be harder to do than we would like—social judging runs very deep, deeper than our conscious mind, and that makes our job even more difficult—but we don't give up. We study and learn and apply, it's what we do. It's what this book is about. *How knowing about nature and humanity can help you be happier.*

The book is about knowing, you have to do the applying—fight fire with fire, your brain got you into this mess, your brain can get you out. But the deck is stacked against you—life isn't fair, and you may be unaware of a certain social sleight-of-hand mental maneuver designed to tilt the scales out of your favor. Ever run uphill or swim upstream? Remember, stay strong in the face of social adversity. Here comes a brisk headwind now...

Claude Steele, a professor and researcher at Stanford University since 1991 *(he also served as president of the Society for Personality and Social Psychology)*, has uncovered the insidious hidden presence of an ingrained social prejudice. We may not be totally immune from its influence no matter how hard we try. This human social behavior that Dr. Steele investigated and named is called *'Stereotype Vulnerability'* or *'Stereotype Threat'*. It has to do with the way we quietly judge ourselves in the social circle— where do we stand when compared to others? And upon our private mental analysis we often conclude that we come up short. We beat ourselves up before we even 'take the field' by silently admitting defeat on a social level; we are so good at prejudice that we perform it on ourselves.

There is a minefield of social stereotypes out there, and we are vulnerable to these social pressures because of who we are and how we got here—it affects our mental performance, as Dr. Steele discovered, but I say it also strongly affects our level of happiness and contentment. Being a human is tough at times, but knowledge is power. Don't just be happy, *learn* how to be happy even when the deck is stacked against you, because it is a lot of the time.

Here is what Professor Steele did. He put together a psychological experiment to see if students would perform differently by affecting some simple social stereotypical cues. How simple? Participants had to record their ethnicity, or not, when they filled out 'basic personal information' on their test form. The test itself was nothing more than a random collection of challenging questions taken from old MCAT's *(Medical College Admission Tests)*, and students were meant to struggle with the questions' difficulties.

Steele noticed something amazing, the Stereotype Vulnerability, by analyzing two sets of results from black males taking the test. The first group who took the test did so by simply filling out their name, they were not asked to check off a box or make any reference to their ethnicity. The exact same test was given to another random group of black men, only this group had to identify themselves on the form as 'black men'. It was the only difference between the tests. This group, just by acknowledging their forced membership in a social layer deemed inferior by a societal stereotype, triggered something amazing. They performed more poorly on the test compared to the other black men, they were less confident. Not only did they answer more questions wrong, but they also doubted and changed their answers more often.

We are intimately affected by our social surroundings and layers—we judge everything, including ourselves, by its social context. *(Compare and Contrast, yes?)* Social connections were needed, they helped us to survive in small groups during the Stone Age. Now when considered on a national or global scale these connections can affect your performance and steal your happiness away—the 'group' today is a lot larger than in the Stone Age, there are groups within groups, and all groups are not created equal in the eyes of society, a group can be ostracized just as an individual can. *(Again, we model on a large scale what happens at the small.)* The unwritten laws, society's preferences and values, we know them and it affects us though we try to minimize this or deny this. We can't isolate ourselves from the experiment—we *are* the experiment. *(For many young black males, getting good grades in school isn't 'cool', everyone knows that the information is skewed toward whites, if you're good in school then you're 'acting white', an outsider... For this subgroup, high academic achievement can lead to high loneliness. It's tough being different, it costs us socially—if you let it. It might be wise to make some new friends, none of us is ever really alone. I say, dare to achieve, even in the face of social fear.)*

Claude Steele also showed how other social groups are affected by their own stereotypes. White males were not immune to social pressures. One control group took a difficult math test, the other took the same test but was told that their scores would be compared against those of Asian males. White males told this fact did worse—*everyone knows that Asians are better at math...* Steele conducted experiments with women and other groups too, always revealing a deep human connection with our society. We care so much about what other people think that it drives us to distraction.

A foreign-born spokesman steps to the microphone and says how sorry he felt for Americans when he first came to this country. Oh, sure, you hear how great it is in America, come to America, it's fantastic, but I had no idea that you

Americans were so bad off. I come to this country and I turn on the TV or I look at magazines and I see now how Americans suffer more than any society on the planet. What am I talking about? Well there is your breath, it's awful, you need mouthwash for that. And then there's the body odor, the hemorrhoids, the foot fungus, the post nasal drip, the dandruff, the yellow teeth, the lack of hair, having too much unwanted hair, the arthritis, the erectile dysfunction, the depression—heck, I'd be depressed too, but America has got a product for that...

It's true, Americans are great marketers, we use fear to sell you more products, to make a bigger profit. And there is a huge fear of not fitting into the social landscape— *Dandruff? Egads man! Do something will you? That's disgusting, and you want to make a good first impression...* Women buy cosmetics to be more attractive, men wear expensive shoes and watches to alert others to their monetary social standing. We all preen and posture and judge others and judge ourselves because that is what we do—only is that the best way to ensure our happiness?

Take a step outside the social circle, see it for what it's really worth. Something valuable that produced you, supports you, and in a sense trained you, and also as something vicious that will take you down in a heartbeat and does so often. The power of the social circle is always there; your friends, your family, acquaintances, complete strangers on the street or campus—it's how *you* relate to them, how much you care about them and their judgments concerning you that gives them power over you, that determines how you will be affected. Many times we let how others *may* think of us to over-influence us, we let others steer and choose our course of action because we are afraid of how we will appear. We put the social pressure on ourselves, do you see it? Stop giving other people the power over your happiness, keep it for yourself. Keep the power.

Keep the happiness. You can have it all, with a change in thinking.

Do you 'have a grudge' against someone? Did someone say or do something that you didn't like? How long were you planning to hold that negative energy inside you—forever? Until 'they' apologize? Don't wait for 'them', that gives 'them' power over you. Their bad act that hurt you in the past, can't you see that it causes you pain every time you think about it, even now? Learn the freeing power of social forgiveness, not for them, but for you. Learn to forgive so that you benefit, so that you can smile and move on, focusing on more important and beneficial connections and relationships. So you weren't treated fairly, join the club. Quit your complaining, what are you gaining? Here it pays heavily to look forward, not behind you. Smile as the negativity swirls away in your wake, you've got better, more beautiful things to do with your time than dwell. Hey buddy! Watch where you're going!

Invaders from Venus

My hat goes off to Dr. John Gray, I read his entertaining 1992 book, **Men are From Mars, Women are From Venus**, a few years after it first was published. I was in a long monogamous relationship at the time, a long enough time anyway that both my significant other and I were driving each other crazy periodically. I read the book first and smiled, then I had my girlfriend, Elizabeth, read it, and she smiled. *I can see now why you act the way you do... The opposite sex is 'mysterious' but I'm learning...* The book brought us closer together as a couple. There is a reason that Dr. Gray's book was a Best Seller, the pages sang with insight concerning the differences between men and women, how we communicate in our own way, what we desire in a relationship, and the mistakes we sometimes make when dealing with the opposite sex.

In the book he uses the Mars and Venus analogy to illustrate that Men and Women seem to come from different planets—we want different things, and when we talk to each other, the same uttered words can often be interpreted differently between the sexes. Of course, there is mythology involved, but Dr. Gray avoids the elephant in the middle of the room—Mars and Venus are generic, stereotypical symbols of masculinity and femininity and he makes no mention of ancient mythology. He also approaches the problems of inter-sex communication in a loving, caring manner. But *why* we are so different—he avoids that. Dr. Gray may be an expert on modern communication strategies; he may understand our differences, but from his perspective you don't need to know why we are so different in order to overcome our communication difficulties. I say, the more you know the better.

He makes many valid points, and much of his book serves as a 'translation dictionary' to shed light on what we really mean when we try to communicate. Men and women can understand each other and fulfill each other's needs better, knowledge here is definitely a good thing. If you are in a committed relationship with the opposite sex, read his book, it is enlightening and entertaining.

But this book, as you may have guessed by now, concerns deeper connections—why are there differences in behavior and thoughts patterns to begin with? Dr. Gray desires you to get what you want out of relationships, but what is it you want? Why do you want it? What animal emotions have evolved to drive you crazy at times, to seemingly stand in your way? For me, it's not enough to know that I *am* a certain way, I want to know *why* I am that way. And once I know what's driving me onward and upward and sometimes backward, I then adjust my perspective. The more I think about it, the clearer my path becomes. And I have to think a lot—things are not what they appear to be.

Women and men, in many ways, have become caricatures that we embrace and strengthen, to give us a better sense of 'self'. Many of us need our symbolic performances like a crutch—the woman who can't leave the house without applying lipstick or the man who has to suck in his gut and throw out his chest as he walks down the street. We know people like this. It's a deep part of who we are, but who are we? There seems to be a treadmill of social behavior that we are placed upon even before birth; if it makes you happy, stay on and keep walking along with most of the masses, it's familiar and comfortable, though not always pleasant and productive.

This book though gives you the power to step off the treadmill if you'd like—here, try this ten-speed bicycle on for size and ride through the world instead of trudging along on a moving sidewalk that doesn't really go anywhere.

Experience the world up close and personal, be an adventurer. By seeing what's normally hidden from you, you can start to make more sense of the world and yourself. You are a product of nature, but just what does that entail? When you are ready for more the world will still be there, hold on tight and try to smile—it may be scary but it's the best way to grow. Upshift, downshift, brake, accelerate— feel the wind. *(For even more wind, literally, get your motorcycle license. Social problems blow on by when I'm cruising calmly down the road with a smile on my face—I call it 'rolling therapy'... Hmmm, have you ever noticed that you never see any motorcycles parked outside the psychiatrist's office?)*

Looking back now at his 'cute' title in perspective with what I have experienced and learned, Dr. Gray was on the right track, but he didn't quite see the total picture based on my interpretation of mythology and human behavior. Women may be from Venus, but they colonized it after leaving Mars, and now their sights are set on Earth. Women are Martians too, first and foremost; we, men and women, are cut from the same cloth. Before I get to 'what is the same' though, let's first trudge up the side of Mt. Olympus and spy Humankind toiling below and analyze the familiar refrain; why man and woman seem so different— the segregation of the sexes.

What am I talking about? For those of you unfamiliar with the mythology, Mars is the ancient God of War, while Venus is the Goddess of Love—enter Stone Age Man and Woman upon the stage of life. Man is the arrogant hunter *(emulating Mars)*, competing on the plain, cooperating silently with other men lest they scare their prey. It's all about the competition between the men: who is the strongest, who is the fastest, who made the killing blow.

When Stone Age men *(and modern men)* come trotting home from a hard day's work, they continue their manly trend, treating a female companion like she is 'one of the guys'. Men aren't used to talking to other men, or women, about their feelings, that smacks of weakness—men should be tough, they don't need help because they are strong, right?

Men also generally don't communicate their daily problems, or any problems, in a relationship—to bring light to problems would also indicate weakness. *(This harkens to the famous, 'Why don't you stop and ask for directions?' scenario with the man claiming—'I'm not lost...' She's thinking, **'He's lost'**, and he's thinking, **'I'm lost'**—but he can't stop now and ask for help, that'll prove her right, she'll 'win', plus then there's the guy at the gas station that he has to get the directions from, he'll smirk knowingly—'nice going buddy...' Ah, relationship bliss)* And the last thing a man wants to appear to anyone, anyone, is weak.

Man... Must... Compete... Always?—No, not always, but you have to opt out of the game for that to happen. It can be done, with the proper mindset, but that takes focused conscious effort. Good luck with that—practice makes perfect, see how many times you can 'not compete' in a week... Hmmm... Do you see what's wrong with this task? That's it, turn 'not competing' into a personal competition. Sheesh—it's hard to get away from, it runs so deep...

Women also were not immune to the social forces in their line of specialized work. They were the principle gatherers in the Stone Age. *(Women may have helped with Stone Age hunting duties, families have to eat after all, but she certainly would have had difficulty helping while pregnant or caring for babies. Men evolved to be bigger and stronger, their brains accept and welcome risky physical endeavors. When they are able to hunt and support a wife and children back at the hearth, that makes a man happy, he feels like more of a man. A flashy sportscar serves this same purpose, to feel more manly. "I can afford this luxury, I have resources and wealth at my command, I can easily support you, doesn't that make me more attractive to you?" It's not that farfetched. When popular Internet dating services are studied, it was discovered just who women were responding to—who were they choosing? One man looks like a professional model, another a stereotypical 'geek' complete with glasses, and they both write to a single woman who is searching for a man—when does the geek get just as many responses as the hot male model? When the 'geek' makes 155,000 dollars more per year, that's when. Don't be surprised, it's the Stone Age way and we are still Stone Age people, it's who we are. We are driven by both physical cues of beauty and youth and also the need for economic security. We make 'prejudgments' all the time; your brain is really good at that, it's how we all got here.)* The women's time was spent in the forest or field gathering needed supplies for survival. Women worked together and talked together—no need to be quiet, they weren't hunting game animals; buried tubers don't scare easily, nor any of the many different plant and mineral resources that surrounded them. Bringing clean water would also be a vital chore.

They also raised the children, talking to them, caring for them, exposing them to the world and teaching them to talk for themselves. *(A scientific study I heard of years ago followed around both men and women recording not what they said, but how many words are actually spoken on a regular basis during normal everyday life. The figure I recall [more info on this at the end of the book] is that women speak up to 3x as many words per day when compared to men; they speak more because our brains are different, and our brains are different because of millennia spent in different, specialized forms of labor. It makes logical sense to my Stone Age brain, how about yours? Do women talk more than men? What do you think? What's your experience? I would like to see this study done again, wouldn't you? And what of 'effeminate' homosexual men and 'manly' lesbian women speaking rates? No studies have been done here that I am aware. Is there a difference? Is it 'who we are' or 'who* *we **think** we are' that makes the most difference? If the gay men do speak more and the lesbian women less, what does this say about true masculinity and femininity? How malleable are we sexually? I hope some curious scientists pick up this ball.)* Women tend to think like women and talk like women, and when they come home from a hard day's work they are no better than the men—they project a feminine perspective upon their male counterparts. Before you know it, these specialized ways of thinking would creep in to cause communication breakdown between the mating pair fomenting strife and unhappiness, social discord even. My how we drive each other to distraction.

But don't forget that we needed this division of labor in order to succeed in the wild—we specialized doing this even before the Stone Age rolled around, it made us more efficient; divide and conquer to focus your efforts is another old adage that remains sound advice. The hunters became better at their job just as the gatherers and child-raisers became better at theirs. People give Henry Ford a lot of credit for inventing the assembly line; he surmised correctly that if a person would just focus on one task, becoming a specialist, then efficiency and productivity could increase. And it did, at first. But specializing at putting on radiators or wheels or a car's bumper is mind-numbing work. Ford took a human's skill at focus and specializing in the hunt and put it to work for himself—*Here, focus on building this car for a while...* We may be good at putting things together, but that is not what our brains were developed for; we were bred in a different time—we love the uncertainty of the hunt, the thrill of the chase. (*Casinos know this very well. The next hand, the next toss of the dice, the next pull of the slot machine... Success is just around the corner... This mimics the style of Stone Age life, one where great exhilaration or sorrow was an unknown outcome. We really like being lucky, it gives us great joy.*)

There is no thrill or joy or uncertainty to putting in a brake pedal, hour after hour, day after day. *(It was Ford who popularized the eight-hour-workday and the forty-hour-workweek. Many Europeans think we're crazy to give up so much time—but we don't 'give it up', we 'invest it'; we trade our time for money. Now if only we didn't want so much money, but there is never enough...)* The dazed workers were bored to tears; their Stone Age brains finally rebelled against the monotony and soon the hired help started leaving the factory assembly line with alarming frequency.

Employee turnover is a problem though, it costs a lot of money to hire and train new workers *(a debilitating 10% of workers were absent on any given day, sometimes from a mysterious illness referred to as 'ford-itis')*—Henry Ford put a stop to this 'quitting', he raises wages, he doubles them *(to a whopping $5 a day; by 1914 his workers were earning 5x the American average—Ford becomes the world's first Billionaire when he amplifies production).* This kept the workers on the line, the money was too tempting, and it saved Ford cash in the long run. And women again are not immune, they are the same as men. They can focus at the mind-numbing work as well.

During wartime there was a shortage of factory labor as men left the cities to fight overseas—enter *'Rosie the Riveter'*, women picked up the slack in the factories, working swing shifts and churning out the goods. Of course the men owning and running the factories couldn't pay them equal wages compared to their male counterparts *(during the second World War 60% the pay of a white male worker was common)*, they were the 'daintier' sex after all... little did they know...

For Henry Ford, it was all about efficiency and cost while using men to his advantage—*You know that fine-tuned problem-solving instrument between your ears? Let's put that to work screwing screws or nailing nails. Here, stand here, now when this part comes along this conveyor belt you do this to it... then do the same thing to the next part when it comes along, and then again, and again... Do a good job and I'll pay you monetary wages...*

Men became the 'bread winners', working in urban factories for money that could be spent on food, housing, clothing, entertainment, transportation, your own car for instance—Henry Ford was offering a new way of life, and men bought into it. *Support your family by living in a makeshift hut and following the skittish herd, or instead bring home the bacon by trading eight hours of your life for flexible money, your choice.* It wasn't hard for your Stone Age brain to adapt to this new industrialized environment; humans and other species have been adapting for millions of years, and we're good, really good, at focusing on a new task when we want to. It gives us pleasure—we are learning machines. When we had to hunt for our survival, each trip to the wild was uncertain, filled with hope and possible adventure—success was not guaranteed, this kept life interesting. In the factory though, familiarity breeds contempt, and tasks were further reduced into unskilled steps. Workers became like cogs in the machine; unthinking, just produce. You are guaranteed a day's wage, no fooling; just do your boring job. How exciting and fun is that?? *(Not!!)*

Men had become specialists in hunting over the great duration, women became the specialists in gathering—and together we loved and cared for each other and raised children and survived the tough times. But this division of labor that made us so successful, it changed us too. Our brains adapted to our chores making us even more efficient at our jobs. That's why we are so good at adapting to new situations today, we're still in the Stone Age, we're used to adapting. Working on a factory assembly line seems like a better idea than subsistence farming and hunting, why with these wages we can have a car, a home, a phone, a school, food for the kids—but at what cost?

There are more resources for your family but your brain is dying of boredom. We were not meant for the factory, though we adapt to it because it models what we have known all along—*specialize and do more*. Specialize in the hunt and be a better hunter—kill more. Specialize in gathering and be a better gatherer—find more. Specialize in farming, be a better farmer (*~15,000 years ago*)—grow more. Specialize in working on an assembly line (*~100 years ago*)—earn more money. We'd like to think that we've changed quite a bit over time, but have we really?

This is a basic sentiment reflected throughout this book. Who we were in the past, as a species, has deleterious effects on who we are in the present. Dr. Gray approached the differences between men and women in a loving and positive way, and he offers very sound advice. But the world today isn't always so pretty; there are hidden Stone Age undercurrents that shape us and steer us. Mythologically speaking, the good Doctor only got the picture partially right. Women may appear to be Venusian, quite different from men, but deep down they can be more Martian than the men themselves.

I grew up as a boy and went to a public school steeped in the social competitions of male puberty; I did not have intimate social details into the mysterious workings of those creatures known as 'girls'—I just knew that they were different and somehow special and that most of the other guys came to that same conclusion about the same time I did. Boys can be cruel to each other, we are bred for competition after all, to struggle and try to rise above the rest. I did not know at that time the true extent that girls will go to socially punish one of their own kind.

I do now. As an adult teacher covering classes from fourth grade remedial math to college level advanced physics, I've seen a lot. And our little ladies, our petite delicate flowers of love from the planet Venus, why, they can be vicious little carnivorous Venus Fly Traps when they want to be—only they pounce on larger prey, namely their own *(and, to a lesser extent these days, 'unworthy' males)*. Now that I think about it, it makes perfect sense. Sure, we had a division of labor for most of our history *(we lived as hunter/gatherers for approximately 96% of the last 4.5 million years)*, and that affected us, but men and women are not as different as you may have been led to believe—time for some truth.

There is that whole 'X' and 'Y' genetic chromosome thing, but the vast majority of our genetic code is identical—boys actually start out female and 'grow into' being boys while in the womb, it is our genetic heritage once again, instructions coming from the DNA steering our physical development. Someone had to come along first *(like the Chicken or the Egg bit, it's the Egg by the way—reptiles laid them long before they evolved into birds)*, and there was asexual reproduction long before the benefits of sexual reproduction *('O' what benefits!)* burst upon the scene.

'Females' came about on this planet before the male form appeared—think of cloning as a society of females giving birth to more females, no need for a man... until the environment changes. When the 'male' appeared it was a happy mistake, a beneficial mutation that allowed life to explode in variety like never before, and variety is good, variety allows an avenue for change. Compete, and the winner advances. And then you do it over again, and over, and over... *(An assembly line in nature, only mistakes are encouraged by the Big Boss—environment)*

Males evolved from the female form, it's true. His large male penis is just an overblown extension of the female clitoris, which, from what I understand fellas *(at least on the human body)*, has over twice the number of sensitive sexual nerve endings as does your 'helmet of love'—and this volume of sensitivity is packed into a much smaller surface area too. You may have an orgasm, she has multiple orgasms *(your results may vary—the female pig supposedly can have an orgasm that lasts over an hour, now you have a new appreciation for the other white meat)*—our bodies are different, but not by much. If you still doubt the whole 'male from female' scenario, do your own research, look into what we know about fetal development—if you know very little going in you'll be shocked and amazed, trust me. As additional food for mental thought men, consider your nipples. Hmmm... Kinda funny aren't they? I mean, why do you have them? You can't nurse a child even if you'd like to... *The fetal transition of male from female kicks in AFTER the feminine nipples have formed, guys start out life as girls in the womb. Our bodies and our minds, while technically different, are based in much similarity. It sounds like science fiction, but we are more alike, Women and Men— Girls and Boys, even from the fundamental level, than we would like to admit.*

We want to be different though, we want to establish definite differences between the sexes. We go out of our way to advertise outward social signs that we belong to one group or the other. What would happen at a large office complex on Wall Street if several 'manly men' came into work one day donning blouses, skirts, and heels? There is no law against it, but yet it doesn't happen.

Even men who would like to wear a skirt, blouse, and heels into work do not dare to—it would cause too much of a 'distraction'; our intrepid cross-dressing men would then have to deal with all of the 'outsider' posturing and ostracizing from other men and women that goes on with social humans. In some cases there is even hate bashing or physical violence waiting for those who flaunt mixed-gender signals. *(Kids these days—oh wait, these are the adults perpetrating the beatings...)* In private parochial schools across the country, little boys are forced to wear pants and button-down shirts while little girls must wear skirts and knee socks to classes—we like things a certain way. We want men and women, boys and girls, to be different from each other.

We also emphasize the differences when dealing with each other socially, when we have more freedom over our attire. The more 'masculine' a man is, or more 'feminine' a woman is, the more attractive they will be to the opposite sex *(and sometimes the same sex, 'not that there's anything wrong with that...')*—we look for known gender signals. Our complex brains see the connection of symbolism and sexuality—a short skirt or a muscle shirt—they speak for us. And these obvious masculine and feminine cues are exaggerated willingly by us, they can do more than speak, they can shout. For example, men have short hair, women have long—is it because our hair is intrinsically different? No, male hair and female hair are identical. If a man wanted to, he could grow out his flowing mane and visit the beauty salon and come out with curls and shine to rival Julia Roberts or Jessica Simpson *(or Fabio)*.

Short hair on men became fashionable as the function of war ran its course. Ancient soldiers noted painfully that long hair on a man was a detriment in battle, it could be grabbed and held, and then a body assaulted. *(Ever see girls fight where they grab each other's hair? I have. Men supposedly know that game, too. Anyone remember an old cartoon depicting a short-haired caveman knocking a long-haired woman out with a club and then dragging her back to the homestead by her long hair? No wonder people think Men are from Mars, but people forget that you ladies know how to scrap...)* Short hair was a hair-style for male warriors, a manly 'doo' for manly men. A Greco-Roman warrior would return home from protecting the household, back to his wife who takes care of the children—and since she doesn't have to fight battles she can grow her hair long. And if long is good, then longer is better... Longer hair means more feminine hair, but again, man vs. woman, the hair on either's head would be just as soft.

Witness a common battle-cry coming from the parents of hippie-boys during the 1960/70's, *"Cut that hair, you look like a girl!"* Parents were using social shame to manipulate their kids, but the shame doesn't work so well when the whole group is doing it... The hippies were happy for more reasons than just the chemical ones—they rebelled socially, they didn't have to conform to the norm. *(At first, they would make their own 'norm' eventually; competition and judgment never really go away...)* But the times, they were a changing, everybody's 'norms' were changing. Women were finally being unhooked from their tethers to stretch their Martian mores; the silk and lace gloves were about to come off.

Women have cosmetics, women have special clothing, special hair-styles—they are indeed different, but many of the differences are external. Mentally she can be just as ruthless as a man, especially if her children are threatened. I've heard more than one generally sweet, diminutive mom say that she could kill easily to protect her son or daughter if endangered. The desire to nurture runs deep—soccer moms today, cold-blooded defenders of the hearth tomorrow, whatever it takes; a dual nature personified. You want some of this? Who's your dainty Venusian now?

And it gets even more interesting. Women have eyelash-curlers. It's this funny looking metal 'clamp' contraption that's supposed to make your eyelashes curl upward—how many millions of these things are in vanity drawers and make-up bags across the world right now? And why? Why do ladies feel that they need eyelash-curlers? Do you know the reason? I do. They do it because they're Martians at the core. *Beautiful?* Maybe. *Delicate?* Perhaps. *Competitive?* Oh my—you have no idea...

Long. Dark. Curly. Yes, these types of eyelashes are more feminine than masculine ones, and we want to emphasize the differences, right? *(hmmm... if the hair on the 'top' of our head is the same...)* But do men really choose a woman based on her eyelashes? There are other physical cues, many of them, that we men are checking out—eyelashes are nice *(we'll notice if they're missing, maybe)*, but there are breasts, and legs, and hips, and an ass, and that long hair, and those red lips, and oh-my-those-eyes... Am I making it sound like the man is a horny hound-dog, salivating at the mere notion of sexual innuendo? Good, because we are that way for a reason, it's the Stone Age way, we need sex to survive, silly—and you petite flowers from Venus, how do you behave, hmmm? If our genetics are basically the same, the hair on our head's the same, our eyelashes are the same—do you think our lustful sexual nature could be the same, too? *Hmmm... I wonder... Reminds me of a story, there was this bachelorette party...*

Ever hear tales of when the ladies go to the strip club—the *male* strip club? Picture if you will a pride of female lionesses taking down a muscular gazelle... And that's just the 'outward' female behavior in a pack environs. It's the 'inward' female behavior that is so competitive, so 'Martian'. Let's leave the noisy strip club and join a normal nearby cocktail party, already in progress.

Soft music, glasses of wine, hors d'oeuvres—and folks dressed up for an adult night out. And how long did many of those women take in preparation for the evening's fun? After all, it takes time to: shave your legs/armpits, moisturize your skin, fix your hair, paint your nails (toes *and* fingers), decide on your lingerie/hosiery/dress, choose your shoes *(Oy!)*, get dressed, curl those eyelashes, smooth on foundation, apply eyebrow pencil, eyeliner, mascara, eye shadow, blush, powder, lipstick, perfume—let's go! Oh no!! Jewelry!!! *(Don't forget your purse, make sure it matches your shoes...)*

Ladies have to do all that because the *competition* is doing all that; it's a feminine arms race—this all gets done to some degree regardless if a woman is single on the hunt or on her husband's arm. She's not doing it for him, she's doing it for herself. Women can be competitive, they can be selfish, they can be ruthless, they can be judgmental—just like the men can be, even more so in some cases, and don't be so surprised. Remember, man comes from woman, he's the original second fiddle. Adam's rib? Hardly—try Eve's Ever-present Social Push for Excellence.

At the party things look civilized *(Please, try another, the secret's in the cheese! — Oh thank you, I can't, I'm on a diet...)*, but there is a hidden Stone Age undercurrent. The ladies know what I'm talking about. Any lady worth her blow-drier or eyelash-curler can tell you what's going on. The men don't go through the pre-evening ritual, so they don't appreciate the work involved, but the ladies know better; with war-paint skillfully applied they ease into battle. At the party they'll do what women have always done—judge each other silently, or in small whispering groups. *(Judge not, lest ye be judged—oh hell, have at it, ye be judged anyway...)*

For a man, much of their personal mental worth comes from 'what they do'—they are expected to compete in the *(economic)* world and get a job, to bring home lots of cash *(kills)*. In today's society, money equals security. Money also signifies potential *(Look at my shiny sportscar/tiny-footed concubine! I must be loaded! I'm more important than you!)*, but 'what you do' is rather internal. You can't always tell what a man does for a living just by looking at him. *Careful, that guy in the cop outfit is actually a stripper coming from the bachelorette party; you can tell by the Velcro® on his pants, plus there's the badge that says Officer FeelGood...*

But for women, it is so much more external. It's how you look that determines self-worth so many times in society, both in the Stone Age and modern eras *(men do desire youth and beauty in a woman, it's a genetic fertility signal that males the world over flock to, for a reason; most critters do check out each other visually—nice rack! That could be a reference to a lady's 'ahem' headlights or an elk's bony skull growth, both are a sexy sight to the right individual. We purposefully look for the healthy, young sexual cues)*—and there is a lot of depression out there among the ladies; they do a lot to cheat nature, to fool those of us (men and women) who might be (are) judging them. Women, desperately trying to be more visually physically attractive, to fit in, are far more likely to develop eating disorders rather than the men.

In America, there is a hidden desire to be thin, to be accepted, to be seen as attractive, that is so strong it can kill; a type of society-induced suicide endures. Don't go there girlfriend, Bulimia is SO nineties... Instead go to your doctor for eye-lifts and tummy-tucks, boob jobs, nose jobs, and lip implants. Go to the salon for hair color, hair extensions, silk-wrapped nails, avocado skin-treatment, a spray-on tan and don't forget the latest rage—eyelash tinting. (That last is no joke.)

Ladies race on that gerbil-wheel of acceptance, and there's always more they can do, always another product or fad diet or fad exercise—it's no wonder that sometimes a woman spins out of control. Marketers will make money off you and feed your addictive desires *(you WANT this, you NEED this...)*—on the way out of the supermarket also pick up the latest copy of a brightly colored *Cosmo* strategically placed near the checkout counter; your eyes are drawn, you have to look—*Who's on the cover? What's she wearing?* Even with eyelash-curlers and cosmetics, the bodies/faces/skin/hair and fashion budgets of the vast majority of Cosmopolitan magazine buyers fall short of the covergirl ideal. And how does that make you feel ladies, to know that you are that far from what the magazine editors *(and obviously everybody in America, dare I say the World)* consider truly beautiful? Warm and happy? Hardly. But recognize that you are being manipulated—it's a 'car salesman's world' out there, and you are being sold a bill of goods.

The advertising images in magazines, your favorite TV shows and movie trailers, none of them are real, they've been manufactured to have maximum impact on you emotionally. They are designed to tap into your needs and your fears. Images cost money, marketers need to trick you into coughing up the cash to pay for it all. But we're just people. Imagine yourself naked, no cosmetics, no clothing, standing in front of a full length mirror. Like what you see? What criteria are you using to judge yourself? I say stop it. Imagine all of America standing naked in front of their mirrors—have you seen regular people walking down the street? Have you seen your relatives? Your co-workers? This isn't Hollywood or the modeling agency I'm talking about, this is America, regular people surround you. And that's who we are. When we stand naked and gaze upon our reflection, we can also reflect—do we cringe or do we smile? Learn to smile. There are reasons to, embrace them.

We judge ourselves, harshly, especially when we are surrounded by visual cues of sexuality and physical perfection. *(Stereotype Vulnerability—what are your odds of getting on the magazine cover? Time to beat yourself up...)* Ladies compete on the external visual field of battle, and it's tough to hide when you are supposed to shine. *Who's the best looking at the cocktail party—is it me? I hope so, it took so long to get ready. Who has the best dress? Who has the worst? Ha! Look at that hair! Who has the hottest guy on her arm? Who has the youngest...? Who is single? (not surprised...) Who has the biggest rock on her finger? I don't give that marriage two years...*

It's our social Stone Age upbringing coming to the fore. And while things may still be the same for us, the competition that drives us, the game has changed for the players; a power shift is spreading. In case you haven't realized it, there's been a revolution going on, the worm has turned for the ladies. Yes, what's good for the gander is also good for the goose—today's modern woman has emerged out of social reform empowered and pulling tightly on the reins of control. Human women have synthesized a power coup against the men—they have been allowed to embrace the Martian within themselves; and power is intoxicating, the women are getting stronger and sometimes drunk on their good fortune. Men, with the specter of unchecked male aggression over their heads, have been dragged down as of late, while women, the victims of dominance, have been raised up.

It is the use of this power socially that causes a lot of woe for the men—but when they were in charge things were pretty bad, much worse. Someone has to be in charge after all, the decision maker, and ultimately it comes down to sex. Men used to call the shots in the mating game, but not anymore. The world, and our behavior, is changing because of this. And since so much of human male and female existence revolves around sex, your happiness is affected by this power shift.

What do I mean by saying the women have taken over? Many men would deny it, many men recognize it and are frustrated, and many men are oblivious—but it's true. Let's go backward in time to the Stone Age and look at the sexes and the social scene. Unlike the female Black Widow, the human male is the larger and stronger of its species. Men have to be big and strong to hunt and provide for a pregnant mate and survive the harsh times—plus women have selected bigger men over the ages, they found that attractive. Even today, thousands of years from the Stone Age, women still swoon over an overtly muscular and tall male form—they can't help it, it's what they like. *(Sexually active males of some African tribes have a ritual 'hopping' dance that they perform for the watching ladies. By jumping straight up they appear taller, and the girls like the tall boys...)*

Unfortunately, along with hunting prowess and a bigger body comes human aggression. We compete against each other, other animals, and the environment—an aggressive stance toward everything will help ensure survival. *(There are other African tribes that participate in ritual 'stick fighting' that can result in broken bones, lost fingers, even death. The girls all watch from a distance and wait for the winner—the boys were asked if they would be fighting and competing this way if the girls weren't watching. The collective answer was 'no—we do it for them—we want their attention'.)*

Perhaps you've heard of the saying, *'might makes right'*. If there is no written law, no government, then nature's law takes over, *survival of the fittest*. Human males are aggressive, they do fight, they do hunt—they get labeled as 'being from Mars' and rightly so. They are aggressive toward each other and aggressive toward the female half of the species. Humans are not alone in this regard, it is animal posturing and the friction of social living that produces it. In some species the Male is the larger aggressor, the controller *(the Wolf)*, in others it is the Female *(the Hyena, the Dolphin, the Killer Whale, the Bonobo, the Bison)*, but someone *must* rise to the top as things are not equal, they are not fair in reality.

For humans, we are steered by our reproductive physiology—that long nine months of being pregnant, then there is the long, long time spent in childhood to reach maturity, many years where the children are not big enough or strong enough to hunt—they have to be provided for then as well. And it is the male who does the hunting, it is the male who takes on the authority pose—male babies became valued.

To imitate reality, in a modern television episode of **ER** *(a fictional Chicago hospital Emergency Room)* a happily pregnant woman finds out that her unborn baby is a girl— and then she wants an abortion. She has done this before, she only wants 'boy' babies, that's what this world values so that's what she values.

The division of labor in producing and raising a child is unequal—men must only contribute a few minutes and millions of cheaply made sperm while women carry the burden of pregnancy. The trials of raising the child continue through to adulthood, and if the father abandons them, the female mother suffers as does her child. Women, it seems, are born to suffer at the hands of men, they are the ones who are cast as second-class citizens, why bring more women and more suffering into the world? *(I am appalled by this thought and behavior by the way.)* Abortion based along gender lines is not unheard of—a woman with many fine strong sons has unspoken value in the social circle; the mother is proud, plus her sons rather than daughters can better take care of her when she's elderly.

Of course the TV show is fiction, but story-lines like this one have played out the world over in many different social human cultures and times for real—we let the group consciousness and standards steer our actions. *(In modern day non-fictional China, something insidious is going on. To combat their exploding population, the government passed a 'one child only' law. Well, if you can only have one child, then you had better make sure that it is a boy... Women getting sonograms could know a baby's sex before it was born, and many times if it was discovered to be a 'girl' the fetus was aborted. The communist Chinese government allows abortion even in the third trimester. A figure of 8,000,000 girl babies being aborted was reported on the PBS news magazine,* **Frontline,** *but I think that the figure is much higher. Today in China, it is illegal for a doctor to reveal the sex of a baby, but 'black market sonograms' are rampant. Girl babies are becoming more rare as less are being born. Many Chinese boys will grow up unable to find a mate. This has already prompted an increase in the kidnapping of little girls and girl babies in order to sell them* *in distant provinces as future wives. We buy and sell each other like animals. This is 2006 I'm talking about, not ancient times.)* So women, whose contribution was needed for survival, were not equal and became labeled as second-class citizens extending back to and beyond the Stone Age. And that male dominated view of the world, based on physical strength and visual size, still surrounds us today, though it is changing, evolving.

Back in the day before law and government, a man ruled his household. He could beat his wife, even kill his wife, and there would be no legal repercussions because the only law was 'might makes right'—*I am stronger than you, I take what I want, when I want, and you can't stop me.* Consider a small hunter/gatherer tribe with several 'pairs' and family units. Just as there has to be a leader within the couple (the stronger male), there has to be a leader of the tribe itself. This is usually the *OVERALL* strongest male. Now what of the smaller, more subordinate males? Do they like being subordinate? Of course not! They are bred to compete, to be number one, but they have been measured and found wanting by other competing males.

But back around their own hearth they are not subordinate—no, at least they are bigger and stronger than their woman. And it was *their* woman, aggressive men competed for and 'won' women *(in later times a man could 'buy' a wife, or wives)*, the strongest get to choose first, they take what they want. The same thing happens in the wolf pack, the Alpha Male chooses his Alpha Female. And when the Alpha Male struts around, all of the other wolves, even the *males*, assume a 'mount me sexually' posture. The Alpha Male will go up to a subordinate male, who drops down and raises his butt up, and perform a quick couple of mock sexual thrusts. He is demonstrating that this lower male wolf is beneath him, symbolically just like a female.

I'm sure it's humbling for a submissive wolf, but he will get his respect later. There is a pecking order in the pack, from lowest to highest, it comes from physical size and competition. Let's return to that subservient wolf later in the day when the Alpha Male is asleep. When this non-Alpha-wolf goes up to another, even smaller male wolf, can you guess what happens? The once subservient wolf now embraces his new dominance and forces the other smaller male to 'assume the position' and makes a few mock thrusts of his own, ensuring even to the other wolves watching who is the boss here...

And what if the other wolf doesn't want to lorded over, what if they think they are just as big, or bigger, than their aggressor? Why, a fight breaks out—snarls and bites produce a bloody nose and a tattered ear. *(The wolf 'playground' can be a lot like the human playground; blackened eyes and skinned knees come from human posturing.)* Someone will be the winner and someone will be the loser—it's never equal, the social circle is designed to be that way.

It gets complicated, this social hierarchy, and I tried to impress on you in an earlier chapter, dear reader, that it is just this social complexity that has driven up humanity's *(and the wolves' and many other social species')* level of intelligence. This aggression and subservience does not look fair, and it isn't, but it served a purpose—you can do more, you can be more as a group, but if everyone is a leader then nothing gets done efficiently. Who's in charge here?

There were many species of early hominids roaming the African landscape for millions of years—but only one out-lasted and out-competed the rest. Fortune favors the bold, and something tells me that perhaps out of the dozen to two dozen attempts of evolution to fine-tune this new bipedal predator, only one species, our own, turned out to be the most aggressive *(only one can be called 'most' after all).*

We called out the other species and bested them all over time—aggression served us well then, but what about now, now that all of our old competitors are gone? Can man relax? Yes, with a change in thinking. Many men have made advances; they've learned to control their aggression *(in order to stay out of trouble with the law, assault and battery will cost you plenty)*, but we've miles to go before we sleep...

Men would beat their women because they could, they were property—and this Stone Age mentality would remain dominant even as humankind slowly advanced and became 'civilized' *(are women being battered somewhere in modern America even at the moment you are reading this? I think so)*—women were still second class citizens, if citizens at all, on the streets of Egypt, the farms of Greece, the forums of Rome, the sands of Mecca, the mountains of Japan, the rivers of India, the forests of the ancient Americas and the fledgling cities of a modern-day America. Law and government had started to be developed, but who made those first official decisions? Not women. They were not considered citizens; even in the United States women were not allowed to vote or run for public office until less than 100 years ago *(1920)*. After the Civil War *(1860's)* black men were 'allowed' to vote, as their status changed from one of 'property', to one of 'man.' *(The term 'slave' didn't originally mean 'black skinned man', it was more of a 'white skin' actually... The unorganized, primitive northern Slavs were easy pickings for the warlike Greeks to the south; they were captured and put to work building temples and cities, and catering to the Greek citizens' every whim—it seems that early democracy was subsidized by slavery, borne on the backs of Slavs.)* We had written down *'All men are created equal'* in founding this country, and while white-supremacists might deny that the black man is in fact a man, he is, and deserves all respect forthcoming with that title. Too bad for the women though, they weren't the ones who wrote the words...

You see, those in power do not want to give up that power, it is intoxicating. Aggressive and stronger men like being in control, we had been for millions of years. When language and 'civility' came along, this domineering position that men enjoyed was not about to be dismissed. Young girls were still told whom they were going to marry and groomed to be submissive in those marriages. Husbands could freely beat their wives, or children, or animals—it was his right as a man.

Del Martin has been active in the National Organization of Women (N.O.W.) since 1967 and has tirelessly fought for the rights of women and other oppressed groups. *(In 1995 she was a named delegate to the White House Conference on Aging.)* Here is an excerpt from her 1976 book, ***Battered Wives***:

> **In America, early settlers held European attitudes towards women. Our law, based upon the old English common-law doctrines, explicitly permitted wife-beating for correctional purposes. However, certain restrictions did exist and the general trend in the young states was toward declaring wife-beating illegal. For instance, the common-law doctrine had been modified to allow the husband 'the right to whip his wife provided that he used a switch no bigger than his thumb'—a rule of thumb, so to speak.**

A 'switch' is an old-fashioned term for a whipping stick, a crude wooden rod usually made from a nearby tree— I hear that hickory was especially painful. Some people think that this practice of beating a wife with a stick is where the term *'rule of thumb'* came about, meaning a generally accepted practice based on experience with no real sense of formality or 'written law' *('might makes right', remember?)*—though there was an English judge in the late 1700's, Sir Francis Buller, who is documented in the Dictionary of National Biography *(first published in 1885, a sort of 'old-timey' British Who's Who)* for making pronouncements concerning just this matter.

The judge was satirized in a cartoon of his day and nicknamed "Judge Thumb" because of it. It's hard to document all the facts now because so much has been lost over time; the evidence is limited but compelling, and it does make some sense knowing what we do of male aggression and dominance. And after all, there were no female judges to hand down decisions to protect 'the fairer sex'. Males pass judgment and hand out punishment in the courtroom, so why not the household too? *Only guys, let's keep the beatings sensible, use a smaller stick...*

Some scholars today think that maybe the phrase 'rule of thumb' had to do not with wife-beating, but with carpentry; the thumb was used as a measuring tool, as in 'ruler'. *(The tip of the thumb to its first joint may be where our 'inch' came from.)* Others credit the term as coming from Brewmasters who would 'dip their thumbs' to see if their beer was the right fermenting temperature—critics of this origin theory cry foul as (1) the thumb is not the digit most sensitive to heat, (2) the 'good temperature range' is a small one, greater accuracy than 'feeling' was needed, and finally, (3) beer making is best achieved under sanitary conditions—plopping your thumb into the wort violates this.

No, women were worthy of being beaten, were worthy of being treated like property. Women were not thought of as being 'created equal'; it was the natural order of things. The Founding Fathers, the *men* in power, wanted to feel more civilized; they were tired of 'the little guy' *(us—the colonists)* being picked on by the big powerful bully *(them— King George III of England with his Armies and Navies and Taxes)* so they decided to write some fancy words guaranteeing their rights and for protecting themselves—a posture of declaring war. *(We were tired of being subservient in the 'pack'; The Declaration of Independence was our 'snarl', the Revolutionary War our 'bite'.)* These words,

however, were written in a time of white male supremacy—
and these words also turned out to be grand in scope and
ultimately damning:

> **We hold these truths to be self-evident, that all
> men are created equal, that they are endowed by
> their Creator with certain unalienable Rights,
> that among these are Life, Liberty, and the
> Pursuit of Happiness....**

The American civil war was later fought over State's
Rights vs. Federal Rights *(more 'little guy' standing up to the
'big bully', more male snarling and biting)*, but that's just
the party line.   President Lincoln, a *Yankee*, freed the
slaves, that bountiful and cheap labor source that made
white men in the agrarian south so wealthy. *You, Sir, have
besmirched my honor by telling me what I can and cannot do
with my property. I demand satisfaction...* Four long bloody
years later the South is forced to surrender—we men are a
stubborn bunch, we don't like to go down quietly *(it's that
Stone Age aggression we inherited)*, but eventually it
becomes obvious when we are defeated. And then the anger
kicks in only to be directed elsewhere. *(...like that time in
1930's Germany...)*
In a similar fashion, the ladies have staged their own
Appomattox, but many men don't realize that the
social/sexual war is over, with women the victors. Those
that do realize this can be bitter, or sad, or lonely, or all
three. No physical sword was handed over. General Robert
E. Lee never gave his ornate sword to Grant; the Union
Commander did not want to see a gentleman humiliated—
men can have such a dichotomy, savage soldiers at one
moment, gracious and honorable diplomats the next. This is
not that far removed from the male core behavior that he
strengthened during Stone Age days—vicious hunter and
competitor among men one moment, laughing fishing buddy

and caring loving spouse the next *(not every man beats his woman to bolster his own selfish worth)*. And women, that symbolized embodiment of love and nurturing, of tenderness and caring, are they so different from the men after all? Do they have that dichotomy, too? I say even more so.

For millennia, women were forced to do men's bidding, to be submissive, to be bought and sold like cattle, to be ridiculed or disciplined or even killed by men. Women have lived in fear of men since the Stone Age, and many still live in fear today. Some men 'can't control their urges', and even a confident self-assured woman who is happily married with a family has to be careful; she isn't ever totally free from fear, from bodily harm. *It's late, and this same woman walks across a dark parking lot alone to her car with a palpable sense of fear. She hears a strange noise, and her heart races...*

It's easy to dub men as the aggressors, the powerful, and women as weak and submissive. But in today's society, the tables have been turned in the 'free' world. Our lives, and happiness, often revolve around physical sex and mental love, and it is here that women have taken over, thanks to men and their written laws. Words have the power to change things socially.

What is 'law'? It's what is judged by society as right and wrong. Your personal views may differ, but 'the majority' feels that stealing is wrong, physical attack is wrong, killing is wrong... and there are penalties (the death penalty?) depending on where you live. *(Years ago I heard of a Central American country, El Salvador, where the penalty for drunk driving was execution.)* Why were such laws invented? Well, if you look closely at most laws, they are designed to protect the weak, the victimized—and at first this wasn't about women, it was about men.

There are a lot of advantages to living in a group. Besides that whole 'increased intelligence' bit and division-of-labor efficiency-of-living, there is also safety in numbers.

The strongest male is not 'all powerful'—several smaller males working together *(a group within the group)* can take down a large aggressive male acting under selfish and damaging impulses.   A 300 lb. drunk football player celebrating a big win starts to feel his testosterone boiling over later that night at the local watering hole, he picks a fight; he's bigger and stronger, he knows that he is gonna kick some ass—throwing punches is sport to him. Call in the bouncers, they'll take care of him. Or maybe a man with a gun holds up a liquor store next door—call in the Police *(more men and more guns)*. On an even larger scale, a man tries to take over the world and kill all of the non-pure peoples according to him—call in the Army, the Navy, the Air Force, the Marines. Law was designed at first to protect the weak *man* from being taken advantage of. There is an obvious *right* and *wrong* to many situations.

It is wrong to inflict pain on another, especially when they are at a disadvantage. You do so sir at your own peril. If you insist on this aggressive destructive behavior we will have no choice but to gang up on you and take you down. You want to live here, in our society? You must live by our rules, our laws. What are those laws? Why, here they are, written down. They are complex, you might need a lawyer, but protection and punishment are provided for under the law.

And women, those submissive beings of old, they have a right to be protected too. They are citizens, they have a right to vote *(again, only since 1920—are we so 'civilized'?)*—they are just as important and vital to society as men are and should have full protection under the written law. At one time a man could beat his wife, even kill her if he claimed that she shamed or dishonored him. It was his right to administer punishment—but no longer. Today this man would be going to jail for violating another person's rights.

Men, who were in total power over women for millennia upon millennia, have made them equal in the eyes of the law, of modern society. At least in America and other 'more civilized' countries—there are plenty of other foreign places where women still must hide their faces and only shop in stores that allow women, plenty of countries where beating and killing and forced marriages are still a way of life for women. But here, the law is written and enforced. Women are protected and enjoy freedom under the law.

That makes women feel safer, but they are not totally safe from the Stone Age brains of men. We still are of a Stone Age mind, only now we find ourselves in concrete jungles and on asphalt plains. And in this new world man has conceded power to woman, and the transition is awkwardly under way. Not so much in the boardroom, there is still the glass ceiling and men's 'good ole boy' club that confers power and privilege at the highest levels of business and economic society, but women have taken over in the bedroom. And sex was there long before a 401(k).

This power came in the form of a pill. The birth control pill, in conjunction with written law designed to protect the weak, was the vector that castrated males, that removed their power *(Margaret Sanger didn't invent the Birth Control Pill, but her feminist philosophy pushed others to 'find a way')*. Men did it to themselves—it was male dominated society that called for protection from even more aggressive males (women didn't do much attacking in the old days), and it was men's thirst for dominance in war that pushed scientific knowledge. Chemistry was born from men's hunger, not women's—iron for steel, sulfur and potassium for gunpowder. But Pandora's box is far reaching—the body's chemistry was decoded, too. There are chemical triggers, hormones, which can keep a woman from getting pregnant.

Male dominated research laboratories and companies could make a lot of money, could create and exploit a whole new market—better living through chemistry ladies, take this little pill and chemically you can control your body. You decide when you want to get pregnant—have sex worry free. *(Warning: the only birth control that is 100% effective is abstinence, but what fun is that...)*

Women today are protected under the law from being beaten or sold or killed. Girls today get to go to school; they can graduate and become doctors or lawyers, business owners or politicians, or even all of the above. Most of us are not that ambitious, but women, who have been under the yoke for so long, are finally getting the chance to compete if they so desire. And they can certainly pick up that baton and run with it. Let's look at the modern dating scenario and see how the female form is adapting in this new modern society with its written laws and scientific chemical body control.

Women, and girls, have sexual power. They get to choose the men for the most part. Why do I say that? Well, the male has to penetrate the female during the sex act, and can be quite aggressive in doing so—some women like this and are attracted to this *(it is manly behavior after all, research '**the rape of the Sabine [SAY-bean] women**' for more info—early Roman [~290 B.C.] female victims who preferred their attackers over their husbands)*, but regardless of what an individual woman desires in her brain, a man in today's society cannot force himself upon any woman; she is protected under a promise of punishment—as Mike Tyson knows only too well. So a man may choose a woman that he finds particularly sexually attractive, but he is powerless to act on his libido unless the woman signifies that it's okay, she must choose him. 'No' does not mean 'yes'.

There is a drug, a so-called *date-rape drug*, which can be slipped into an unknowing woman's drink to make her lose her sexual inhibitions. In other words, the male has removed her ability to choose her partner. He decides for her, and that is against the law. And why do men resort to such nefarious means? Two reasons. They are horny, and they don't have the power to take what they want anymore.

And that is so frustrating to so many men. There are men out there that you ladies don't really find all that attractive. And some of these men have desires, have needs, but in a free-market society where you ladies get to choose the men, they find themselves constantly picked over, they are constantly judged by you and found wanting in the social sexual arena. And this can have extremely deleterious effects on the male Stone Age brain—this is not the environment it was developed in. The male is supposed to be in charge, the male is supposed to take what he wants. And women are not the only victims of men's carnal nature, 'men' are also the victims; men get raped, a lot. Would you be surprised to hear that more men get raped in this country when compared to women? I was. And the numbers aren't even close...

Stephen Donaldson was raped while in jail. *(This is not popular fiction author Stephen R. Donaldson, best known for his six-book series, **The Chronicles of Thomas Covenant**, whose main fictional character became a rapist; the similarity in names and topic is a surprising coincidence.)* During the 1970's, at our nation's capitol, he participated in a peaceful Quaker anti-war rally (a 'pray-in') to protest what was happening in Cambodia. He was arrested and thrown in jail, and over the next two days was gang-raped 60 times. This physical abuse did damage, he needed surgery, and if that was not bad enough, he contracted AIDS from this incident and died from complications in 1996 at the age of 49. No one deserves to be raped, men or women, imprisoned or free, but the numbers I've researched are staggering. Stephen would eventually help to spearhead awareness of this problem. Stop Prison Rape (**www.spr.org**) became incorporated in 1994 with Stephen as its president. Here is an excerpt from a May 1, 1995 article *(**Stephen Donaldson, Can We Put** *an End to Inmate Rape?)* appearing in USA Today magazine. You can read Stephen's entire posting at the web address listed below. Frankly, an estimated 60,000 men a day are sexually assaulted. It appears to me that imprisoned human males behave a lot like the canine males in a wolfpack... Read on:

> **The precise number of sexually assaulted prisoners is unknown, but rough estimates can be derived by extrapolating previous studies of a jail system *(by Philadelphia District Attorney Alan J. Davis)* and medium-security prison *(by sociologists Wayne S. Wooden and Jay Parker, their data confirmed by a 1994 survey of an entire state prison system)* to estimate conservatively that more than 300,000 males are sexually assaulted behind bars every year. This compares with a 1992 Bureau of Justice Statistics estimate of 135,000 female rapes a year outside confinement. By all accounts, the situation is even worse in juvenile detention centers. Once victimized, a prisoner is marked as a continual target for sexual exploitation and repeatedly is subjected to gang rapes, or must trade sexual use by one or a few men for protection from the remainder. An estimated 60,000 prisoners are subjected to involuntary sex each day. Very few of these rapes are ever reported to administrators, much less prosecuted.**

www.spr.org/en/sprnews/archived/050195.asp

I remember learning a long time ago that rape was a 'crime of violence' more so than a 'sex crime'. I was young and going through puberty when I first heard this so I didn't really understand it. To my young male mind, sex feels good; it was about the sex, right? But now I know better, it's not so much about the sex as it is about the power.

(Consider my logic—a man can have an orgasm by himself while in the shower aided only by his imagination and a fistful of soapy suds, or later in the presence of an unwilling woman. Both culminate in fleeting physical pleasure, but only the latter requires violence to exercise control. Rapists are drawn to the 'forbidden power' of control, and power is like a drug, it's intoxicating. Once the rapist tastes this power, he is drawn to it. It's not the orgasm that turns him on, he prefers attack and control rather than the solitary hot shower.) A rapist with a knife, or a gun, or even just with the physical threat of violence at his own muscular hands— he takes away a woman's power to dismiss him. Without this threat of aggression the woman would say no, but he is tired of being told no, and now he doesn't have to, she has to do as he says. A chemical date-rape drug makes the job even easier, it doesn't seem so violent, but the result is the same, the woman is forced to be submissive again in a society that has raised her up as an equal.

But women are not equal, not in the sexual world— where men once had the power, now women hold it, and flaunt it, and use it, and are corrupted by it. Women can very easily become *'sexual bullies'*—and why not? Power is intoxicating, women and men really aren't that different, it's just that our roles have recently been reversed—and the ladies are loving it, for the most part. It's fun to be the one on top, in control for a change.

Now when I said that the ladies get to choose, not all ladies get their every sexual wish. For example, perhaps a very horny, very buff Justin Timberlake or Lenny Kravitz is hanging out at your local disco one night. Justin and Lenny are exceptions to the rule, just as any 'most popular boy' is when surrounded by sexually active women. They all want him—he is the epitome of male attraction, but they all can't have him... He gets to choose in this case, who is most physically attractive to *him*... Justin gets to wield the female power *(you go girl!)*, but we all can't be Justin

Timberlake or Lenny Kravitz *(or Buddy Holly or The Beatles)* now, can we.

But let's say that Justin is not in town, both he and Lenny are out on tour singing and gyrating for lucky fans, in fact it's just another normal local night out cruising the popular locations.   Men and women mingling, laughing, drinking. There is sexual tension in the air—shoes, clothes, cologne, perfume; all have been chosen with care. And men, you better do a good job because you are being judged. The women are being judged too, but the men have to wait to be chosen. *(In the animal world, the one that does the approaching is seen as submissive. People come to see the King after all.)* As the night goes on, count how many times a woman refuses a man's advances instead of the other way around.   It's good to be the Queen. *Also, in proposing marriage, a man often kneels, and asks respectfully for the right to marry her, offering a diamond—**then** she gets to decide... Who's the submissive one in this scenario? "A gift, your Majesty..." There are some notable exceptions to the rule, there is my best friend who is married with two beautiful daughters (heartbreakers both)—only he didn't ask for his future-wife's hand in marriage, 'She' asked 'Him' instead! (Guess who said, 'Yes'!!)*

I knew a very attractive woman, not romantically, who was so tired of being hit on when she was out with her girlfriends that she took to wearing a wedding ring even though she was single. She got tired of the endless parade of 'non-worthy' men (her word was *'losers'*) coming up to her and hitting on her. Did the wedding ring always work? What do you think? Of course not, some men just had to try, there are some that always try.

The male sexual players are playing a numbers game—not every married woman is faithful after all and maybe I'm attractive enough to seduce her. *Hey baby, what's your sign...* But men are not the only players out there in the mating game. Women hold the trump cards, and they are learning how to play them, and the men *(the fake wedding ring came off when she spotted a 'hottie' I heard)*, to their advantage—but is playing one another the path to happiness? What do you think? We do it because 'everybody else is doing it'—but how many lose in the long run? Sincerity and honesty sometime take a back seat to lust and animal passion.

Consider writer/director Bill Condon's Hollywood biographical depiction, ***Kinsey***, for clues into basic female statistical dominance *(and basic human sexual behavior)*. In the movie, Alfred Kinsey *(played exceptionally well by Liam Neeson; Laura Linney was Oscar®-nominated for portraying Mrs. Kinsey)* is sitting around analyzing 'dating' data, and he's surprised to uncover a connection between sexual performance and 'attractiveness'. It appears that a woman's physical attractiveness level had no limiting factors concerning her ability to attract male partners. In the woman's world—everyone gets laid. The men were not so lucky... This makes sense when you logically apply the **Anatomy of Dominance**, 'beggars can't be choosers'; the men were doing the begging and the women were doing the choosing.

There has been some modern data studied on the subject of male and female levels of attractiveness and their sexual prowess, data that uses the scrutiny of a computer *(try 'Google'ing Randy Thornhill, Distinguished Professor at the University of New Mexico)*. 'Symmetry', or the 'sameness' of the left and right side of the face or body, has been quantified by looking at actual photographs and physically measuring the distances and directions between 'left' and 'right' points. Some of us are more symmetrical than others *(i.e. look at most models or movie stars, Elizabeth Taylor and Clark Gable come to mind)*, and surveys the world over, to include quite varied cultures, have all placed pictures of people with greater symmetry above people with lower symmetry when folks are asked to rank them.

Things became even clearer when the people in some pictures were analyzed against their sexual history. Kinsey's results were duplicated. For a woman's first orgasmic experience, or number of sexual partners, it made no difference how 'attractive' (symmetrical or asymmetrical) a woman was—there was no correlation for **the choosers**. But for men, **the beggars**, it was a different story. The more 'attractive' the men were, the higher their chances of sexual encounters and orgasm. And here's an interesting side note—women who have sex with more symmetrical men also report having more orgasms themselves. For me this makes sense, sex starts out in the brain. Men, while sleeping, can have a 'wet dream' *(a nocturnal emission)*, an orgasm, just by thinking, by dreaming. *(The brain is the biggest erogenous zone of your body, and no physical contact is needed to 'turn us on'.)* Are women so different? When they are with a hot symmetrical guy, that subconscious *(or conscious)* mental knowledge stimulates the physical machinery. So, it's been proven, a 'hot' guy turns a woman on (duh), but look deeper ladies. "All the good ones are taken" is a lament I've heard before, but it's not true. We're out there, hidden amongst the Stone Age remnants, you'll just have to try harder to see our value when we don't look like Matthew McConaughey.

But that's on the casual red-hot orgasmic libido end of the short-term sexual spectrum—ah, to be young again... *Wham, bam, thank you ma'am* only goes so far, there are the concerns of marriage and commitment and children to raise. Women are tied more closely, biologically and emotionally, to the children *(often in a divorce the nurturing parent gains custody; women find it harder to walk away from their children, they represent too much a part of themselves and their own dreams)*—in the long term the power then shifts to the men in a relationship.

Once the deed is done they have the power to stay or leave, they have to choose for themselves when the kids come into focus. They can do the right thing, work and invest in the relationship *(18 years to reach adulthood, and then comes college tuition)*, or they can do the selfish thing, leave those responsibilities behind and live for the moment—only for physical pleasure and the joy of winning in being chosen to bed a revolving bevy of beauties *(don't forget to add the cost of child support)*. Life isn't perfect, though we want it to be—we chase that rainbow at times, smiling as we do, not realizing that it is an illusion; you'll never arrive. Rainbows are always out of reach. Perfection is a pipe dream. It's time to take the blinders off.

Psychologically, men don't want to grow old, they don't want to die—and sometimes they do like Hitler did, they go into denial. Emulate youth guy, even though you are fifty. Shave off those whiskers, smoother is younger. Fret over your thinning hair: take your Rogaine®, create a comb-over, attach a toupee—bald is NOT beautiful... Bald is old. *(Ladies do it too—that 'eye wrinkle cream' is expensive, but it takes years off your appearance, plus there's always cosmetic surgery, almost 12 billion dollars worth in 2004 alone...)* And don't forget Stereotype Vulnerability, you're an 'old guy' now, everyone knows about old guys... *Do you 'still have it'? Will the hot young babes still pick you over the rest? Can you still compete? Time to buy a shiny new sportscar to compensate perhaps... My best friend and I readily joke whenever we see an older guy driving the quintessential sportscar—one of us will usually point and say, "Nice penis!"*

This chapter is a long one, my apologies. When I decided to write this book I spent the most time thinking about this chapter—it picks at the core of male and female behavior, it looks at the physical and social inequalities of the sexes, AND there's also been that quiet (?) transition of power—there is a lot to write about. Volumes have already been put to page on the subject, I've added my 22 cents worth *(inflation)*, and you've spent your life to date dealing with members of the same sex and the opposite sex—how do you feel now? What you learn changes you—everyday you are a new person, similar to the one a day earlier, but different just the same. You are older, more experienced today—some days you make greater jumps forward than others, how's the day going for you so far? Learning anything new?

There are no magic answers here, you are also a long-term work-in-progress and build yourself physically, mentally, and socially year after year. It takes time to be a human, time to be born, time to grow, time to learn and mature. I've given you a lot to think about, from men's nipples to women's eyelashes, and later in this book I'll return to regale you with more witty notions. My goal, and your goal, should be happiness and serenity and belief in ourselves—this is easier said than done in today's competitive and complex world. We beat ourselves up so easily. Life doesn't have to be that way.

We can all do a better job. This is a credo that drives me to be a better teacher, a better writer and a better person—but being better isn't as easy as snapping your fingers, it takes some focus and effort, anything worth having does. You can't change the group and social dynamics, you can only change you—your perception, your reaction, your long term action. Knowledge is power, not an answer.

Different people have quests for different answers—I urge you dear reader to continue reading, not just this book, but other books—never stop reaching. Not all the time mind you, you have other things to do after all, but budget some time daily or weekly or monthly where you can pursue your own quest of science, or nature, or of anything that further explores your world. You are a learning machine, remember? Language is a gift, use it to your advantage.

You're allowed to explore outside the classroom walls, you don't need to be assigned homework to find out more about anthropology or stellar structure. It will pay dividends in the long run helping you to smile, both when things are good, and when things are not so good in your life. Evidence is also mounting that the brain benefits from learning new things the way normal muscles benefit from physical use. The more you learn the stronger and more able your brain becomes. If you want to stave off Alzheimer's, a good offense is to never lose the wonder surrounding your world.

How do you deal with imperfection in others? In yourself? As you continue to learn about all sorts of related and interconnected things, you'll find that you'll change. You'll have to, it is you who are connected. *How you deal with imperfection and unfairness now and over time, well, that depends on you. See yourself as water—being pulled, touching and being touched; are you stagnant or flowing freely? You know, you are mostly water to begin with, like the surface of the planet that spawned you, and yet you are so much more than just water. Be so much more than just a man or just a woman—be a thinking human, a considerate human. You've got that big brain, you are able to consider lots of things—do so. What's holding you back? Do you know? Do you know why?*

Ghost in the Machine

I mentioned earlier that we are intimately tied to this planet via air, water, and food. Why do we need them? Did you partake today? You are breathing right now, yes? You will get thirsty and hungry later, too, if not presently—you'll probably do something about that. *(I like food a lot, I eat almost every day...)* If you are a baby who can't walk to the fridge or pop open a can of soda—cry darlin', someone will hear you and come running to help. *(What is it now? Hungry or Wet?)*

We feel physical pain without these three essential things. In the Stone Age we lived and died struggling to stay alive. Clean Air, that's easy enough to find—unless you live near an active volcano. Poisonous gases are a nasty no-no. Clean Water, that's not too bad either; it flows in rivers, collects in lakes, falls from the sky—unless you live in a notoriously arid area. *Hello evolution, nothing like a challenge to bring out the best in a species—and in you too.* And finally, there is Food. Aye, there's the rub. *(mmmm... a spicy rub on an order of country-style ribs...)* Humans will eat almost anything; it's one of our great advantages. *(Insects, anyone? 65 million years ago this was our preferred dinner... And we haven't changed enough even in all that time to eliminate this food source from our diet—a fat white grub hiding inside a rotten log was a tasty treat to Native Americans for millennia. You wrinkle your nose at the idea because you're spoiled; in some ways we do live 'a dog's life'...)*

Welcome to Omnivore World—here, the menu has fewer limitations, have at it and bon appétit. It's true that our diet is rather narrow these days (corn, oats, beans, rice, wheat, fruit, beef, chicken, pork and fish, sometimes goat, sheep and deer), but if push came to shove, and eating became equated with survival, well, your diet would start to include some unorthodox choices.

There is a popular reality television show, **Survivor**, where rather average Americans are thrust into some rather uncivilized wilderness areas where they have to rely on the land to provide for them. They get really hungry over the weeks, and in many cases the contestants lose a lot of weight. While stranded, they learn to stomach and eat whatever they can find—they forage in the forest and the ocean, eating whatever they can gather, catch, and kill. (*Hmmm... That sounds so familiar...*) Why do we need air, water, and food? In the end, all three are about the same thing. Food. If you don't get enough to eat then your body will turn traitor on you—your body will start to consume itself, you become your own food. That's why the Survivor contestants lose weight. You have to have a **constant** supply of energy, your body and existence demand it.

The oxygen in the air, the water that you drink—both of these are needed to help break food down. All are needed in the life-process called Respiration, this is the scientific label we put on the release of energy from food. Food is energy, and you need energy, you need a lot of it. You need energy to blink your eyes, to turn the page, to think, to digest, to defecate, to smile, to dream, to breathe, to walk about, to keep your body a relatively even 98.6 degrees Fahrenheit most of the time... If you get the right amounts of energy as released from food, then you benefit, you stay alive. No energy means the end of days.

Energy is the true name of the game, the end-all get-out mover and shaker of your personal world. The war for energy has been waged since viable DNA was unleashed on this planet—the DNA you possess is a molecule, a complex one, but it is only a collection of atoms. The first war, and the one that's still being waged to this day, is an atomic one.

Yes, you heard me—atomic war I say. But not the one you think; I'm not referring to the nuclear weapons that cause so much devastation and human suffering and social fallout. The battle I'm referring to takes place in between the sub-microscopic atoms—the art of hooking and unhooking on the smallest scale. Think of it as street-to-street fighting, or hand-to-hand conflict rather than a massive beachhead assault.

There is energy our bodies can use that is stored in certain molecules, and we exploit that energy source. For the uneducated, a molecule is a collection of atoms linked together. These could be as few as two, as in common table salt, Sodium Chloride, or there could be hundreds to thousands hooked together, as are found in many proteins. Living things *(Organic)* tend to have very complex molecules, while non-living *(Inorganic)* things, like minerals or water, are rather simple atomic collections. *(Pour out a few salt crystals onto a dark table top—look closely. Do you see some little cubes? You should, in salt the atoms often stack themselves at right angles, they make cubes in 3-Dimensions (3D). A shiny diamond is 100% carbon—no right angles there, the carbon atoms stack up a little differently—still, we benefit from those angled and flashy facets. Diamonds are pretty, but can you also see beauty in a tiny cube of salt? Which would you rather live—a life devoid of diamonds or the one without salt? Here's a hint: without salt in some form you will die... Why do you think our taste buds are tuned to it? Your body knows what it needs to survive; you get 'steered' toward foods as well as sexual partners. Do you want fries with that?)*

So how do you get from simple, inorganic non-life to complex, organic living things? The DNA does it all, but how? The underlying answer is logical. What do you do to take yourself from the simple to the complex? How do you get from being naked to being clothed? How do your shoes go from being untied to tied? How do you get from home to anywhere else?

Perhaps you've heard of a bizarre little part of nature called entropy. What is it? Well, it's not a physical thing so much as it is a quality of nature. Entropy is about energy and systems, it's about how things run down. But in a nutshell, it states that the natural way of the universe is to go from order to disorder, from things being organized to things being randomly distributed. *If you've had an opportunity to see my home/office/car you can certainly glimpse entropy hard at work—things tend to get disorganized around me, how about you?*

There are some folks out there willing to twist this property of nature around to prove the importance of their religion and its ruling deity(ies). How else can you explain the order and beauty of a rainbow's arc or a butterfly's wing or an eagle's eye? How can these organized and specialized structures arise when the universe instead wants to tear things down rather than build 'em up? How can we move opposite the current that pulls at the rest of the Cosmos?

The short-term answer is satisfying and logical—the key to the complexity of the eagle's eye lies in your shoelaces. Look at them. They were untied. How did they get from unorganized to organized? They can't do that by themselves. And they didn't, they had help. It came from you. People don't get all the facts sometimes when it comes to entropy. Things do tend to disorder and slow down in nature—**when there is no external energy source.**

Your shoes are not an isolated system—but you can experiment with this if you'd like. Go ahead, isolate your shoes. Untie them, take them off, and put them in a box (a *shoebox* perhaps?), then slide them under your bed for a year or two. Let the suspense build as long as you can stand it, then open your cobbler-esque time capsule and lo and behold—the shoelaces are still not tied... *Hmmm... Maybe they needed a longer time in the box...*

No matter how long they remain though, you know the ending—no knots, no nothing. Leave them there long enough and bacteria will break down your laces and turn them into powder, try to tie them hushpuppies now. Entropy takes a hike when external energy, like you for example, is pumped into a system—that excess energy, why, it makes things happen. It can cause things, if the conditions are right, to go from disorder to order. As long as there is energy there is the possibility to build, to organize, to tie some laces. Take away the energy, and it's another story. Dead men tell no tales, and they also tie no shoes.

Available energy is not the end of the story—that energy has to be put to use, and it is, at the very smallest level of our bodies, the atomic one. It's happening inside you right now—simple sugars are being taken apart and then hooked up differently, their atoms are being rearranged to make your bodily tissues, muscle and blood, nerves and bone. And not only do the raw materials come from those sugars or others molecules that you ingest, but power to do all the unhooking and rehooking, why, that comes from the molecules you eat, too.

With food, you get it all, everything your body needs. It's all right there in one compact awesome little package of molecular happiness. *It's concentrated treasure!* It's what we all want, and by we, I mean every living non-plant on this planet. *Plants are able to make their own food, lucky things—read Walter Jon Williams' award winning novella,* **The Green Leopard Plague [Asimov's Science Fiction, Nov. 2003]**, *for an interesting perspective on a society of people who are able to photosynthesize their food. You can find it online:*

www.asimovs.com/_issue_0406/greenleopards.shtml

Your animal molecules need to benefit from the demise of others. It's cellular survival of the fittest. Selfishness, efficient division of labor, search and destroy— your body is the Coliseum *AND* the lions rolled into one, and here come the Christians, I mean food... They don't stand a chance—someone's salivating. Check out those teeth, nice.

You spend your entire life moving around, building your body up from the 'ground' level. *('my, look how you've grown'—remember?)* You've made it a mission to collect and concentrate nutrients inside your body, and you've done a very good job, all automatically. *(As long as you get the right proportions—too much rice and no protein lead to a deficiency related disease called kwashiorkor [quash-ee-OR-CORE]. If you've seen the stick-limbs but bulging bellies of starving third world babies on TV charity ads, then you've witnessed atomic war where the body is losing. It needs the right food, the right raw materials, in order to build—you can't eat just rice. The DNA needs a wider palette to paint the fuller picture. You need better food.)*

Let's look at your food now. What is it that you've eaten to date? How long have you been alive, how many years? How many pounds of food have you consumed? Hmmm... Meals that add up to many times your body weight have passed through your lips and over your gums I imagine. Regardless of whether you are a vegetarian or a judge at the local big rib cook-off, all of the food that you have ever consumed has had something in common. It was alive at one point. Anything that can be classified as food, meaning anything that can give you energy, it was a lot like you, it had actively working DNA.

That corn plant, those soybeans, that chicken or pig— they were alive. That burger bun came from flour, an end stage of wheat, a living plant. Plants and animals took in nutrients to make their bodies, they concentrated the atoms and built their own molecules *(a lot like you)*, that's why we like to eat them so. They are concentrated sources, they worked hard at building up their bodies, and now we eat them, the plants and animals. They become us—we don't have to work so hard if all of those atoms we need are right there for the taking, and besides, it's really the only thing that we can eat—we have no choice in the matter.

Everything you eat was once alive. Can you live off of 'inorganic' vitamin pills and water? I'm not sure it's possible, but those vitamins didn't just appear in pill form, it took a living 'organic' person to gather the bits, to concentrate them, to manufacture it, to transport it—to be truly inorganic means to be untouched by any living process. Plus some of those pill ingredients are distilled down from once living plants anyway.

You don't have to survive on pills. It's an easy thing for you to perhaps grow *(they're alive)* some vegetables or fruit and raise chickens, pigs, sheep, goats, and cattle for yourself. The vegetables, they grow from next to nothing out of the ground, pulling and concentrating atoms from the soil and the air to build their tissues. *(Fertilizer, like cow manure, is spread over the farmer's field to replenish those atoms that the crops extract. I once saw an episode of **The Tonight Show** where Doc Severinsen gave Johnny Carson a tomato that he grew himself at home from a 'cowpie'—the tomato looked large, red and delicious, but you can imagine the look on Johnny's face when he heard how Doc grew it...)*

Funny stuff, believe me. It's hard to imagine that there are millions of young people out there who have no idea who Johnny Carson was. Johnny was the King. He had the timing of a Timex. Johnny with his jokes, like Eric Clapton with his guitar, made it look deceptively easy. Trust me. It isn't. Talent cannot be denied.

Lunch with Cadence

Please think about this as you eat a tomato

That tomato and you share a 4-letter code

You are both related by life

A long time ago bred a common ancestor

But then there was a split

You go your way I'll go mine

But now after eons there is a reunion

How are you?   It's been so long!   mmm-kiss

But this meeting isn't that friendly

You dine and you smile as you pick up your napkin

It's you eating the tomato

Instead of the tomato eating you

Animals eat the concentrated plants *(chickens scratch for feed, mmmm... or an unlucky worm perhaps; cows graze on grass—tasty animals ALL eat living things too)*, where atoms get further concentrated into their own tissues; meat (especially fat) is a higher source of concentrated energy than the plants from whence they came—and packaged quite nicely for human consumption. What was put together carefully by one animal *(to make itself)*, can certainly be taken apart by another, you. Your stomach has a tough time with tree bark, but a tenderloin, or a liver, this is another matter entirely. Termites are tastier than two-by-fours for a reason...

And you, you ingester of things once alive, you are alive too. You are food yourself—just ask the sabre-toothed cats of the Stone Age. Hominid skulls have been found with puncture marks on the back that match the pointy incisors of the big cats. Humans were a tasty collection of nutrients I imagine.

We don't think of ourselves so much as food these days, but we were then and still are today. Currently your body must be ever vigilant against a constant onslaught of tiny predators *(Bacteria and Viruses)* that surround us with their own 'teeth'... As long as you stay alive and energized, your immune system—the antibodies, the white blood cells and other evolved entities—will try to keep these intruders at bay. *(AIDS, Acquired Immune Deficiency Syndrome, affects your immune system's ability to fight off the intruders—victims can die from acquiring secondary lethal diseases while their defenses are down. And it's hard to combat the Human Immunodeficiency Virus, HIV; it mutates too readily, it continues to evolve even as we fight it.)*

After we die however, it's a different story I'm afraid. Without stabilizing energy infusing your body the inmates will start running the asylum—your tissues and my tissues will become dinner for the living microbes found everywhere. We will live again as our bodies become a multitude of beings. *(Ashes to ashes, dust to dust—You are a living thing born from a non-living planet. You come from the Earth, you will be returned to it.)* Even if we are cremated our physical collection doesn't disappear, atoms never disappear, the bonds just get broken. Our atoms get recycled—some will even rise again as part of another person. When I say that there is a little Einstein in all of us, in one sense I may speak the truth.

So, in the end energy in certain forms has been provided, and the struggle for food has really been a battle over atoms, the atomic war, and there is no end in the fighting—a person's gotta eat, right? Life doesn't wait around for the answer. It's proactive, a living organism goes out and finds those atoms it needs, organizing them for itself; it grazes, it hunts. *(Cattle and other ruminants benefit from a genetic mutation that produced four stomachs. Four are better at extracting the tightly bound energy found in grass. Our one stomach can't handle the grass, but we allow the cow to turn grass into steak via her four tummies for us. Then our one stomach can handle the steak— mmmm... grass never tasted so good. Pass the Sodium Chloride...)*

And how did this organized behavior all get started to begin with? Does this finally go against the tide of entropy? No, the Earth is not a closed system. There is plenty of energy to go around—energy to start the process, to shake things up a bit through evolution, and to keep the ball rolling. If something dies something living will soon take its place, until it dies, then another comes along—all of them built from DNA, all sharing communal atoms powered by energy and going about their days staying alive as long as they can.

Energy comes to the surface of the planet in two main forms—thermal energy *(heat, from the internal Earth)* and Electro-Magnetic energy *(light, from the sun)*. It is these forms of energy that spawned life and powered it, allowed it to change. With energy, a lot is possible. Most of the life forms on this planet exist because of the good graces of the sun pumping down free life-giving energy for those organisms lucky enough to take advantage of it *(green plants at first, and then the others, animals and fungi, take advantage of them)*. I say 'most' life forms because we have found an interesting and isolated ecosystem, the only one that we know of, that does not need any energy from the sun for sustenance. Creatures here thrive from a different energy source, the other one—the Earth's internal thermal heat.

There are volcanic plumes of super-heated mineral-rich water that spring up periodically from the deep ocean floor distant fathoms from any type of visible light. These natural outcrops resemble tall, crude, rocky chimneys that continuously belch dark clouds into the cold water. Scientists call these natural 'hot spots' Hydrothermal Vents, but they earned the nickname *'black smokers'* because of their appearance, though the dark 'smoke' is really that heated mineral-rich water I described above streaming upward.

Around the base of these volcanic vents an alien-looking world moves with life. Here there are heat loving bacteria and tube worms and albino crabs, all thriving in the deep blackness, supported by the chemicals, atoms if you will, and the volcanic heat, energy, all spewing forth in abundance powering this bizarre ecosystem—a nutritious feast for those evolved enough to exploit this energetic environment *(a process called chemosynthesis)*. And where did all this volcanic life-supporting heat come from? It had to come from somewhere; energy is a funny thing, it never really disappears. You may have come across the famous **Law of Conservation of Energy** in school that says something on the order of *'energy cannot by created or destroyed, but it can change form'*—and that is what happened in the Earth's case, energy from earlier processes changed form into life giving and sustaining heat.

There are three sources of the Earth's internal heat. The first and foremost comes from the formation of the Earth itself. This planet is a collection of space debris, the cast-offs from previous exploded stars. When the bits and pieces come together under the mysterious pull of gravity, they start to rub and bump up against each other. As the planet builds it further squeezes its insides harder—all of this friction, this rubbing and bumping and squeezing, it produces heat *(rub your hands briskly together to feel the heat of friction; when you 'shiver' from the cold your muscles are involuntarily rubbing together to keep your internal organs 'warmly operating'—if you stop shivering and get sleepy, that's a bad sign)*. Gravity is the ultimate cause of this energy transformation, it does the work, the squeezing, and the Earth gets hotter—the surface of the Earth is *not* a closed system, all of that original heat is still trying to escape even today.

Gravity also plays another but smaller secondary role in the generation of planetary heat—Earth gets heavily bombarded in its infancy by meteors attracted by gravity, and there were a lot more whizzing around back then. These chunks of rock fly through space at incredible speeds—and when they smack into the Earth all of that 'motion energy' has to go somewhere, it doesn't get destroyed, right? It changes, it turns into heat. And finally, there is a third area of natural energy that is turned into thermal heat—radioactive decay.

Some minerals are unstable, their large atoms break down spontaneously into more stable smaller atoms—this process releases energy stored in an atom's nucleus, and this energy has to go somewhere—it gets turned into heat, too. Humans have discovered how to do this for themselves in building nuclear power plants and nuclear weapons; this internal energy of the Earth can be released, slowly over time as in the case of power plants *(the heat is used to boil water—the steam energy is turned into electrical energy via a spinning turbine)*, or relatively quickly, as in the case of the atomic bomb which produces a massive mushroom of a fireball. *(All of an atomic bomb's energy comes from the Earth, the unstable atoms were buried below. Their energy would have been released naturally into the Earth slowly over time, heating it, if humans weren't around to dig up and concentrate them—we use our big brains and food energy to make it happen, to gather and build. We need energy to create, even if our creations end up causing destruction.)*

There is one bold genesis theory that life first started because of the ready energy found near deep underwater volcanic sites, the Black Smokers—perhaps here is where life first began before it morphed and moved on to take advantage of other energy sources, namely the sun. No one knows for sure, but curious scientists are looking into it. Interestingly enough, we are looking for volcanic life far from this planet—our gaze has lately turned to a lonely and cold moon of Jupiter.

Lonely and cold on the outside, Europa *[yer-OH-pah]* seems to be a frozen world. But the thick and cracked ice on the surface is deceiving, it conceals a vast liquid ocean underneath—the only other place in the Universe where we know for certain that liquid water exists. And there is plenty of volcanic activity on the moons of Jupiter too, the Jovian micro-system has lots of energy left over from its own formation, just like Earth. *(Those dark areas you see on Earth's moon, they are ancient lava fields, a blackened basalt. Volcanoes, both active and dead, are quite prevalent throughout the solar system. The largest, Olympus Mons, can be found on Mars—it's the size of Texas and taller than Mt. Everest, multiple times taller, worthy of the Gods...)*

The sun is too dim to support life way out by Jupiter *(the giant planet 'glows' in thermal light, it gives off more energy than it absorbs)*, but what if volcanic heat supplies the energy for life on the ocean floor of Europa the way it does here on Earth? Our own planet shows that it is possible.

A mission is planned that will be looking for the telltale signs of atomic life within the seas of Europa; Sherlock Holmes has been loosed upon the solar system. *(Mike Cameron is a scientist, he's also the brother of famous Hollywood director James Cameron. During the filming of* **Titanic,** *Mike invented new cameras that could withstand the crushing depths of the ocean floor near the famous shipwreck. Now he's turned his expertise to Europa; he's busy working on a robot that will melt through the alien moon's thick ice and release data-gathering probes that will swim and 'taste' the dark waters for life. Go Mike Go! By the way, his brother James did cast him in one of his movies. What part did the 'non-actor-scientist-brother' portray? As a dead body in* **The Abyss,** *he held his breath and allowed a crab to crawl out of his mouth. Now that's acting...)* We've already landed on Mars, a freeze-dried planet that used to have an abundance of free flowing water and volcanic heat of its own *(there's no stopping the 'Cameron Boys'—James has joined The Mars Society and is busy helping to design a more advanced rover for a possible Martian landing in year 2010)*—we don't expect to find life there now but it could have formed there, telltale atoms, organic molecules, would be left behind; our magnifying glasses are out and about, come along Watson... And what does this mean if we find evidence of ancient life on Mars, or Europa, or anywhere in the solar system? *(The Sirens of Titan, anyone? Kurt Vonnegut rules! For a good time exploring evolutionary life on fictional Earth, read his novel,* **Galapagos,** *too.)*

What this means is something incredible. It means that life is relatively easy to get started. All you need are the right chemicals; atoms can collect and become abundant, they get concentrated into planets—and then you mix in some energy from the sun or from the planet itself, and

BOOM—life, look out world... You see, there are these groups of atoms that start replicating themselves by using other surrounding atoms in the environment, and they use available energy to make it all happen... I'm not saying that the freaky good stuff happens all the time, but is life a relatively simple and abundant commodity in the universe, or are we alone? Are we an incredible odds-defying mega-lottery winner? How lucky are you? Are we freaky good stuff? What's the deal?

These are important questions, ones in which we are spending billions of dollars to find the answers to. *(I can see the federal grant application now: The Search for Freaky Good Stuff)* And don't think that these government dollars are being wasted—investment here multiplies and comes back down to consumers: computers, digital cameras, medicines, cell phones—they arise from the pursuit of cosmic answers. And as we pursue the evidence mounts. Who you are and how you got here, why, that's a big part of the search. That's one of the benefits of living in today's modern social world, the one left over from the Stone Age— some folks, scientists, are busy dissecting that rainbow for you. I am just one knowledgeable person, but I am here for you, we are all here for you. We are all in this together. And we all have to eat. For some reason, I'm hungry. *(I know the reason.)*

Think of what happens in your car's motor, the 'internal combustion engine'. The car will thumb its nose at entropy as long as the gas tank is full and the battery is charged. It's raring to roar into life—turn that key, press that accelerator, feel the entire car shake and shimmy into life. Soon you'll be barreling down the road. How is this possible? The car isn't organic, but it was built by organisms; it's a complex machine, and it works a lot like a living person, even though it isn't alive.

The engine needs to breathe—just like you. It needs food, too. There is combustion going on here, raw fire induced by spark plugs, and while this fire looks like flames, it is synonymous with what goes on inside your cells. Look at a campfire or a candle flame or a Chevy Big Block engine cylinder; they have the same need as a human bicep. Oxygen is needed.   Oxygen atoms combine with the concentrated organic carbon atoms of the fuel, they combine with hydrogen atoms, too—oxygen assists in ripping apart the atomic bonds between the molecules, massive oxidation occurs, sometimes called *oxidation reduction*.   (Bigger molecules are reduced into smaller ones, but technically this term has to do with *'changing an atom's electron ratio'*.) **This process releases energy that was stored there, in the organic atomic bonds, and then this energy turns into other forms of energy, like heat, light, sound, and motion.** But just what is getting torn apart? What really is the fuel? Do you know? Where does all that energy come from? You should. Your crackling Yule Log will burn more brightly when you know the reason why.

Your campfire requires wood. For your candle, it's not the wick that's really burning, it is the wax. And what is wood? What is wax? What is gasoline? What is food? If you add oxygen in just the right way, energy is released from these and other things. What else burns? Can you think of other things? Any substance, any fuel—if it burns you can bet on one thing, it used to be alive. That energy came from somewhere, it was gathered and collected and concentrated by a living thing with DNA, and now the energy is being released. Maybe it enters the environment as waste heat, maybe as life energy to get another body going. If it burns it burns for a reason—it burns because it was once born (there are exceptions, a few elements like magnesium and sulfur can combine with oxygen and produce heat).

There is a great demand for fossil fuels—we can turn their chemical atomic energy into heat easily by adding oxygen, by burning. This heat energy can move us *(in our* _cars)_, can keep us warm _(with home base-board heating)_, or might even light our way via electricity—fossil fuel is quite versatile; we need it, we use it, we hoard it, we kill for it. And it used to be alive. Why do you think they call it _'fossil'_ fuel?

A popular myth is that the oil and natural gas we use came from the dinosaurs—they died and were buried and their bodies turned into fuel. _Close but no cigar._ The large dinosaurs were not involved, but rather their teeny tiny cousins. Picture living micro-organisms, plankton and algae for example, floating in a nutrient rich sea—they lived, they soaked up the sun's energy into their tissues, building themselves up, then they died. Their tiny bodies, monuments to gathered solar energy, they drift down and collect on the bottom of the sea.

But the sun shines on, more micro-organisms are born to breathe, to gather atoms, to take in the sun's energy—they too mature, reproduce, and then die. Soon there is a rain of corpses coming down through the water, collecting and concentrating on the sea floor. Day after day, year after year, century after century the tiny bodies build their pile, layer after skinny layer—after awhile though, this can really add up.

The planet doesn't always stay the same though, it moves and shakes with energy—maybe conditions are just right to turn our tiny concentrated critters into present day oil. After many stable years of happy-go-lucky living and dying, things change massively for our ancient undersea cemetery. There is a dumping of inorganic sediment into the system—flooding rains or a large landslide could supply the goods. The sediments need to be special in order for our oil to form though; if sand came in and buried our collection of countless dead microscopic bodies, no oil would be made, it is too porous. What we need to make oil is clay.

This is not the clay you find on a potter's wheel. Clay doesn't start its life out that way. Like you, the clay you enjoy molding with your hands started out smaller, a lot smaller. Dare I say microscopic. *(So many things start out that way, have you noticed? Good thing there's energy around to change that, to help build things up by concentrating...)*

A lot of soft clay actually comes from really hard granite. Granite, that speckled rock of mountainous fame you find the world over, is a collection of different inorganic minerals that solidified a long time ago deep underground from hot molten magma. You can easily tell if you are looking at a rock that cooled underground if there are large, sparkly crystals that you can handily see. The bigger the crystals, the longer the atoms took to organize and cool underground. *(Hot lava that pours into the ocean cools too quickly—no crystals form, there is no time to grow large and orderly. This is sometimes Obsidian—this dark volcanic glass breaks down to form Hawaii's famous black sand beaches.)*

These big, solid, underground crystals get forced toward the sunlight in a slow planetary process, called Plate Tectonics, that pushes mountains into the sky. Everest is getting taller every year by the way—mountains grow, did you know? How do you think they get to be mountains after all? *(Sea-shells and marine fossils have been found miles above sea-level in the Himalayan Mountains—they weren't put there by Noah's flood, they got lifted by the internal energy of the Earth along with the rest of the surrounding ancient seabed—GPS sensors show that Mt. Everest isn't the only mountain that's STILL rising...)*

Granite is a rock, and rocks are made from more basic minerals, they are a collection of different concentrated atoms *(sort of like you, flesh and bones—but the arrangements are much more simple)*. Granite often includes the minerals quartz and feldspar in abundance. Quartz is tough. Sand is a form of quartz—it is an incredibly strong collection of only two types of atoms, silicon and oxygen *(if pure the actual chemical formula is SiO₂—it would be clear, like glass, but impurities can change the color and produce brown, white, and even those famous black sand beaches)*, locked together in a way that nature finds hard to beat down.

Have you ever noticed a lot of sand at the beach or in the desert? There is a reason for this—quartz is the toughest stuff around, it's outlasted everything else. Everything else gets pounded or dissolved away until only the quartz remains. Not much is tougher. *(Some gemstones are harder than quartz, topaz and diamond for example— but you don't find too many 'diamond covered' beaches...)* This is feldspar's fate, it's weaker. It is to be pounded and dissolved and atomically changed.

It comes out of the Earth hard, not as solidly formed as quartz, but it is hard nonetheless. However, it is not durable—the chemical structure is attacked by other molecules, weak acids found in rainwater, which tug at its atomic bonds. As pure water descends from the sky *(lifted up high by evaporating energy supplied from the sun, remember? Boy that sun sure gets around—powering ecosystems, lifting water, making rainbows...)*, it falls through the atmosphere. Here the innocent raindrops pick up other atoms along the way, the water gets 'dirty'—some common atomic hobos that hitch along for the ride are the gaseous molecules of carbon dioxide found in the air.

This creates a weak acid *(called 'carbonic acid')* within the raindrop; you can't taste it, and it does no harm to you if it fell on your skin, but this acid does attack the feldspar chemically in the granite *(a process called Chemical Weathering)*. It tries to attack the quartz too, but the strong atomic structure is immune to its chemical ways. The feldspar though, it kneels in defeat. Its tough molecular bonds are broken, and the once proud mountain outcrop starts to bleed—it bleeds clay. The granite's feldspar is turned into tiny, soft, clay particles; particles that look like little mini-sheets of paper under the microscope.

They get pulled down by gravity, by a rivulet of water, by the creek, the stream, the river until the flow enters the relative calm of the sea. Here, our tiny flat sediments sink downward through the water, settling like leaves upon the forest floor—fluttering, interlocking, layering. Only these aren't leaves and this isn't the forest floor. The flat clay particles build up on top of those dead micro-organisms that have already fallen and collected over hundreds of years, remember? This clay will protect those dead bodies, laminating them in a tough natural covering. Over time even more sediment is dumped on top of the clay, now it doesn't matter if sand enters the picture or not—the clay is already where it needs to be and is about to do its job.

Both the micro-organisms and the clay will start to change with pressure and time. The once living bodies will be liquefied and crushed from the burial. The clay will harden into a sedimentary rock we call shale, trapping the newly formed oil beneath it. This overhanging layer of shale is called 'caprock' because of its position on top of the oil bubble below it. If sand had buried our tiny once-living bundles of solar energy, then any liquid oil that formed could be squeezed out through the pore spaces between the sand grains. *(Sandstone looks solid, but it isn't, not at that scale...)* There are no pore spaces in the clay/shale—the flat sheet-like particles overlap each other, the rock is impermeable, liquids can't flow through it.

Yes, liquids can flow through seemingly solid rock, as long as it's permeable. Drinking water is pumped from wells, right out of the ground—*Where does it come from? How is that water replaced?* Rain falls from the sky and sinks into the ground—here it flows underground, slowly, through the pore spaces of the seemingly 'solid' sedimentary rock and into the hole that was pumped dry. Old Faithful, the hot-spring geyser out at Yellowstone *(powered by volcanic heat mind you, the Earth's thermal energy does the pumping)* gets its name because it erupts with a regular frequency. This 'timing' occurs because of the regular rate of flowing underground water through the permeable rock— *it takes time to fill a teakettle; and when the water drips this constantly, about every eighty minutes should do it, it'll whistle when it's ready...*

I've tried to illustrate geologically how our fossil fuels form—the needed processes to trap the solar resources invested into a living thing's bodily tissues; we benefit from these once living microscopic creatures, we fight over these. I hope you see how the pockets of stored petroleum energy are fickle, they are few and we are pumping them dry with alarming velocity. It's not the first time this has happened in our history.

Earlier I spoke of candles, how it is not the wick but the wax that provides the light and comfort. For many years the very best candles in the world, the ones used in lighthouses and for medical applications *(and therefore were purchased for use in the homes of wealthy aristocrats, when you can afford the best you want the best),* were those made from sperm-whale oil. Yes, the cranial fluid and distilled fatty blubber of a giant living creature made a most comfortable living for us—we've learned how energy is concentrated in living things. *(Did the colonists understand that the heat and light for their homes came from 'burning whales'? How many people today understand that the heat and light for their homes comes from 'burning microscopic sea creatures'? In some poorer cultures, people burn 'dung', both animal and human, to heat their homes—thankfully you get used to the smell quickly, something called 'olfactory deafness'. Living things are energy, even the dung/waste products are not totally destitute of energy—that's why the flies and beetles go for the poop, there's still some energy there—of course you can burn the poop for yourself and deny the fly its feast...)*

The light the sperm oil produced was superior, and the smoke/soot was negligible, much better than burning other animal fats. *(Seal candles are rather smoky I've heard.)* Today you take for granted the turning on of a light switch. Part of this book was written in the heart of a New York Adirondack Mountain winter—power went out three times in four months here. I wonder as I shiver at the challenges our ancestors endured. We are so lucky, we inherit so much—the wind was just the beginning.

The sperm whale and 'right' whale *(called this because whalers considered them the 'right' whale to hunt; 40% of a right whale's body is low-density blubber—they float when you kill them)* were not so lucky. In our quest for colonial energy we nearly hunted these 'living fuel' sources to extinction—fossil fuels are needed today, but the need for oil from living things extends farther back; a Nantucket whaling economy ruled the world before OPEC called the shots. *(Organization of the Petroleum Exporting Countries— 'petroleum', by the way, actually means 'oil from rock'. Saint Peter is sometimes called 'the Rock of the Church' for two reasons, one is his name; 'petra' is Latin for 'rock'. Londoners also forget their literal language—silly Brits, filling your tank with 'petrol' means filling it with rocks... But then again, Americans fill their cars with 'gas'...)* There was a national need for energy even back then. A wise Benjamin Franklin saw the light, the 'candle light' that is.

Many of us practice 'daylight savings time' by setting our clocks an hour forward or behind, but we don't know why. *(It's 'spring forward'—'fall backward', recent legislation has been passed that will increase this 'time shift' to include more days. Prepare to be confused, though your Stone Age brain can adapt, eventually. I know someone who missed their plane once because they forgot to change the clocks.)* The practice comes from Ben Franklin's time, a time of whale oil and a need to keep energy costs down—if you work when there's more sunlight, then you'll burn less candles! *(Also, try to avoid burning the 'Midnight Oil'—Oy! Stop working and get some sleep! You're 'burning the candle at both ends'...)* Today we don't burn candles so much, we make most of our electricity from burning even better, more abundant resources, like buried fossil fuels. Let's face it, whales can only take us so far...

When you turn on the lights, you are burning a once living thing. When you take a hot shower, ditto. TV, radio, computer, phone, microwave—anything electronic, guess what powers it? Something with DNA, something that used to be alive. Batteries look innocent and inorganic—guess what? They aren't. That energy all had to come from somewhere...

Okay, that's not entirely true. Some energy comes more or less 'directly' from the sun instead of filtering 'indirectly' through once living things. Consider Niagara Falls. The falling water comes from the Niagara River that flows between Lake Erie and Lake Ontario—along the way there is that nasty drop in elevation. *Water is heavy mate, about eight pounds per gallon, why, that kind of falling weight can turn a crank and do some work... Nicola Tesla built the world's first major Alternating Current electric generating plant there (industrial Buffalo benefited from Tesla's Niagara notion), much to Edison's chagrin—the 'Menlo Park Wizard' was promoting less efficient Direct Current at the time. Did you know that Marilyn Monroe popularized this famous location for honeymooners in her 1953 film, **Niagara**? It's a nice place to vacation with your 'honey'—the splashing waters supposedly produce lots of floating charged ions in the air, our feelings of love get an electric boost!* And how did that water get up there so high inside Lake Erie to begin with? Why, the sun lifted up the water from the Earth's surface via evaporation—later the energized water rained down from upon high. The rivers flow because of the sun.

The sun powers the rivers? The sun does far more than that my friend. You walk and talk because of the sun. The food you eat, its energy is distilled sunlight. You can also be considered as distilled sunlight. Every creature on this planet, besides the ones crawling around the base of a Black Smoker, is here because of the sun's kind charity. All food and all energy that we enjoy and need are gifts that continue to be bestowed by that glowing orb in the sky— water power, wind power, fossil fuels, and even the nuclear fuel we use in reactors received its original energy from an exploding star, a sun much bigger than are own. And now we've learned to turn our sun's energy directly into versatile electricity—solar panels.

These thin wafers of silicon and glass are made such that when the sun shines down upon them, the abundant energy kicks out some electrons from the silicon atoms, making them flow, powering them to do work. Electricity. We've learned the value of pushing electrons, they can be pushed around, but they don't want to be, that takes work. *(You do 'work' on the electrons, giving them energy, and then they gladly do 'work' for you... In basic Physics, Work and Energy are the same thing, they are measured with the same units.)* And where do we get the energy to push electrons to and fro? By burning fossil fuels of course—lots of stored sunlight there, until we use it all up that is. Ever notice how the cost of oil and gasoline and electricity keeps going up? Other goods and services rely on these energy sources too; their costs will increase as well.

Energy is a rather young science. We didn't know why the wood burns in a bright fire, making it brighter, until less than two hundred years ago. *(The metric unit of energy is called the Joule [JOOL], after Englishman James Joule who experimented with waterfalls on his own honeymoon and later falling weights and a water barrel circa 1841 in the family brewery—work done on water can raise its energy level, its temperature. Joule discovered that all forms of energy can be converted into heat. Many considered him a genius, including himself...)* The world had by then discovered coal—compressed and fossilized plant material from ancient buried swamps—and was powering the Industrial Revolution from its stored sunlight. Pushing around electrons in the early 1800's was a hundred years ahead of its time, only a curiosity; Michael Faraday invented the electric motor in 1821. No one saw the potential at first, but then no one knew the ubiquity and versatility and basic nature of the electron, or of the atom either.

Your body runs on electricity, we know this now. Sometimes we install pacemakers to ensure that the heart receives its regular rhythmic electronic signal, either from the brain or a battery—you know, back-up. *When the power goes out, it's nice to have a generator in the shed.* Your heart is a muscle, and all muscles contract under electric duress. Evolution laid the first electric circuits, not man.

Your brain is not a muscle *(exercising your brain is not about lifting physical weight)*, however it also runs on electricity. There are a hundred billion nerve cells in your brain, and even more numerous synaptic gaps between all of those neural neighbors *(the nerve cells don't actually touch each other)*. Picture the nerve cells as houses and the synaptic gaps between them are the lawns—each lawn bumps up against several others, no 'row housing' here... When you think *(or breathe or move or hear or anything)* electrons and neurotransmitters are fired between the neurons, across the gaps—like a baseball thrown between the houses and over the lawns. This energy of moving electrons triggers memories or physical action. *(And yes, according to Einstein, the electrons strangely gain mass as they accelerate; $E=mc^2$ applies to electrons, baseballs, even stars and galaxies.)*

Your body is swimming in moving electrons—and where did all those electrons get the energy to do all of that moving? It came from your food, it was found in the bonds between the atoms. It was released by 'burning' with the oxygen you breathe. And where did the food get its energy? The sun—all of that energy came from the sun. And now the million-dollar question—where did the sun get its energy? It might be nice to know, it's an awful big part of who you are and how you got here, but please be patient, I will reveal many of the sun's secrets (and your own) in the next two chapters.

Energy is the genie in the bottle, the ghost in the machine. What makes it go? What makes you go? Just because we are now talking about stars and neurons does not mean that I have abandoned the Stone Age. Hardly, the great advancements we've made have been done so by Stone Age brains. We have not evolved that much in tens of thousands of years, and agriculture is less than 15,000 years old, a blink in evolutionary time—if you could bring forth a baby through time from the Stone Age, from 20,000 years ago, to today, they could do what you could do. They could go to school, learn your language, graduate, study the workings of the heavens or the workings of the brain. They could unlock the chemistry and structure of the universe, just like you. Did that baby get here from the Stone Age to do all of that? Yes, that Stone Age baby is right here. That Stone Age baby is reading this—that person from the Stone Age, it's you. Welcome to the well-house, we've been waiting for you. Here, hold out your hand, you should know something about your world...

Do you want to hear the Daily Specials?

There was a time before humans, that much is clear—we weren't always here. And this confuses us—because if there was a time before, and the time now, then there had to be all of that awkward 'in between' time. This includes our developmental days, the hominid days, the Stone Age days. We see the evidence of these times recorded in our artifacts and in everyone's DNA. And we know that all of this accomplishment and organization would have been impossible without the influx of some energy source.

The sun powers us, it feeds us in a round-a-bout fashion. Both visible and invisible pulsing energy waves pound this planet continuously, but this energy comes in several forms. The sun's energy comes packaged as Electro-Magnetic waves, that enigmatic carrier of radio and television programs, the invisible hand that forwards your cell phone calls like magic. In essence, radio waves are really light waves, they are just invisible to your eyes. _(German scientist Heinrich Hertz was the first to discover many properties of radio and light. What's your favorite radio station? 102.7 on your FM dial? That's 102.7 million 'waves per second' slamming into your radio antenna, or 102.7 Megahertz... You may sometimes see it written as 102.7 MHz in honor of the discoverer.)_

Your radio, TV, computer, even your cell phone; they are all about a technology that codes information into pulses of Electro-Magnetic light that can be beamed around the planet where other devices then decode the information. They easily transform this light energy into other 'flavors' of energy—sometimes as sound waves that reach your eardrum and make it vibrate back and forth. Funny thing though, this physical ear-motion is turned back into Electro-Magnetic energy as the signal is sent via electricity through your auditory nerves to your brain *(frequency, or 'how fast' the eardrum is vibrating, the 'Hertz', is translated by your brain as 'high or low pitch', soprano vs. baritone, Mariah Carey vs. Johnny Cash. Loudness or softness of the sound, however, depends on the 'range of motion'—is the eardrum pushed a lot? That takes more energy—the sound must be louder. Consider a gentle string quartet concert vs. AC/DC on their 'bleeding ears' tour. Your brain decodes the speed and violence of your moving auditory membranes and the three tiny vibrating bones called the 'hammer', 'stirrup', and 'anvil' found there—it's music to your ear. Sometimes you just gotta rock...)* where the 'decoding' takes place, it is compared against other 'sounds you have heard', your auditory memories. *(Ah... I've heard that before! That noise is a bell ringing, I know what that means... The pattern is decoded, start the salivating!)* But what are memories? How is this information stored? This is still a mystery, but none of this happens without energy doing its chameleon dance.

Somehow, all of this gets done by your body and brain by using electricity, electricity that got its energy from the food you ate, but which first came to the food courtesy of the sun. It all sounds crazy and round-a-bout like I said, and it is, but this is the universe we inhabit, we can't change the rules. And since we and everything else in the Cosmos have to 'live' and exist by these rules, it's best to understand them. It's best to be prepared, to be knowledgeable about your situation, don't you agree?

Energy, by scientific definition, is the ability to do 'work'. And work is defined as a push or pull *(an applied force)* that moves an object over a distance. Sound energy does work on your eardrum—it moves back and forth when the energy gets there. *(Some elderly folk have trouble hearing—the ear's moving parts don't move so well over time, they get worn out, they need more energy to effect the same motion. The stored electrical energy of hearing aid batteries mechanically increases the energy of sounds.)* Your muscles do work in order to make you walk, your feet push on the floor backward and your body moves forward. Your car's engine does work too—it pushes on the road and you move merrily along, as long as you have energy, gas in your tank that is. Gasoline is just another form of energy, chemical energy. This 'stored' energy is sometimes called 'Potential' Energy—it has the potential of 'making something move' sometime in the future, when it is later burned. *(Of course now you know that oil really got its wealth from the sun—it's just like your food, food is also stored sunlight, it is also chemical potential energy, sitting around waiting for you to 'burn' it. The food 'calorie' that we so readily count is actually a unit of heat, of energy—one calorie is officially the amount of heat needed to raise the temperature of one gram of liquid water one degree Celsius. Your body 'burns' food— it keeps you warm among other things. If you run a mile you'll have to burn more fuel—your body really heats up then... A dragster engine gets pretty hot when it burns a lot of fuel, too. So does a racehorse.)*

And as we use that chemical energy, it does things—it turns into motion *(called 'kinetic' energy)*, it turns into sound energy *(rumbles of V-Twin pleasure if you own a motorcycle like I do—twist that throttle, hear that roar)*, it turns into heat as well. If you could see inside an engine's cylinder, just under the spark plug where the explosion and burning occur, you would find the gasoline also turning back into light energy, back into the original Electro-Magnetic light that was begat inside the sun. It's gotta be *bright* when it goes *boom.*

Energy changes form in the human body, just like in our car engines—though the cell is rather sophisticated compared to an engine piston. But energy doesn't need complex bodies or machinery to make this form-change, it can do this spontaneously in nature without our help. For example, the sun shines down upon the ocean where the water absorbs this energy and heats up. *(This is an energy change—sunlight is turned into heat, and heat is actually the tiny movement of atoms, the so called 'Kinetic' Energy, tiny movements that can increase or decrease depending on the energy flow. Add enough energy to a hunk of iron and the atoms will vibrate apart—energy is motion, heat is really motion—the cold solid will turn into a hot molten metal. Add even more and the liquid iron could turn into even hotter gaseous iron, careful, don't breathe it!—I kid, that would take too much energy, that's too hot for natural Planet Earth, but 'iron gas' exists in the sun's atmosphere...)* The water molecules at the ocean's surface gain so much energy that they break their chemical bonds and escape as water vapor, gaseous water, into the atmosphere.

Eventually, the vapor-gas will condense and fall as liquid-rain, but for that to happen those energized water vapor molecules have to get rid of all that energy they absorbed earlier, they need to dump it. The lucky recipients of this energy-gift are the surrounding air molecules, pairs of Nitrogen and Oxygen atoms mostly, found in the upper reaches of the Troposphere. This is a fancy word for the densest part *(air is 'thicker' at the 'bottom', 50% of all air molecules are found in the first ~4 mi/6.5 km above the ground)* of the Earth's atmosphere, and it's only about 11 mi/18 km thick. This is where we live, you are breathing in the lower part of the Troposphere right now.

Nicknamed the 'Weather Sphere', only in this rather skinny lowest layer do you have clouds and water collecting. In other words, all 'weather' and storms happen here. Commercial aircraft normally do not fly in the incredibly thin and clear air above it—the Stratosphere. In the classic 1963 Twilight Zone episode 'Nightmare at 20,000 feet' (written by Richard Matheson and directed by the now famous Richard Donner), a young William Shatner looks out the window and sees a gremlin fooling around on the plane's wing. 20,000 feet sounds far away, but it's less than four miles up. When planes do fly 'above the clouds' they are still safely inside the Troposphere and below the Jet Stream— that's the fast moving 'river of air' marking the boundary between the stormy Troposphere below and cloudless Stratosphere above. And where does the Jet Stream get the energy to move? Where else? The sun. It's all about the sun.

These air molecules in the upper Troposphere that receive the water vapor molecules' energy, they move faster too. But just like in a relay race with several runners, when one runner passes a baton the race isn't over, the baton will get passed again—the sun gives up the energy to the water, the water lifts and gives up the energy to the air, now it's air's turn—who do they hand off the energy to? What's next in line? Cold, cold outer space my friend. The air molecules absorb water's energy but then pass it off themselves, they give off that heat as invisible Electro-Magnetic light waves outward into the void of space.

Yes, I said light waves. The Earth, and its atmosphere and oceans, are glowing and giving off invisible energy, all 'warm bodies' do, even ice cubes, only your eyes can't see it, they aren't 'tuned' to it. Your eyes are like a radio permanently set on one station, *visible* light, but there are many more invisible 'flavors' than the visible colors that we can see; the sun is broadcasting more than you know, visible light is just her main gig. You can't tune your eyes the way you tune your radio, bodies aren't as physically flexible as machines.

Right now NASA is working on very sensitive telescopes, called interferometers *[in-ter-fer-AH-meh-ters]*, that can see the faint invisible light shining from 'extra-solar' planets themselves *(meaning 'outside the solar system', just like **E.T.** was the Extra-Terrestrial, meaning 'outside the Earth')*—that 'used' light energy carries lots of coded information, it always does, and we'll be able to tell if the planet we are looking at has life just by analyzing its light energy signature *(once we eliminate the 'interfering'* *light of its much brighter companion sun right next door—Stone Age brains learned how to do this, we'll see life from a distance relatively 'easily').* Living things alter the chemistry of a planet's atmosphere, they alter the way it absorbs and emits energy, and every planet has its own unique combination of gases, its own weak but distinct energy signature that can be amplified and analyzed using computers.

Life cannot hide—it needs atoms, it collects them and reorganizes them to suit its own needs. It uses the energy found there then casts them off like garbage. *(The oxygen you breathe is actually the waste product coming from green plants. One man's garbage is another man's treasure...)* Well, we can detect these 'garbage' atoms produced from living things just by looking at them—their light tells us information, and everything gives off light, living and non-living alike, even you. *(Fans of the movies **Predator** or **Blue Thunder** know what I'm talking about.)*

Stars are easy to measure, *lots* of energy being emitted there. Planets however are not so easy, they are relatively cool—but we are learning to tease this weaker information out. *(Remember how television satellite dishes used to be huge, as big as a car? Dishes now are tiny, DirecTV® sometimes gives them away—we can do a lot more with a weaker signal as we get savvier, as we get smarter.)* By knowing how our own planet Earth works in the energy scheme of things, we discover how other planets work. And it helps to know how planets work. Life needs planets. You're alive, you need the Earth, you're dead without it. Even when astronauts blast off they bring copious amounts of the 'Earth' with them in the form of air, water, food and batteries *(chemical and electrical energy)*. And what lifts those rocketeers into the sky, away from their Earthly home? Rocket fuel? Try concentrated sunlight...

Speaking of sunlight, let's return to those solar-powered water vapor molecules now located in the upper atmosphere.   The water molecules that delivered their energy on high, the ones that got lifted off the ocean's surface, they will fall to the ground with moving kinetic energy. The drops will splash and tinkle on your windows— the sound energy you hear, that bit that reached your ear, it wasn't born here my dear. *(Anytime you hear a sound think 'Sun'—all weather and life on the surface of Earth is powered by the sun, but also most sounds, whether a chirping bird or thunder's boom, live because of the sun's benevolence.   The only non-solar induced sounds on the planet come from volcanoes—they're powered by the Earth's internal heat.   Old Faithful's geyser-hiss happens because Yellowstone National Park is actually part of a VERY large sleeping volcano.   It erupts violently every 600,000 years on average.   By the way, the last time it flared up was about 640,000 years ago, so it's a little overdue to make some noise of its own...   Step right up, place your bets, cover your ears...)* The water delivers its heat energy and sound energy to any available molecules, and then it journeys back to the sea to start the whole process over again.

Most of us have heard of this 'water cycle', but have you really understood the implications of this 'conveyer' of energy? Water is like a perfect rechargeable battery—it never wears out. You put energy in, then it delivers the payload perfectly and returns ready to repeat the process none the worse for wear. However, what if water went on strike and decided to stop with the delivery aspect of its job? What if it brought all of its heat *back* to the oceans with it on its roundtrip journey? That may sound innocent, but this would really be insidious. Thank your lucky stars that this scenario does *not* take place. Little do you know how hard the lowly water molecule works to protect you. That's about to change. Not the protection mind you, that's still there, it's your knowledge that will be altered.

We desperately need some of the sun's absorbed energy to leave this planet. People talk about 'Global

Warming' now, and this crisis stems from a predicted 2 to 4 degree temperature change of the planet. This doesn't sound like a lot, but we're talking about a *LOT* of molecules moving a little bit faster—on a planetary scale this is a tremendous amount of heat, and this energy manifests itself in the form of: hurricanes, tornadoes, thunderheads, floods, mudslides, droughts, glacier and ice cap melting, expanding sea-water, desertification, etc. In a nutshell, it means more extreme weather in all categories. *(There were a record 27 named storms in 2005, including a record number of dangerous Category 5 storms. Four hurricanes made landfall in Florida last year, five hurricanes struck Japan the year before. Other violent storms are on the rise, too. The slowest month traditionally for tornadoes in the U.S. is January, the average is 22—this makes sense since tornadoes are powered by the sun; you get the most outside the winter months, when the temperatures are higher. The all-time record for January tornadoes used to be a lowly 52, but in 1999 that record was broken. Most weather records, like human sports records, get just barely broken. Weather records in the U.S. have been established since around 1895. So, how much was the old record broken by? Was it barely broken? Hardly, try 'shattered'—the number of tornadoes tripled. There were 169 recorded tornadoes that January. From 52 to 169. You do the math. And that's the 'slowest' month... On a more modern note, 2006 is turning out to be a record setting year, too. According to the Weather Channel, the first six months, with an average temperature of 51.8 ^0F, is the warmest Jan-June for the 'lower 48' EVER... The months of May and June in Boston are the wettest two months there, EVER... Hmmm... Want to watch the records fall? Just wait 'til next year, and the year after that, and the year after that... Things are getting more energetic, have you noticed?)*

Every thunderstorm you experience, the lightning and thunder and rain, that's the stored energy of the sun being 'let loose' in the upper atmosphere—the energy that is allowed to 'bleed off'. *(A lightning bolt heats up the surrounding air molecules to a temperature greater than 5x the surface of the sun—the air molecules vibrate with this extreme energy, that's the thunder, and when it gets to your ear it vibrates this too, and how. It's hard to understand that this violent sound is born from the sun 93 million miles away, it just gets delayed a bit. Crazy, isn't it? Energy gets delayed on its trips just like you. Nature can be that way, it's weird and yet familiar.)* We take the rain for granted. If this cycle didn't happen, pumping the heat into the atmosphere's upper reaches, the surface of the Earth would be far warmer than it is currently—imagine about 60 degrees Fahrenheit warmer every single day. How cold does it get around where you live in winter? 30 degrees? Add 60—now it's 90 degrees in February. And what about the summer—instead of a comfortable 80 degrees, how does 140 sound to you? *(And then the tornadoes and hurricanes really kick in... So don't fret when it rains, that's the Earth's radiator working to make it more comfortable every day of the year for you. Ever try to operate a car without a working radiator? You won't get too far, your car may start on fire...)*

So the sun gets around and has water playing the part of chauffeur; the energy changes fashion, its appearance, but it can always do some kind of helpful work if applied correctly. But not all forms of energy are helpful. Take us for example. We can lie at the beach soaking up the sun, hearing the waves crash *(also powered by the sun—who knew surfing was a solar sport?)*, but the light energy striking our bodies doesn't feed us, it burns us instead. A sunburn is literally a burn—your skin absorbed the energy and now it's cooking, browning quite nicely, here, add some cooking oil, *oops*, I mean 'tanning' oil... Don't stay out too long though, that brown covering will start to blister and peel as it absorbs more than the maximum allotment.

Does all of this cooking damage your skin? Yes it does—just ask the prematurely wrinkled folk who spent a lifetime chasing a healthy summer glow only to find that it killed the collagen in their skin. If you don't mind early wrinkles, or the increased possibility of skin cancer, have at it. The fastest way to leathery aged skin is to live the life of a sun-worshipper. That *'P'* in the sunscreen label *'SPF'*, it stands for 'protection'—protection from too much energy. The sun does good work, but too much of a good thing can hurt you after all. *(Careful, most sunscreen lotions, even SPF 100, only block the 'burning' UV-B rays of the sun. You should also be aware of the MORE dangerous UV-A rays; these penetrate your skin to a deeper level and can cause wrinkles and even deadly skin cancer. To block these Electro-Magnetic light-rays as well, be sure to use a product that contains Zinc Oxide or Titanium Dioxide. There is also another chemical, Avobenzone, that also works, but this one 'wears out' quicker when up against the onslaught of the sun's intense energy. Is the sun that dangerous? You bet your bippy it is—it can kill you if you're not paying attention. Skin cancer cases are on the rise... Let's be careful out there...)*

No, before we can use all of that abundant free energy inside our bodies, it needs to change form. Enter green plants. With green chlorophyll a plant soaks up the Electro-Magnetic rays and turns them into something else, chemical energy found in the molecular bonds of sugars and starches, the building blocks for its own planty body.

The plant also stores some of this energy inside its seeds and the nutritious sugary-fruity-pulp surrounding the seeds—this was not originally intended for our benefit but for the plant itself. Just as the egg yolk is supposed to give a growing chick its first nourishing energy boost in life, the same goes for the sugary pulp found inside the rind but around the seeds of an orange—it's there for the same purpose, to feed the seed in order to grow a tree. *(Please remember that the similarity in these life functions is not a coincidence, chickens and orange trees do share some common DNA, they are alike for a reason, there was a common living ancestor... But it wasn't a half-chicken half-orange tree Frankenstein kind of a monster—the time of common ancestry happened well before any land colonization occurred, the single cell stage, but DNA can be measured, unlike humans the chemical signatures are incapable of lying.)*

Animals have learned to eat the plants, to steal the stored energy for their own life-use. Plants of course don't like to be eaten, they've evolved defenses—thorns, spikes, poisons *(I'm suffering from a bout of Poison Ivy as I write this)*—it's all in a day's work of absorbing energy and trying to keep it for yourself. Even plants are selfish, but some plants have evolved social connections, check out their sexy flowers—nothing like colored and fragrant sex organs to attract a multitude of insect courtesans... *(Yes, a flower's genitalia are the blossoms that advertise with color and scent. A rose by any other name would smell just as sweet to the flying six-legged critter whose hairy limbs are perfect to assist in pollinization. Some plants have even evolved flowers that mimic the female form of an insect species. The males copulate like mad with the planty imposter—little do they know that they are impregnating it with another flower's pollen instead of animal sperm. Plants seem smart, don't they? Evolution rocks, get a load of what it did with us! Careful, don't feel that superior, look what happens when we animals become accustomed to cocaine or heroin. A plant can still enslave us—what are we but chemistry? See Gene Hackman portray fictional New York cop, Jimmy 'Popeye' Doyle, in **The French Connection**, both 1 and 2, for a wild ride, figuratively and literally, through human society and drug addiction.)*

When animals eat plants they turn the plant's energy *(originally solar energy)* into their own. Our bodies are temples to meals past, they are brimming with protein fueled by the transformed atomic energy in vegetables. Plants turn sunshine into sugar, we in turn transform vegetables with their sugary payload into meat, into flesh and bone, blood and brain. You are what you eat—if the plants you consumed were disguised energy, then what of the animal tissues it's turned into? They also are energy— they can be burned, they have the ability to do work.

My mind goes back to a short story, a fictional one, that I read over twenty years ago *(okay, now I feel old)* written by Stephen King *(who must feel older than I)*. Titled **Survivor Type**, and included in an anthology of King's short work called **Skeleton Crew**, it concerns an unscrupulous and greedy New York City surgeon who was attempting to increase his wealth by smuggling in two kilos (~5 lbs.) of pure heroin from the Far East. But there are problems; the boat he is on sinks and he is washed ashore on a tiny desert isle...

> **Two days since the storm washed me up.**
> **I paced off the island just this morning. Some island! It is 190 paces wide at its thickest point, and 267 paces long from tip to tip.**
> **So far as I can tell, there is nothing to eat.**

This story didn't have the usual King flair up to this point, but Mr. King understands fictionally what is reality; we forget that we ourselves are food.

A starving man who gets thinner as his body 'eats itself' from the inside, that's not dramatic. *(Unless it's King's great gypsy-curse thriller, **Thinner**, of course. The man covers all the bases.)* A skilled but desperately hungry surgeon who uses heroin as an anesthetic before lopping off his broken leg—in order to physically eat it—now *there* is some human drama for you. Gruesome yes, but biologically sound, the man needed food *(his leg was broken, but not* _useless..._); it's painful when we starve, and this demand for energy, it's constant. Stop eating to experience it for yourself, I dare you. _(Just kidding—please eat, I do want you to live.)_

How did castaway Dr. Richard Pine _(a.k.a Richard Pinzetti)_ fare in the long run? Well, he was writing his bizarre experiences down in a type of diary, that's how we know everything we know, but his writing reveals a mind slipping into madness, and the maddening hunger drives him on until only his precious and medically skilled fingers remain—when they are gone the story can no longer be written.

lady fingers they taste just like lady fingers

This is the haunting ending I remember twenty years later. _Man, I love words... Yo Steve, way to go! You and I are of a mind._

There was a somewhat similar real-life precedent for plane crash survivors turning to cannibalism. In 1972, members of an Uruguayan rugby team, who crashed in South America's snowy Andes Mountains, survived on the only energy available to them—corpses. You can read of their human struggle in Piers Paul Read's riveting account, **Alive**, a former Number One Best Seller. Ten weeks spent in a frozen hell—16 survived, 29 ultimately died.

Animal flesh is a more bountiful energy source than vegetable flesh—it should be, it's more concentrated. In many cases a carnivore can digest almost all of its prey's bodily tissue. A hyena doesn't balk at brains or bone—she eats it all _(the Alpha Female is in charge of the family, she gets first dibs, then the cubs—males are ranked the lowest)._ Harry Potter's owl, Hedwig, would love to eat a nice mouse, that grazer of grain, instead of the grain itself. She eats the mouse whole and then coughs up a small pellet of indigestible fur and bone. The rest of the mouse though, that's been turned into owl and flight. The owl is a great hunting carnivore—it is like a cat with wings: excellent hearing *(fluffy head feathers and 'horns' focus the sound)*, sharp claws, and a taste for small mammals; those little furry bundles of concentrated energy...

People do a pretty good job of dividing up the cow and consuming it all. *(Ever see that famous butcher's chart outlining all the different cuts of beef over the entire cow? And what's left becomes hot dogs...)* But we have options the owl does not. It's possible for us to eat the corn we would normally give to the cow if we like; humans can extract some energy directly from special plants around us, we're omnivores, remember?

There are some parts of the plant that humans cannot digest though—tough cellulose fibers and starchy pith may be a smorgasbord for termites, but we prefer the tender nuts and fruits produced by a plant's reproductive sexual organs *(the 'ear of corn' is this).* And now you know that the plant places its special 'easy to use' sugars there, easy to use energy for its seeds that is—the next generation.

Some people may cry foul at the way we humans treat our vegetable cousins, eating their unborn young and all, but it is those tasty sugars surrounding the plant's package of DNA, the pulp around the seed, that drives us to propagate even more of that species. The ones that are good to us, that are especially tasty, why, we're good to them. *(That big, delicious ear of corn actually started out a lot smaller—ever see those 'tiny ears-of-corn' that come in some Asian food dishes? ALL corn used to be that small; we've manipulated the plant over time, protecting bigger offspring and shunning the smaller.)*

We spend our days placing their seeds in the ground and taking care of the tender young shoots that emerge— urging them up into the sunshine, watering them artificially if the clouds forget to rain, lighting the smudge pots throughout the grove to keep the Florida orange trees alive and warm in times of uncharacteristic killing frost. We grow lots and lots of tasty plants these days—it's hard to imagine that this effort didn't even occur to us until about 15,000 years ago. Before that, nature did the planting, and she is a sporadic farmer.

As you can see, we've learned how to speed up the process, how to grow our own plants and concentrate the free solar energy with the help of some atomic powered seeds. Our brain adapts to the problems at hand—that's why you're here. There is hope, we're good at adapting to new knowledge, look at us go.

With more food more people can survive. With more machines and more energy, more food can be grown. Fossil fuels, and the advent of science, has subsidized the human species, allowed us to explode in numbers. How well would the multitude of humanity survive when the electricity goes out, when the heat goes out? You owe a great deal of gratitude to the power grid on which you feed. Nowadays you can just pop on down to the supermarket, but few of us realize the immense expenditure of energy, of burning, to bring these goods to your favorite marketplace.

Electricity and fuel go into everything you buy—from the effort to grow and harvest the food, to produce the plastic packaging, to build the store and shelves themselves, to pave the road that leads to the supermarket, to the fields, to the cities... More machines, more engines, and more fuel are needed all the time. A caravan of food must be delivered to areas of population everyday—people gotta eat! _(I've heard that in the U.S. all food travels from fields an average 1,500 miles to reach human mouths.)_

Because of this massive continual burning of fuel, each of us possesses something called a 'carbon footprint'. You may at one time or another have heard of us humans referred to as 'carbon based life forms'. How quaint. _ALL_ living things are carbon based life forms actually. The carbon atom (slightly smaller than an oxygen atom) is very versatile—it's at the center of most organic molecules; every living thing on the planet uses carbon in some way and always has. *(Could extra-terrestrial life be non-carbon based? I don't think so. The next atom with similar electrical properties is silicon—carbon is a lot more prevalent in the universe, plus when you add catalytic oxygen to silicon you get quartz; sand is good for beaches but bad for bodies.)* You should be made of carbon as well, it's what you eat after all—the once living things you ingest are all made of carbon, too. *(Perhaps you've heard of* **carbo**-*hydrates? Simple sugar is a string of 6 carbon atoms surrounded by some hydrogen and oxygen atoms, $C_6H_{12}O_6$ The starches, fats, and proteins you eat also contain long chains of carbon atoms.)* And the fuel that's burned to make machines, to power the machines, to make the electricity—this fuel was once living too, it is made of carbon as well.

All of this carbon that used to be part of living things, it is 'burned' meaning 'combined with oxygen'—this happens in your cells and it happens in your car's cylinders. The carbon is 'plucked' from its molecular chain—*say goodbye to your buddies carbon, oxygen is back in town and she needs a dance-partner...* Stored atomic energy is released from the fuel as the carbon breaks the bonds with its neighbors and hooks up with the oxygen instead.

You've probably heard of the end results, both carbon monoxide *(chemical formula 'CO'—one atom of carbon and oxygen each)* and carbon dioxide *('CO₂'—one atom of carbon and two of oxygen)* can get produced. On a spaceship there needs to be special air filters that take out the carbon dioxide in the air when it builds up from the astronauts' breathing—your body is constantly 'burning' fuel, blood sugar called glycogen is the preferred fuel, but followers of the Atkins diet know that the body can burn fat and protein as well. *(On a popular science television show called* **Mythbusters***, hosts Adam Savage and Jaime Hyneman built a rocket fueled not with normal propellant, but with* *salami. That's right, they combined oxygen with protein and fat and got a rocket to fly. Any hydrocarbon would work— the deli-meat actually burned too well and exploded the rocket on the first attempt, oops.)* Regardless, fuel in your body is being 'burned'—the carbon atoms found in fats, proteins, and carbohydrates are being bound with some handy oxygen atoms as you breathe. Your body greedily uses the energy released from the act of plucking these carbons from their 'food' structures and ejects the waste product, the carbon dioxide, pell mell into the environment with nary a thought.

Carbon Carbon everywhere—all of this carbon adds up, some comes from your breath, when you exhale, some comes from the exhalations of the cow that turned into that steak you ate. Solid food is turned into wispy gas, similar to the way a heavy solid log burns in your campfire and becomes carbon-laden smoke. *(Most of us don't burn logs anymore, we burn a better fuel these days, oil.)* Some of the carbon associated with you comes from the exhaust pipes of the cars and trucks and factories and power plants that are required to support you. *(Even electric cars are not as 'clean' as you think.)* Yes, all of this carbon adds up—it becomes pounds and pounds, tons and tons *(one 'ton' is 2,000 pounds/~900 kilograms)* of carbon. This is your 'carbon footprint'—how much carbon needs to be burned and released because of your existence? How many tons?

Here is a sobering example—your car. How much does it weigh? A couple of thousand pounds perhaps? A ton or two? What if I told you that the average American car, because it is being driven, produces its own weight in carbon dioxide every single year.

That doesn't sound right, does it? But it is true— thousands of pounds of carbon come out of your tailpipe every year. How is this possible? Well, think of your fuel— gasoline, this is refined from oil. Lots of carbon there, pounds and pounds of it actually; oil used to be alive, feeding off the sun, remember? 'Generic' gasoline could be described with the chemical formula C_6H_{18}, though in reality it can be much more complex—regardless, there are lots and lots of hydrocarbons there *(get it? hydro[gen and] carbon atoms)*. When you add good old oxygen to those hydrocarbons, the atoms get unhooked and rehooked—they turn into water (H_2O) and carbon dioxide or carbon monoxide (CO_2 and CO respectively). **The funny thing is, no atoms are actually lost in this process.** Atoms don't really get 'burned' or destroyed, the atoms never go away—they just get combined with available oxygen, they get 'reshuffled'. It's why you must always breathe *(Haven't you wondered? Why not? You're doing it now. You do it for a reason, a reason you ignore because you do it without thinking)*—this 'reshuffling' process never stops. The breathing must continue. Stop breathing and you die.

But as long as you breathe, or your car's engine breathes, then the atomic tango continues—carbon is freed from the food and fuel and spewed back out into the environment with a different partner. Pounds and pounds of it—thousands of pounds. Tons even. And all of this is happening because of you. Your car needs fuel. *(Air doesn't weigh much—but you need a lot of it to combine with your gasoline. For every 1 lb. of gasoline you need 15 lbs. of air! Dragsters need more power than a normal car engine, they use a fuel called Nitro-Methane; it's a type of hydrocarbon that has some handy oxygen atoms already attached. This means that you can pump more 'gas' into a dragster cylinder—8x more! No wonder dragsters fly... I ride a motorcycle, the 'Iron Horse', but the organic version, the thoroughbred racehorse, needs air too—Seabiscuit needed to inhale/exhale 10 gallons of air every second when running to victory. Over a distance of one mile no animal is faster than the horse, and just think, it's powered by oats and air.)*

Gasoline is mostly carbon, sure there are more hydrogen atoms in the organic molecules, but carbons are huge compared to hydrogens—normally a single carbon atom 'weighs' as much as 12 hydrogen atoms. Yowza that's a lot of carbon. And how much does a gallon of liquid gasoline weigh? Almost 6 pounds. *(Most of that weight, about 4.8 lbs. worth, is carbon. If you've ever wondered why we abbreviate 'pounds' with the letters 'lbs.' when there is no 'l' or 'b' in the word 'pound', wonder no more—Libra is the astrological name for The Scales, it originally comes from the Latin; a 'libra' was a unit of ancient Roman weight...)* And that's pounds per gallon. How many gallons fit inside your gas tank? On average I would say about 12 gallons—12 gallons times 6 pounds equals around 70 pounds per fill-up. And where does all of that poundage go? *Out the tailpipe baby, out of sight, out of mind...*

And when your gas-tank goes empty, just fill 'er up with another 70 pounds, then another 70 pounds, then another, and another. Each week, every week, all year, every year. And that's just from your car. Think of all the products you need and use, the roads, the buildings— everything surrounding you and touching you—it all takes machines and energy, it all takes the burning of carbon to produce. Humanity's carbon footprint gets larger and larger each year as more and more people populate the planet and demand goods and services to make their lives more comfortable.

Just like in a spaceship though, the carbon is starting to build up in the air, it's becoming more concentrated due to all of our 'activities'. Not enough to asphyxiate us like on the spaceship *(or in a closed garage with the car's engine running)*, but enough to throw off the energy balance of the planet; the scales get tipped. This is the **'Global Warming'** that you've heard so much of, and carbon is the culprit causing us grief. *(Well, technically, we're the culprits, we're the masterminds, carbon just plays the dumb-but-strong henchman...)*

Another catchy name for the same problem is the **'Greenhouse Effect'**. It makes sense, the Earth is warming, just like a greenhouse in winter. It's all about energy, and of course the one that's hurting us is the one that powers us *(the source of most of our energy, the sun)*. Simple carbon dioxide, the molecule, has an interesting special physical property when it comes to the sun's energy—it is selectively absorbent. It behaves a lot like the glass found in a greenhouse or the windows of a parked car sitting in the sunlight.

The glass is selective—it's like the big bouncer down at the posh nightclub. Some types of energy get ushered right through, they are given the V.I.P. treatment—when the energy is in the form of visible light for instance, the 'door is opened' and it's allowed inside the greenhouse or parked car via the glass. However, the energy doesn't stay this way, it's always changing, remember? And a very common form that this light energy turns into is heat.

Atoms inside the interior, behind the glass, absorb the energy and vibrate faster; your car's leather seats, for example, get quite warm, but hot things don't stay hot forever, they cool down darling. And how do they do this? They dump their energy *(sounds like the water cycle for a reason, all atoms do this energy dance)* in a special way, in the same way that air with extra energy behaves in the upper atmosphere. They 'bleed' it off in the form of light, but a special type of light called IR, short for Infra-Red. *(This is the fancy scientific name for heat—'infra' means 'below'; this invisible form of red light is 'below' the red light that your eyes can detect. On the other side of the visible light spectrum is 'UV' or Ultra-Violet. 'Ultra' means 'above'—this invisible light is 'above' the violet light that your eyes can see. A rainbow in the sky has more striped colors than you know, maybe the invisible parts are where the Leprechauns hide...)*

Your TV remote control uses flashing beams of this Infra-Red light to change your channel or crank the volume. You can't see the pulsing light-beam shooting out of your remote, but it's there. It's not like the 'heat beam' you'll find in the comic books or **Godzilla** movies, it's been weakened to make it safer. *(Television can be bad for you mentally, why make it bad physically, too? Actually, the remote control is the least of your problems, most televisions today can be classified as 'electron guns'—TVs get hot because metal inside is being heated on purpose. Hot metal ejects energized electrons at high speed that are then steered by controlled magnets to strike the inside of your TV screen, imparting energy, making it glow certain colors. Steer enough electrons and you can make the colors dance. The picture on the screen, created by energy, will appear to move—it can dance too...)*

The leather seats of your parked car, or the concrete floor of the greenhouse, or a sandy beach on a sunny summer day—these atoms absorb the sun's energy, they vibrate faster, but things don't remain the same forever though, do they? All of those hot atoms then dump this extra energy, they get rid of it, not in the form of electrons as inside your TV, but as Infra-Red light. Your car seats glow with invisible light as does the hot sand on the Earth's surface.

And when this 'heat as light' tries to leave your parked car's leather seat, or the inside of a greenhouse, it encounters the glass windows blocking its path. *The virtual bouncer steps up—visible light may pass easily inside, but invisible light like heat, I'm sorry, you'll have to try harder, you can't leave right away...* And a type of 'traffic jam' ensues as all of that absorbed and emitted 'heat energy' tries to get out, to escape. *(Another delay that is found in nature—movement doesn't happen instantaneously, it always takes time, and you might be blocked. Try harder, obstacles should only slow you down, not stop you.)* Things on the inside of the glass, your car's interior, or a greenhouse's interior, they stay rather toasty compared to the outside of the glass. The Infra-Red heat gets trapped inside, at least for a while. Once the heat builds up it will slowly escape, too slowly for our tastes though. Things get plenty hot in the meantime.

But what about the sandy beach? There is no giant glass dome keeping in the heat, right? Why is the Earth heating up like a greenhouse then? Glass isn't the only material that behaves like a selective nightclub bouncer. The carbon dioxide that we produce from living, and also from burning fuel, this works just like the glass.

And we produce tons of carbon dioxide, especially Americans, every year. *(We have 5% of the world's population but produce 25% of its carbon exhaust, though China and India are catching up unfortunately.)* Our products, our food, our clothing, our buildings, cars and vacations—they all require the burning of fuel. The carbon has been there, locked up in the fuel, but we need energy. We burn the fuel, we take and use its energy by unhooking the carbons from their home and rehooking them with oxygen we find floating free in the air—CO_2 now exists in the air where there used to just be a 'C' safely tucked away inside a tree or buried deep underground as coal, oil, or natural gas.

Tons and tons of carbon atoms are liberated from their Earthly confines; the wisps of carbon vapor now float free in the air connected to the oxygen atoms they were forced to marry *(with humans holding the shotgun)*. The sun's light comes in through the air, through the invisible CO_2 molecules, but when the heat tries to leave back through that same collection of gases, it can't escape right away, the carbon dioxide selectively grabs onto the energy— it likes it, it holds onto it. *(Yes, even non-living molecules are prejudiced; it's no wonder we judge.)* The atmosphere starts to heat up. Weather is really the absorbed energy of the Earth flexing its muscles, and more energy means more flexing. More violent storms with higher frequencies shall abound—have you seen the shattered storm records as of late?

The key is to switch over from carbon based fuels to non-carbon based fuels. I applaud the latest initiative into Biodiesel—with an increased production of corn replacing part of the foreign oil we are dependent on, but 'corn' alone is not the final answer, it's just a short term way to ease us off of our dependence on fossil fuels. An acre of corn can produce approximately 300 gallons of Ethanol (pure corn whiskey). Burning pure Ethanol as fuel does not increase the Earth's carbon load *(and that's very good)* as the carbon released into the atmosphere came from the atmosphere to begin with, when the plant 'sucked' it out of the air to grow itself. Some people believe erroneously that increased carbon dioxide levels in the air will create an environment with more robust plants everywhere, that increased tree and shrub growth will continue to 'suck' the CO_2 out of the air and solve our greenhouse woes—but people forget that plants die, and that bacteria, in the process of munching the dead vegetation, release this gas. Nothing is gained.

No. Non-carbon is the best way to go—but what else is there? There is Hydrogen pointing the way. When you combine Hydrogen with Oxygen this yields power, electricity even, and the waste product is water. *(It's been officially announced; BMW is introducing the world's first hydrogen powered production car, the 7 Series, early in 2007. It will have 12 cylinders, 260 horsepower, and is designed as a 'hybrid' to run at first on both hydrogen and petroleum products. BMW is offering the hybrid since it will take a little time for 'hydrogen filling stations' to become as accessible as 'gasoline filling stations', but BMW has seen the future and apparently embraced it. The German car company has also expressed hopes to offer hydrogen power plants eventually in ALL of its cars. Now that's impressive, and will probably be quite lucrative for BMW in the long run. It is my sincere hope that America jumps on this hydrogen powered bandwagon, and soon, in order to kick some Bavarian butt. The Europeans have a head start, but we hate to lose... Let's go Detroit, the alternative gauntlet has been thrown down—are you gonna stand for this?)* But how do you get the hydrogen to begin with? Well, herein lies the trick. There is plenty of hydrogen already stored up in water (H_2O), all you need do is run an electric current through the water, and then you separate the hydrogen atoms from the oxygen atoms—but where to get the electricity without burning fossil fuels? Solar, wind, and water energy (which is really all solar) are available for exploit, and then there's the other source of energy, the Earth's internal heat.

Iceland is a land of volcanoes—they have plenty of cheap electricity given up by the Earth. Places like Iceland can use non-carbon geothermal power to make hydrogen, and then this hydrogen can be altered *(a catalyst can turn it into a solid for safe transport; see* **Stan Ovshinsky** *and his 'Ovonics solid storage technology'—Stan also invented the nickel-metal-hydride rechargeable battery in 1982, he knows a lot about chemistry and electricity)* and then shipped around the world, in the same way the Middle East digs up and exports its oil. Iceland will become the new Saudi Arabia.

The U.S. has geothermal power too, we have volcanoes as well (in Hawaii, Alaska, Washington, northern California, and don't forget Yellowstone). We also have a desire to wean ourselves from the petroleum teat; we are starting to develop more wind, solar and water power. *Underwater turbines are being tested in the flowing rivers around New York City as we speak. Also, I have heard of biologically engineered strains of algae (look up* **Dr. Maria L. Ghirardi**, *Senior Scientist at the U.S. Dept. of Energy's* **National Renewable Energy Lab**, *even their website is* *powered by renewable energy) that will take in sunlight, but give off hydrogen gas as a waste product—we could 'farm' hydrogen...* Who knows? Maybe someday folks will have solar panels on the roof of their house that will collect enough energy to make some handy hydrogen to power their car. To hell with the gas pumps, make your own fuel. Current hybrid autos that still use gasoline are not the final answer either, hydrogen baby, that's the key to transforming the planet, and our lives, for the better.

For more information on why we should be trying a whole lot harder, check out former Vice President Al Gore's planetary passion: ***An Inconvenient Truth***. It's a movie and a book, and Mr. Gore's voice needs to be heard. And Al is finally getting some charismatic assistance from his friend, Bill Clinton. The 'Clinton Global Initiative' raises funds from varied sources to combat widespread problems such as Global Warming. Al Gore managed to sit down with 'Rebel Billionaire' Richard Branson of ***Virgin*** mega-fame while at the 2006 Clinton conference, and it appears that Sir Richard was impressed with Al's sales pitch; he has pledged 3 Billion Dollars *(all funded by profits coming from his airline and other transportation ventures)* to tackle the concerns of Global Warming, to include the promotion of alternate fuels. At a separate news conference, while standing next to Bill Clinton, the über-wealthy British philanthropist said:

We must not be the generation responsible for irreversibly damaging the environment. We must hand it over to our children in as near pristine condition as we were lent it from our parents.

Stand up and take a bow Al, you're doing great work, we need more people like you. *'The tragedy of the commons'* can be avoided; we don't have to trash our planet.

We are an intimate part of this planet. However, we've been approaching it with a Stone Age mentality—unfortunately a selfish mentality. All that matters is *me*. Well, that may have been a nice way to survive volcanic catastrophe, but it's not the way to true happiness or planetary bliss. And America with its SUV's and individually wrapped moist towelettes, we are setting the selfish Stone Age pace for the rest of the world to emulate.

It's all about us, us as individuals. Part of the reason that the planet is in such dire straits *(and about to get worse)* is because we only live for a few short decades. We have to eat while we are here, you can't take it with you. Disposable diapers are so much easier, cans of soda are so convenient, that 320 horsepower engine is so fast... You have to live—it's just that your life has more of an atomic impact than you know. Have trouble believing me? Would you rather believe that the Earth's temperature woes stem more from 'natural cycles' instead of from human activities? Hitler would, he's good at denial. Don't just take my word for it, you may not know 'Dave Gardner' as a respected expert, not yet anyway, but perhaps you'll listen more closely to a respected journalist, like Tom Brokaw. He has lots of experts at his beck and call. Listen to Tom as he talks to you through his recent documentary: *Global Warming, What You Need to Know with Tom Brokaw*.

Of the 21 hottest years on record, 20 have occurred since 1980... All over the world computer models are now saying the same thing—Global Warming is real. The planet will continue to warm... The science is overwhelming... On the ground scientists are now seeing with their own eyes the very changes forecasted by computers... Many scientists believe that temperatures are rising so fast, the Earth's climate may reach a threshold, the tipping point, when there will be nothing we can

do to 'un-do' Global Warming. If they are right, by the year 2100, within the lifetime of our children or grandchildren, our world will be a drastically different place... The Chinese plan to add 1 coal-fired power plant every single week for the next 7 years. China's CO_2 emissions are rising rapidly, it is already the world's second largest source of Greenhouse Gas emissions. Number one? The United States...

Tom does a really good job *(go ahead Tom, you get to take a bow too)*, he eventually spotlights Americans and what we can do to help solve the problem without giving up our familiar standard-of-living; most Americans have no idea just how much 'burning' is going on because of living, per year every year.

Add it all up and the 'Smiths' (an average American family living in an average American home outside an average American city who also happen to use an average amount of energy) produce 50 tons of CO_2 every year.

50 tons per family per year; that's 100,000 lbs. of 'light and wispy' carbon dioxide getting produced by you and your loved ones (on average). If that sounds like a lot, it is, and there are a lot of families out there; multiply that 100,000 lbs. by millions... Are you starting to see the scope? All this living, all this oxidation, all this unhooking and rehooking of atoms—it's part of who you are and how you got here. You are connected not only to everyone else socially, but you are also connected to the planet. You come from the planet, you will be returned to it, and while you are here you will play your part in the atomic dance, building your body, driving your car, turning on your computer. How many people take it all for granted—do you? Or should I say, "*Did* you?" Once you know how things work around you, your perspective changes, your value system changes.

Never again do I look at a carrot, or a car, or a light bulb, or the sun the same way ever again. My way of thinking has been changed. Things are different now.

The same applies to the problems in my life. I look at them differently as well. And those problems, they don't mean a whole lot in the grander scheme of things. Who you are and how you got here—isn't that more important than the drunken insult socially given at the cocktail party? I guess that depends on how much value you place on social posturing compared to promoting your own serene state of mind. You can't stop being angry or sad, frustrated or offended, but you can understand the motivations that caused these emotional states, and you can lessen their negative impact. That takes human thought and a paradigm shift to occur though, conscious effort on your part. All of which are helped along by the information written in these pages. If this effort sounds like work, it is—but if you desire happiness and serenity in this mean old world with its stacked deck, you can have it. You just have to figure it out. Think about it. Have a snack, you're gonna need the energy. I'll try to help you when I can, but don't thank me, thank the sun.

The Machine is a Ghost

Atoms, those building blocks of nature, they never get destroyed, they just get reshuffled. That's weird, isn't it? Even burning doesn't do them in. For all intents and purposes, atoms are indestructible. Well, 'normal' intents and purposes—we've discovered that atoms can be altered under *very* special circumstances. It happens in nature, in the heart of our own sun, and humans have also tinkered with atomic structure in developing nuclear power plants and atomic bombs.

If you've read some interesting and bizarre things about humanity and nature up to this point, hold onto your hat. Humanity, in its quest to understand everything, including ourselves, has uncovered some bizarre truths about those 'basic building blocks' of nature we call atoms. We should be concerned, after all this is ultimately who we are and where we come from. There is new information out there, answers that raise more questions—we are peeling back the layers of the Cosmos like an onion, and what we are finding reveals more than Einstein ever dreamed. There is a bizarreness to the story of the atom, and of us.

Before I get into the bizarreness, lets quickly look at human perception and bring everybody up to speed on the basics. It was only about 100 years ago that we first figured out atomic structure. *(Check out New Zealand's favorite physicist, **Ernest Rutherford**, and his amazing and revealing experiments.)* Atoms, as it turns out, aren't really 'there', at least not in the sense that we think they are. Atoms are like ghosts.

We are fooled. It's not that hard to do. You see, we base a lot of our understanding of natural processes on our own personal experiences, unfortunately though, just because something looks similar, this does not make it correct in the eyes of reality. For example, look at the light and feel the heat coming from a campfire; there's 'burning' going on, yes? Look up at the sun on a summer day—do you witness its light? Do you feel its heat? Of course you do, and as such you may assume that the sun is 'burning'—*it looks like a fire, right? It feels like a fire, right? The sun is a big burning ball of gas, right?* You would be wrong. *Bzzzt! Thanks for playing!* There are no flames, the heat and light you feel and see get generated in a different manner, there is no 'burning' going on. You wouldn't be the first to be fooled.

Even great minds are fooled. Aristotle saw the sun and the moon travel overhead each day. To him it was obvious; the Earth was stationary in the heavens. He didn't feel the Earth move—if the Earth moved, wouldn't a powerful wind be generated? If the Earth moved, wouldn't falling apples hit the ground miles from where they left the safety of a tree branch? *(It took almost 2,000 years and an obstinate Galileo to overturn this incorrect assessment—and he was rewarded for his hard work by threat of death and house arrest. Some people, especially people in power, don't want to hear the truth, it frightens them. It's more comfortable to promote and believe in the lie. Change is bad for people in power, they fight change.)*

This information can be a bit scary—why? Because it challenges much of what we experience and have been taught as true. Some readers will be shocked and appalled by what is written in these pages, but hiding from and denying the truth does not make it go away. And what we've discovered has been because of careful measurements and the application of logic.

From simple experiments Galileo showed how the Earth could and should be moving through space. We take it for granted now, the movement of the planets and the structure of the solar system, but the average person can't 'see' the solar system. Sometimes things don't make sense to your senses, and it's hard to accept the things that you haven't personally experienced. Galileo had a telescope, to him it really was obvious, open your eyes, see for yourself.

But it was scary for people in the 1600's to think about a moving Earth, it resulted in vast confusion and human mental torture—we're analytical tool makers and problem solvers, remember? If the Earth moves then: Why is it moving? How is it moving? Why don't we feel the effects of this motion? Will the Earth stop moving? Will it crash into the sun? Scary yes, but now we actually know the answers to these questions. *(They had to be asked before they could be answered—and thankfully French mathematician* **Pierre-Simon Laplace** *found the moving planets to be stable in their solar orbits, the Earth is safe. There is cosmic cause for concern, things do change as they move. Mars is not so safe, one of its two tiny moons is spiraling downward on a slow collision course. Our own moon is actually getting farther away from the Earth each year, it has been ever since it formed...)* Of course more scary questions have arisen, and why not? We don't know everything, but each day brings new discoveries, new answers, and of course new question marks...

We sit in our seats, smiling, as flight attendants pour drinks out of cans as though nothing is the matter. *Nothing the matter??!!* We're flying 40,000 feet above the ground at an air speed of 250 knots! Why doesn't the soda spill? *Excuse me, could I have some more ice cubes? Thank you so much...* Galileo would be freaking out right about now, but you, you calmly sit and sip—it's as if the plane is stationary, back on the runway... We understand that a moving thing, like a plane or a ship, can seem 'stationary' to the cup, the soda, even you if everything is actually moving at the same speed.

An astronaut on a spooky space-walk to repair a broken satellite feels and looks as though they are stationary—look down, and you are over California, you _work some more on the satellite. Close your eyes—it still feels as though you and the satellite are stationary. Look down past your feet again a few minutes later and you're over Florida... You are traveling 16,000 miles per hour, that's over twenty times the speed of sound—you're going faster than thunder. If it takes you eighty minutes to effect repairs you'll go around the globe. **'Around the World in Eighty Days'**; hey Jules Verne, get with the program! And again, if you closed your eyes you'd swear you weren't moving at all..._

Look around you, see something stationary nearby? Is it really? The ground just happens to be moving at exactly the same speed... In a plane the 'ground' is now the floor of the plane. As I mentioned much earlier in this book, motion is relative. It depends on your perspective. _(Kind of like your happiness, eh?)_

A moving Earth challenged much of what we thought we understood, now, with education, it doesn't seem so unpleasant. Learning about atomic structure can be viewed the same way. It's scary and there are unpleasant implications when you analyze the 'atom'—but to deny the truth is to deny who you are. Don't pull a 'Hitler', step up and face your fears. Are you afraid of a little question mark?

Humans evolved from a lower primate form. All life is related by DNA and common ancestors. We're still Stone Age humans with reactive animal emotions. Men's nipples—Women's sexual dominance, go figure. We come from the Earth born as a single cell, we will be returned to the Earth. Energy from the sun is converted into life and motion, heat and sound, on this planet. Atoms are not destroyed, even by burning, they get recycled.

And now for the next—things that feel solid really aren't. Remember, your senses can fool you. How is this possible? Things 'feel' solid? Hear that? Those are my knuckles rapping on the table top—solid as the day is long...

Ah, but now you luckily know more than Aristotle, the way things feel and look may not necessarily be how they actually are. Look closer, nature is behaving like a miniature P.T. Barnum, you are being fooled mainly because you want to be fooled. It's easier to believe you are solid, that all atoms are solid—but that isn't the truth, it's a hoax.

Atoms **behave** like solid little spheres, they bounce off each other the way 'solid' billiard balls bounce off each other and the bumpers of a pool table. When we make models of molecules in the classroom, the atoms are represented by golf ball-sized 'solid' wooden or plastic spheres, color coded to indicate which atoms are being used. We live in a world where solid things certainly seem solid. *Air? Sure, that's a gas. Water? Yes, water is not solid, it flows—but a rock, or this table top, surely these are solid...* Of course now we know otherwise; air, water, rock or table top, none of them are solid—it's all an illusion.

Atoms are almost entirely empty space. I might even be inclined to say that the atom is *entirely* empty space, there is nothing there physically, more on that in a bit. Basically though, how 'empty' is the average atom? I want you to envision a giant sphere, like a vast glass apple. This is no normal glass apple *(as if any glass apple was normal— but it makes for an interesting visual)*. No, this apple is so big that it could fit the entire Empire State building *(1250 ft / 381 m tall)* inside its hollow framework. Now THAT'S a 'big apple'—*ba dum bump; I blame my father's sense of humor...*

If you've never been to New York I can still help with a different frame of reference, imagine your favorite large sports stadium—the Superdome, Dodger Stadium, Lambeau Field—now imagine two *(yep, two)* of those side by side... Now imagine a giant glass sphere that encompasses **both of them** entirely... Pretty big, eh? This is our basic 'atom' blown up in size to demonstrate just what I'm talking about, to put things in perspective, to show you just how empty every atom really is.

And this giant glass model we are visualizing is not the structure of a complex atom, but rather the simplest atom there is, Hydrogen; this atom has an atomic number of '1'. *(Helium is '2', Lithium is '3'... Carbon is '6'... Oxygen is '8'... Iron is '26'... Gold is '79'... Uranium, the 'heaviest' of natural atoms on this planet, is '92'... They are all listed in ascending order on that atomic alphabet we like to call 'The Periodic Table of Elements'—why 'periodic'? Because the structure and properties of some atoms are similar and repeat, like Carbon and Silicon or Helium and Neon; the basic atoms can be organized into a meaningful chart.)*

Back to our giant glass sphere/apple, only now lets take out the 'Empire State building' or 'twin sports stadiums' and replace them with more symbolic parts that make up the hydrogen atom—what would our model look like? Well, atoms may be tiny, but they are truthfully made of even smaller objects, three of them, the so-called 'subatomic' particles; 'sub' because they are 'under' the size of actual atoms *('sub' comes from the Latin—submarine literally means 'under' the 'water').* Of all the atoms on this planet, from 'tiny' Hydrogen to more massive Uranium, there are only these three tiny subatomic particles that make all of them, and ultimately you, up. They are the protons *(electrically **positive**),* the neutrons *(electrically **neutral**),* and the electrons *(electrically **negative**—thank Benjamin Franklin for coining the terms positive and negative when discussing electricity).*

This book, in its completed form, symbolically demonstrates the different levels of atomic structure. The book is like you, big and solid. But you are made of smaller things, atoms, and these are made of even smaller parts, the tinier subatomic particles. And each collection of parts makes up a unique 'whole', with them you can make a person, or a rock, or even a rainbow—there is a lot of beautiful variety with atoms, but you have to follow the rules. Atoms have definite structure and behavior.

This book has structure too, it's a big thing but it's made of smaller things, the words... The book is a collection of words like you are a collection of atoms. And like atoms, words also have some smaller parts, the letters. There is an alphabet there, 26 different letters, and with them you can spell words and create an entire book. With those 26 letters you can write all kinds of different and beautifully varied books depending on how you link them together—not just any way mind you, 'jsiajpdgfrsa' isn't a word. For the alphabet to make sense the smaller parts, the 26 letters, only fit together in certain ways, there are rules. Letters have specific jobs in building larger words. Words need definite structure and behavior in order to be organized into a beautiful and meaningful language.

With atoms, there is only a 3 letter alphabet. If you look at everything physical on this planet *('Physics' is about the physical universe, it's all measurable)*, you, a rock, the air, the water, Hitler, hummingbirds—all of it is made from only these 3 'letters'. You are made of protons, neutrons and electrons—that's it. But those 3 letters are so, so versatile—look around you, look at what nature has 'written' in a beautiful and meaningful way.

But there are rules even with these 3 letters. Vowels have certain characteristics as do consonants in our written language, they have different 'jobs'. Our 'atomic letters' are no different. Let's finish filling in our giant Empire State sized model of the simplest atom there is, Hydrogen, by briefly describing just where and what can be found if you were to look more closely.

So, in your mind's eye you can picture this huge glass ball—the outside surface, the glass though, this is an issue. There is no solid surface to the atom, that's an illusion. This 'outer boundary' is the realm of the electron, orbiting around the nucleus at a prescribed distance like some insane out-of-control satellite; it zips around and around in all kinds of crazy tilted orbits—it moves so fast that it looks like it's everywhere at the same time, a 'surface' seems to appear... *(One way to look at it is a 'probability cloud'—there isn't the electron at a certain spot, there is the 'probability' that the moving electron is here at this moment—somehow the ghost of probability generates this pseudo surface; research Werner Heisenberg and his famous* **Uncertainty Principle.** *You can't apply normal laws at this level—behavior down here is strange and real and ghostly all at the same time, Einstein hated it. His famous "God does not play dice" with the universe quote spoke of the distaste he had for probability and quantum mechanics. If this stuff freaks you out at least you're in good company.)*

Travel down toward the center of our huge dual-stadium-sized sphere, away from the frenetic perimeter dance of the electron, and you'll approach the nucleus. It is here that you find the home *(or should I say prison cell—the roving electron acts like a constant pacing guard keeping outsiders out and inmates in)* of any neutrons or protons—that's all she wrote for your atom, those are your three parts: electrons on the outside, protons and neutrons in the center. And in our hypothetical giant hydrogen atom it's even simpler, there are no neutrons here *(the only atom found normally this way—none are as 'primitive')*. A hydrogen atom contains only one tiny positive proton in the nucleus, and one negative electron *(even tinier)* orbiting around it.

If we could see them, these atomic 'parts' would look and behave like little spheres, similar to the spherical atom itself, only tinier of course, these are the 'sub'atomic particles we're talking about—how tiny? Well, in our giant model the size of the atom has been greatly increased to show more detail, to help you wrap your brain around what's going on. How big is our tiny proton in the center? Well, imagine a sphere the size of an apple seed...

When I say apple seed, I'm not talking about a giant-sized apple seed to go with our giant-sized glass apple. No. Regular size. That's what's at the center of our giant sphere. Hmmm... No, revise that. Not a regular sized apple seed, instead think stunted, malformed, teeny-tiny irregular-sized apple seed. *Yikes* that's a tiny thing at the center of a big thing—and you thought atoms were small, well, guess what's smaller... This lonely little proton is our nucleus, THIS is where the atom gets its mass, it's all concentrated here. Only protons and neutrons matter that much because those distant orbiting electrons are next to nothing compared to our nuclear prisoners.

How small is the outlying electron? Well, please remember that the proton is the size of a teeny-tiny apple seed in our model, *the electron is about **a thousand times smaller**...* It's miniscule really, a bare whisper of existence. And yet it zips about so fast that a weird 'hard' energy shell forms in its wake. There is nothing there at the surface of the atom, just the paths that the electron traced through space.

Strange yes, that we are made of these bizarre little spherical atoms of mostly nothing, but we are. And those subatomic particles, the even tinier protons, neutrons, and electrons, we think of them like 'little balls' doing jobs inside the atom, little 'solid' balls... But as we've seen, successful forms in nature tend to repeat, if the 'atom as solid' is an illusion, just a dance of smaller particles, then what of those smaller particles... *Are they really solid? Are they made of even smaller 'things' doing a strange dance?? Is there anything solid at all about the atom???* To answer these questions: *No, Yes,* and in my experience—*No,* the atom is really all energy that masquerades as solid matter. Nothing is real the way we think it is. *(Research **'Quarks'** for more information.)*

We don't see things as they are, we see them as we are.

– Anaïs Nin

So, time to change the way you think. Who you are is what you think after all—you could be paralyzed or lose all your limbs, but you would still exist, I think therefore I am. *(If you haven't read Dalton Trumbo's 1939 novel,* **johnny got his gun,** *you should. What would you do if you lost your: arms, legs, eyes, ears, nose, and mouth?)* But what are thoughts? You're having them right now, you have a personality, you think, but where do thoughts and memories reside? Your wonderful brain is filled with nerve cells that never touch. It is filled even further with atoms that never touch, and those atoms are filled with parts that never touch and are themselves a lot of nothing, just some squiggly dances of energy fields—and yet this is who you are, you are special enough to know this secret and strange blueprint. You can think about it, you can envision it. But again, what are thoughts? Thoughts have no physical reality, but it seems as though your tangible body is a lot more like intangible thought than you may have imagined.

For many of us with a traditional religious leaning, we are brought up with the notion that science and religion are at war, or at least at odds with each other. This is not true, instead see that they compliment each other. *(Copernicus and Kepler, Galileo and Newton, Darwin and Einstein, they were all scientists who saw the beauty of existence and discovery running parallel with their own religious beliefs. They all professed their faith in God. Giordano Bruno, a 17th century ordained priest who lived alongside of Galileo, was at first excommunicated for adhering to the Copernican idea that the sun was the center of the solar system, blasphemy! Later Bruno was burned alive on a stake—the Inquisition demanded a full recanting of his concept that the stars we see are the same as our sun, also that there might be other planets out there inhabited by* *intelligent people. Bruno became a martyr—he would rather* *die than lie about his beliefs.)* Science is about cosmic order, measurement, while religion focuses on cosmic purpose. Science can show you how big or how old the universe is *(~14 Billion-years-old),* but it fails to ever explain why it exists. There is more to understand.

Do you think—or were you taught—that we are solid physical beings here on Planet Earth while God, or The Creator, is ethereal, knowledgeable, and exists on a higher plane? You are closer to God than you know. You, my friend, are ethereal. You are knowledgeable. And yes, as you're maybe finding out for the first time, you too live on a higher hidden plane of existence. *(It's okay to say this, right? You're not going to burn me alive upside down on a stake, are you? Some people would rather kill than admit they might be wrong, in order to stay in power—it appears that Hitler's horror wore Vatican robes, too; Adolph was far from original in eliminating opposing voices. Things in Rome have changed since those times, it may have taken 400 years, but Pope John Paul II did apologize for the wrongful persecution of both Galileo and Bruno. But modern Christianity is still far from accepting, how many Black and Homosexual individuals have been ridiculed, beaten, or killed in this country by so-called Christians? The Ku Klux Klan wasn't run by atheists... Jesus would be appalled by our lack of acceptance. If only we could forgive others for being different from us. The Stone Age is not about forgiveness, it's about power. I see the Stone Age all around me and even in me, but being human allows us to rise above our beastly ways. Learn to forgive. Learn the value of life.)*

$E=mc^2$, Einstein's Mass-Energy equation, shows that mass is energy and that energy is mass; they are interchangeable. In other words, 'mass', or the atoms and their parts, are more malleable than they seem. Remember, none of it is really solid. We haven't spent much time talking about our boring friend, the neutron, but he is hardly boring. Hmmm... a neutral thing where you have a big positive proton and a tiny negative electron... I wonder what would happen if you could somehow 'melt' together this proton and the electron—sure, they are separate now, but if you could somehow get them together, what would happen? Would you end up with something where the charges cancelled each other out, making it neutral? If the tiny electron joined the bigger proton, wouldn't that make an object just a smidgen larger than the original proton? What is your logic telling you? Guess what neutrons are...

This is indeed a good description of the neutron, sometimes 'boring' neutral neutrons break down under radioactive decay by **changing back** into a proton and a fast moving ejected electron that can cause bodily damage. This type of atomic breakdown is called *Beta* radiation (*Alpha* radiation causes damage too, but not from ejected electrons). But let's go the other way, let's build some neutrons instead of tearing them apart, for an interesting phenomenon that illustrates just how empty normal atoms here on Earth really are.

There is a special kind of star out there called a Neutron Star, you may have heard of it. *(Some Neutron Stars spin and give off rhythmic energy in a special way— they are a subset called Pulsars.)* It is a monster, much larger than our own sun in mass, but not large enough to cause it to explode in a Supernova or implode becoming a Black Hole. No, this is a special large star where gravity is only slightly insane. *(A Neutron Star can emerge from explosion though—the outer layers of a star can get blown away, and the remaining large 'core' will start to condense under gravity. Also, even monsters have monsters, there is a Neutron Star in the Constellation of Sagittarius [SGR 1806-20] that has a magnetic field a thousand-trillion times stronger than the Earth's—it's the most magnetic object in the known universe.)*

Gravity squeezes stars, it's where their heat and light come from. But before we get to the energy-manufacturing part of a star like our own sun, lets look at gravity gone mad with our Neutron Star. Atoms in our sun get squeezed, but they still look like atoms with nuclei and orbiting electrons—not so in a Neutron Star. Here we have a star so massive that the very atoms get altered *(more so than usual)*. The squeezing pressure is so high that the electrons can no longer do their job—for their entire existence they've never been near the nucleus, that's about to change. Negative electrons are forced down, down to the nucleus. Here they 'melt' into the positive protons *(opposites do attract, usually)* forming neutral neutrons—but what of all that empty space that existed between the tiny nucleus and the atom's distant outer 'surface'? This space used to be an atomic no-man's-land, a whole lot of nothing could be found here. The electrons are gone so the empty space they patrolled and protected is also gone. Instead of ghostly atoms of distantly separated nuclei, now all of those nuclei of separate atoms can cram next to each other inside a much smaller area. There are no longer any protons or electrons to be found, there are only neutrons all pulled and packed together by gravity *(nothing has been destroyed, just reshuffled, compressed more efficiently)*. How much would this star-stuff 'weigh' if you could remove the empty space and fill it with neutrons? Check this out.

Let's somehow bring a spoonful of Neutron Star material back to Earth to weigh it. This is concentrated stuff, so we have a special scale built—and it's huge. It's one of those old-fashioned 'pan' balances *(like 'Libra')* where you put something *unknown* on one side and add *known weights* to the other until it delicately balances. We put our spoonful of pure neutrons on one side, and on the other we will put... a full-sized fully loaded aircraft carrier. It balances.

The aircraft carrier seems huge but remember, all those heavy metallic atoms are really mostly empty space between the electrons and the nucleus; real atoms are ghostly. If you could somehow squeeze down that aircraft carrier, crushing the electrons into the nuclei the way you would crush a paper bag, it would fit inside the spoon. The empty space inside would be gone, but the 'weight' remains *(crushing something makes it smaller, not lighter—nothing was added or removed after all).*

In a Neutron Star, normal atoms are squeezed down, concentrated, devoid of empty space, but what of those neutrons? Are they mostly empty space too—can they be squeezed down even further? Can they be squeezed down until ALL the space is gone and yet the mass still remains? What do you think? This bizarre curiosity was predicted by Einstein and is today called a Black Hole. It's not really a 'hole' at all, it's what's leftover when a giant star is massive enough to collapse into 'nothing'—and yet it's still there... *(Perhaps all Black Holes and the Big Bang 'point' do possess a little 'size' as some scientists conjecture; they are not 'zero', but they are infinitely small. What does this mean? Well, take an inch and divide it in half. Then divide that half in half again, and again, and again, forever. You'll never get to 'zero', right? You get closer and closer and closer without ever reaching it. This mathematical argument is the basis for Calculus; mentioned earlier this was first explored by Archimedes and then again by Isaac Newton. This topic gets a little complicated for obvious reasons, much of what we think we know about 'singularities' and Black Holes comes from mathematics and inference; we 'see' and measure Black Holes based on their effect on nearby stars. Some Black Holes are classified as super-massive monsters. However, any bit of mass, to include the Earth, could become a Black Hole if it was somehow squeezed down far enough. Research the 'Swartzchild radius' for more info. By the way, mathematics say the mass of the Earth would need to be mashed down to the size of a pea to turn our planet into a Black Hole—it looks like we're safe for now.)* Our knowledgeable friend Stephen Hawking has spent a good deal of time thinking and writing about just this scenario in books. *(His 1988 Best Seller, **A Brief History of Time**, I'm happy to say, sold more copies than Madonna's book, **Sex**. There is hope.)* Yes, atoms are strange, and we think of the stars as distant and separate from us, but think again. We are made of atoms, but atoms had to come from somewhere. The atoms that make up you had to be born somehow.

They come from energy. As the story goes, there was no universe, there was no space, no time, no stars, no atoms, there was just a void. And then, at the moment of creation, energy came roiling forth from a point that had no dimension, no length, no width, no height. This is affectionately known as the Big Bang. *Let there be light!* Was this energy actually light, or even like light? No one knows... No one was there to see it... There were no stars yet, just energy. Can you fit huge amounts of energy into an area that takes up no space? Evidence is leaning toward yes... but why or how this could take place is a mystery *(not surprising then that it was first proposed by a scientist-turned-priest, **Father Georges-Henri Lemaître**; he called the expanding universe's origin the 'primeval atom' and based his hypothesis partially on Albert Einstein's theory of relativity. Lemaître, first meeting Einstein in 1927 while wearing his priest's collar, is soon ridiculed by Einstein, but he would later be vindicated by measurements made by Edwin Hubble in 1929. Even Einstein would concede; the universe was expanding. In 1966 George Lemaître dies—but before this happens he hears the amazing news from New Jersey; the Cosmic Background Radiation left over from the Big Bang has been discovered),* regardless, we are here with our magnifying glasses trying to make sense of what we now see. It is Galileo's legacy, he would be proud. Humans everywhere are opening their eyes.

From this supposedly dimensionless point ethereal energy spewed forth, not atoms—atoms are like the raindrops that form from gossamer vapor on high. When things are too warm the water stays as vapor, only when it cools do the drops take form. The Big Bang, it is proposed, was similar—as the new 'energy universe' expanded, the energy spread out and cooled, it condensed into simple matter, the protons and electrons (very few neutrons at first) that we know and love. But that's not all that was born from this energy soup, other strange particles also popped into existence. Anti-matter lives. *(Dan Brown, author of the now famous book, **The DaVinci Code**, previously penned a novel, **Angels & Demons**, with the same main character tracking down a stolen parcel of anti-matter through the streets of Rome and the tunnels under the Vatican.)*

Anti-matter sounds exotic, and it is, at least around here. *(Though we can manufacture it using high-energy 'atom smashers'. The so-called 'super-collider' of Texas, that went 'super-over budget' in 1993, was one of these.)* But it did exist in abundance at one time—we are twins that got separated at birth. There could quite possibly be anti-matter suns and planets and entire galaxies in this universe if the conditions favored them at certain early times and places. As strange as it sounds, there may be distant living things right now, made of anti-matter, going about their lives as if nothing is out of the ordinary. *(Bruno did not die in vain, I've seen his vision.)*

And just what is anti-matter? Anti-matter is the opposite of matter, sort of—while the atomic structure is identical in both *(a tiny nucleus guarded by another, smaller, distantly orbiting object),* the electric charges of the subatomic particles have been 'reassigned'. Our proton is still in the nucleus, only now it has a Negative charge, it's called an anti-proton. Our tiny orbiting electron has also been repolarized, it now carries a Positive charge, it's called a positron instead of an electron. But an anti-atom, like anti-hydrogen for example, 'looks' the same as its brother, the 'normal' atom of hydrogen. *(Just think, there might be intelligent anti-matter beings out there pondering the same thing, only they consider us the strange ones. Negative electrons indeed...)* There could be anti-matter stars that shine, and their light, if it fell on you, would feel just as warm as the light of a normal 'matter' star, like our own sun.

The energy soup that cooled down into matter also cooled into near-equal amounts of anti-matter. *(In 2001, a sophisticated NASA satellite named* **WMAP** *[Wilkinson Microwave Anisotropy Probe] takes sensitive readings while in outer space. We learned a lot, and many of our questions were answered. According to measurements, 'matter' just barely outnumbers 'anti-matter' after the Big Bang—about 0.000001% more atoms than anti-atoms...)* Isn't that a neat trick? Energy turned into two types of 'ghostly' atoms that are opposite and compliment each other. Unfortunately *(or 'Fortunately')*, the young universe didn't stop there with its newest tenants. Once these two physical manifestations appeared 'out of nothing' gravity also was born—gravity is the tendency for items of mass, like matter and anti-matter, to drift toward each other, to attract each other. You have mass, you are attracted to the Earth. The Earth has mass, it is attracted to the sun. But gravity does not care if there is matter and anti-matter in the room, she treats them equally.

No one knows why gravity exists. Yes, you wouldn't be here without this strange Big Bang, but you also would not exist without the helping hand of gravity. In the beginning *(scientists surmise based on cosmic measurements, keep reading)*, when the pure energy condensed into matter and anti-matter, much of it didn't remain in this state for long. These simple physical 'things' were born from pure primordial energy, energy that turned into tiny atoms and anti-atoms that 'popped' into cosmic existence, and that 'popping' is important.

When they appear, they aren't stationary, just loitering around; these primordial specks are born with motion. When these particles 'wink' into existence, they fly off in opposite directions. But gravity changed all that, gravity pulled these similar-looking cousins back together, and when matter and anti-matter do finally find each other something interesting happens—an explosive family reunion occurs. They flash back into a form of pure mysterious energy reminiscent of their birth, but this is a different form *(energy changes forms readily, remember? The signature radiation started out in the Ultra-Violet range but has since cooled to -455 °F and shifted to the less energetic 'Microwave' range)*, one we can measure, one that still permeates the universe today. We call this the Cosmic Background Radiation, or CBR for short *(or CMB; short for Cosmic Microwave Background radiation)*. You can hear it for yourself—turn on your radio, but don't tune it to a radio station, tune it to some 'white noise static' instead. Some of those scratchy hisses that you're hearing are from space *(up to ½ of 1%)*—your radio is designed to pick up Electro-Magnetic energy, and the Big Bang is still broadcasting.

Two American men, Arno Penzias and Robert Wilson, stumbled upon this leftover 'flash of energy' by mistake *(It's still out there!!)* while taking super-sensitive measurements of energy reaching the Earth from space while using a house-sized horn antenna based in Murray Hill, New Jersey. *(In some ways it resembled the giant ear of a 'housecat'; and cats have good hearing for a reason, the natural shape of a cat's ear is an excellent 'collector and concentrator' of energy.)* They tried to get rid of all the 'white noise' scratchy static that their antenna was picking up, but found that they couldn't quiet completely this annoying hiss—was it broken? No, their sensitive antenna wasn't broken, it was working great. Soon this rogue energy that was fouling up their readings would become the focus of their wonder. They were awarded the Nobel Prize in physics because of their serendipitous 1965 discovery— sometimes it's better to be lucky *and* good.

It didn't take long until we were sending up even more sensitive telescopes into space *(COBE; [KOH-bay or KOH-bee] the Cosmic Background Explorer satellite launch was delayed because of the Challenger explosion. It was put into orbit in 1989 and then took measurements for over two years. The analyzed results were exciting and made the front page of the New York Times. Eventually the WMAP satellite would be built and launched to tease out even more detailed information)*—and what we've seen astounds us. There are measurable patterns and ripples still detectable in the ancient energy signature. *It's like DNA, we're learning how to read the details, to tease out the answers to our questions, we're witnessing our history, our epic story and what a story it is. Every day helps us to decipher it.* Since the stars shine and we exist, it's easy to see that not all matter was obliterated soon after it was born, some pockets survived. The early universe must have been asymmetrical in form; *IF* there had been a perfect distribution of matter and anti-matter, then everything would have eventually 'curved' back into each other thanks to gravity, everything would have flashed back over into energy. But that didn't happen, some bits of matter 'made it safely to the ocean' just like those turtle hatchlings I described much earlier.

Some early atoms missed bumping into their anti-twins and instead clumped together with themselves, again thanks to mysterious gravity working its magic on this asymmetrical distribution—this is the proto-universe. *It's like a soup of strange but loose ingredients, there are no stars, not yet anyway. There is no 'light', not as we will come to know it.* Simple atoms of hydrogen weakly pull on each other, they slowly form small groups that start to squeeze each other tighter in the young darkness as more gather together. The ones at the center feel the onslaught, but still the electrons orbit, still the atoms at the heart of this cluster resist collapse. However, there is more ammunition coming. More and more atoms of hydrogen find their way to the pile.

Why am I spending *(investing)* time talking about all this? Because this is the crucible of creation that I mentioned much earlier. It is here at the heart of a cluster of hydrogen atoms that you will be born, piece by piece, atom by atom. This is the start of a sun. When the cluster of hydrogen *(or anti-hydrogen)* atoms gets large enough, gets 'heavy' enough, something dramatic happens. Things change. A star is born. It becomes a nursery where the bits that make up you, and everything around you, will be manufactured. A star is a stellar factory, but it doesn't churn out cars, it makes the stuff of life. And it's all born from change.

The simple hydrogen atoms at the hub of the growing globule of other hydrogen atoms can't resist forever, the pressure becomes too great—all of the atoms on the outside are trying to get to the center, but the ones that are already at the core have the luxury of being crushed, but crushed into what?

Helium. The hydrogen atoms do not get crushed down into nothing—a simple star does not have the muscle to completely remove the jealously guarded empty space found inside the atom, but it can try... The hydrogen atoms get squeezed and the subatomic particles shift and re-align to form a new, larger, more complex atom, still with an empty no-man's-land space surrounding a new, larger nucleus. Under intense pressure, **Four** smaller hydrogen atoms have been combined, or 'fused' together, to make **One** larger helium atom. *(There are two protons and two neutrons in a regular helium nucleus. Putting smaller atoms together this way is called* **Nuclear Fusion.** *Breaking big atoms down into smaller atoms is called*

Nuclear Fission. *Just like in life, it's harder to build things up than it is to tear them down.)*

This isn't easy to do—it takes temperatures and pressures found at the heart of a star, like our sun, to make this happen. *(How big is the sun, our star? If it was a giant glass bowl and the Earth was a marble, you could put over a million marbles inside the bowl, and the sun is rather average, there are much bigger stars out there.)* This hot, growing globule of hydrogen atoms—this becomes a star once this fusing of four hydrogens into one helium begins— this is how a star shines, it's not burning, it's Nuclear Fusion. *(All higher elements, not just helium, are formed by the joining of smaller parts, smaller atoms, together somehow. And you are made of a lot more complicated stuff than hydrogen and helium—haven't you ever wondered where you came from?)* This is how the energy of our sun is 'manufactured'; it can give you a tan, make it rain, grow some corn, generate thunder and lightning, push around some wind and waves. All of this is possible on Earth because of our simple sun—it all comes from hydrogen turning into helium.

How does this happen? The mystery was decoded thanks to that famous $E=mc^2$ equation. You see, luckily for us the transition from hydrogen into helium isn't a smooth one. *(It was also a good thing that the universe wasn't perfectly 'smooth' either, otherwise matter wouldn't have eluded anti-matter and 'clumped' together—it seems that we benefit from some interesting imperfections, yes?)* If you measure the mass of a helium atom and compare this to the four hydrogen atoms that went into making it, you'll come up a little short *(about 0.7% short)*. There will be some mass missing, not much, but it's just not there. This is what makes the star shine—the missing mass has been transformed into light, into pure energy that spews outward eventually reaching the Earth.

Thanks to the famous equation, $E=mc^2$, the 'm' is transformed into 'E'. But we're talking a tiny bit of mass, right? Isn't that converted into a tiny bit of energy? Not exactly, you see that 'c²' that I have deftly avoided discussing? Now is the time. That tiny little bit of mass must be multiplied by c^2, and this is in actuality a very large number, the **'speed of light'** *squared. How much energy does a little bit of mass have? If we could completely convert normal matter into the pure energy that formed it, by combining it with equal amounts of anti-matter, we could launch a spacecraft to reach Mars and return—and it need only be powered by a few paperclips... The sun has a bit more mass to play with—in 1938 Hans Albrecht Bethe figures it out, every second 600 million tons of hydrogen atoms are fused into helium, and in the process 4 million tons of matter get transformed into pure energy. That's every second. That's a lot of paperclips, and the sun has plenty to spare.)*

This newly transformed solar energy doesn't reach the Earth instantly though, when that tiny bit of hydrogen mass turns into pure energy, it has to go from the inside of the sun to the outside, it has to travel through the hell unto which it was born. But the furnace/nursery that is the center of the sun is crowded—so crowded and dense that energy born here has to run the gauntlet of all those other atoms crammed into the sun's core. It's so crowded and hot already *(15 million degrees Celsius here—also very dense, liquid water normally has* **1** *gram of mass per cubic centimeter, iron is 'denser' at* **11** *grams per, gold is about* **19** *grams—at the sun's crowded core the density is a whopping* **160** *grams of matter crammed tightly into every tiny 'sugar cube' sized box)*, that newly formed energy doesn't know which way is up... The energy bounces around, atom to atom, like a runner's baton being passed in a disorganized race with no visible finish line; it is absorbed and re-emitted, zig-zagging around in many different directions, often retracing its steps. Unlike Moses though, this energy doesn't take forty years wandering around to reach the promised land, it takes *a million years* instead.

The light energy born at the core takes a million years to reach the surface of the sun *(on average that is, some photons of energy have **never** left the sun, they have been wandering, lost and confused, for over four billion years, and counting...)*, and then it finally leaps out unencumbered toward the Earth, at the impressive speed of **186,000 miles** *(or **300,000,000 meters**)* **per second**. Notice, this is not miles per 'hour'—lightspeed is measured in miles per 'second'. *(This numerical value is also 'c' in our famous equation, $E=mc^2$. It's a big number, light is very fast when compared to our experiences—Galileo once tried to measure its speed by timing a lightbeam leaving an uncovered lantern atop one Italian mountain and arriving moments later on a nearby neighboring peak. Light was too elusive, too fast and slippery for Galileo, though give him credit for trying to time it. It would take almost another hundred years to figure out how fast light moves—research Danish astronomer Ole Rømer's 1676 ingenious experiment using the 'Galilean' moons of Jupiter as his larger laboratory.)* About eight minutes later it has zipped at top speed across the 93 million miles of rather empty outer space to slam into your skin at the beach, or the green leaf of a corn plant, or some water molecules in the ocean, or the dark leather seat of a parked car with its windows up.

We know what happens then, the light energy gets absorbed, it changes form. Well, now you know how that energy got there to begin with. It's Mr. Einstein's formula showing the way. Mass, under gravitational duress in a star, is being squeezed so hard that it changes, and in the process it releases some of the original energy that it was born from. *(The Hydrogen Bomb is this, only we create the pressures of the sun's core not through gravity, but through implosion—see the 'Manhattan Project' movie, **Fat Man and**

Little Boy, starring Paul Newman and John Cusack, to better understand how explosive energy waves can be focused inward, an 'implosion', attempting to crush the atoms at the center. The movie is not about the 'hydrogen' bomb per se, but the principles are the same. It shows how humans severely squeeze atoms. We don't know how to artificially manufacture gravity ourselves, not yet anyway. Nature is elegant where human devised processes are much uglier, dirtier, and less efficient, but at least we are trying... Always reach upward, Galileo's legacy lives on in you.)

Food and oil, that's distilled sunlight, we understand this now. But take it a step further. The sunlight that comes from mass at the heart of the sun being squeezed—this mass itself is distilled energy left over from the Big Bang. It's all the same energy. It all comes from that moment, it just takes on different forms over time. Sometimes it's pure energy, sometimes it's atoms of matter and anti-matter, sometimes it's light, and sometimes it's you. *(Let there be light, right? Consider this—'you' are made of condensed light...)*

Let's get back to our simple star. What happens to the newly formed helium atoms that are now found at the heart of the young star? They were formed from the squeezing of hydrogen. Using human logic, it's easy to see that the squeezing game isn't over. Helium is a larger, more complex atom than hydrogen to be sure, but it too will succumb to the pressures at the star's heart. The squeezing forces will take *three* helium atoms and 'mash' them together, forming a new larger atom at the center—and in this process **again** the constituent atoms sacrifice a small amount of their mass, and **again** this is turned into pure light energy doomed to spend a million years bouncing around inside the star. This new single atom that the three helium atoms 'morph' into, it is one you know only too well. It is carbon.

Every atom of carbon that you are, every atom that you ingest, every gallon of gasoline that you burn—those carbon atoms found here on Earth were born in the heart of a star. My how the energy changes form. It used to be hydrogen, then it was helium, then it was carbon, and now it is a dandelion, and now it is a cow that ate the dandelion, and now it is you who ate the burger. It's gone a long way, that energy, from the Big Bang to you. But it's still here, disguised as stars and light and living and non-living things.

Our sun is a relatively small star, there is hydrogen on the outside squeezing and fusing into helium on the inside even as we speak. But there is no carbon formation going on now or even in our sun's near future; it just isn't large enough *(you may have heard of the heavier elements being found in the sun, it's true, but the sun didn't make them, they were 'adopted')*. However, there were other stars, larger ones, that used to exist before our sun did. These monsters were stellar factories, producing layer upon layer of heavier and more massive atoms, all of them stacked and densely organized by size and weight as you travel toward the star's center. If you could slice these massive stars in half they would look like giant cosmic candy 'gobstoppers', with the outer layer being lighter hydrogen and the 'heavier' layers found below. Each spherical layer forms a 'density step' at a time, the number of layers being determined by the size of the star—bigger stars mean more gravity, better squeezing, and heavier atoms get to be manufactured. *(The Earth has 'density layers' like a star as well. Lighter air is found on the outside, but travel further in and the next layer you hit is the denser watery ocean, then comes the rocky crust, below that a 'plastic mantle' surrounding a liquid outer core of molten iron and nickel that finally encases a solid and very dense inner core. Who knew the planets looked like candy coated treats? We do. We owe a lot of our understanding of the Earth's interior thanks to the study of earthquake waves.)*

As a young astronomy student, I was originally led to believe that this is how all of the heavier atoms were formed, until you end up with an atom of Uranium, itself a collection of 238 protons and neutrons crammed together inside the nucleus with a complicated swarm of 92 tiny protective electrons buzzing around the outside. In my mind I tried to imagine a star so massive, so much bigger than our own puny sun, that it could squeeze this 'massive' atom into existence at its core.

That's not what happens, such a star does not exist. The uranium and heavier elements like gold and zinc that exist on this planet come from stars, but not in a way that you might think. Many of the super-heavy atoms found here on Earth were born when these older super-massive stars exploded outward in a cataclysmic death spasm. *(Some stars go boom, and how!)*

Our star, the 'Sun', will not explode. It will go out with more of a whimper than a bang. It's just too small. But as I mentioned, there were other stars, more massive, more gravitational, more relentless in their squeezing. Helium was made, carbon, nitrogen, oxygen, neon, calcium, iron—layer upon layer, and as the atoms are formed the energy oozes out, it leaks out as light. The star heats up, expanding some, but still the squeezing continues. Gravity is squeezing inward, while the energy and heat that get produced from atomic fusion try to blow a star outward. Many times there is a balance between these two forces, and a stellar détente called hydrostatic equilibrium is reached. *(Even the sun operates under its own intrinsic duality. Are you both pushed and pulled like the sun? Nature is speaking to you, you come from nature, you are nature.)* Our own sun is in balance now, its size and energy output are relatively stable. *But we are born from imperfection, remember?*

An imperfect distribution of original Big Bang energy allows hydrogen to exist.   An imperfect transformation of hydrogen into helium allows energy to leak off as sunlight, to infuse Earthly ecosystems and power DNA and life itself. *(In a way, all life is like a dung beetle surviving on the meager energy that is cast off as a waste product.)* And now we find that an imperfect balance between heat and gravity allows the higher elements to form.   The 'big' atoms of uranium and gold, they are not born in the hearts of stars like carbon and oxygen, they are more easily created when the star dies, in an unimaginable fury of violent explosion and collision.

Some super-large stars, with their atomic layers and abundant heat, are not in balance forever; they blow apart when the scales are tipped.   The energy being manufactured from mass at the core finally overcomes the gravity squeezing it down.   The star goes **Ka-Boom**, but in a way that's tough to imagine.   Material from the interior part of the star, atoms, are forced outward, where they collide with other atoms that are already there, other atoms that aren't moving that fast.   I suppose that you can think of it as a speeding car slamming into a slower moving car from behind *(something that happened to me once in New Jersey)*, but this is like no collision on any Earthly highway.

These 'outer' atoms collide so violently with the escaping 'inner' atoms that they 'melt' or 'fuse together'— this is how you make huge uranium atoms. *(There is also a process called 'neutron absorption' that allows atomic nuclei to grow in size—but this is rather boring compared to a massive star's explosive phase.)*   The pressures from these collisions are greater than those found at the heart of even the most massive shining stars.   It is in the outer wisps of an exploding star that the fusion of even higher elements happen under extreme cataclysm.   These explosions and collisions not only give birth to bigger atoms, but they also serve to scatter the other 'simpler' atoms, like carbon and oxygen, that were built-up inside the core and hoarded together—they are now liberated and free, free to wander the Cosmos.   It is here that we find you floating, the scattered atoms that make you up, all of them, well before our Earth or sun could begin to take form.   *(Like the scattered seeds of a 'dead' dandelion—seeds that just might get blown away and later be given a chance to become organized, to grow again somehow...)*

Here, in the coldness of space, is where you exist as separate pieces, pieces that were born at different moments and places, but they find themselves slowly coming together over time.   You are not made from just one star, no, your atoms come from many that have been born, have lived, have died and exploded just so.   *(A lot of special things had to happen to make you appear on this planet, not just your parents 'getting it on', are you starting to feel a greater connection to the Cosmos?   Massive stars have to live and die so that you can be born.)*   And then, after some time passes, a single cell, you, gathers together some available atoms to make your body and mind.   You grow, your body gathers together the billions and billions of atoms that used to be separate.   It puts them in order, into organized structures that work.   And because of struggle and sex and food and evolution, you've been given a brain that can analyze, that can see this basic structure and marvel at the implications. You get to think about you.

Most of us don't think about ourselves in this deep manner, and what is deeper than pulling back the curtain to see that everything we think of as real and solid, including ourselves, really isn't?   And why do we find these thoughts unpleasant?   Because it goes against what our senses and our parents have always told us.   It's strange and different, and not very comforting.   Says who?   Where do your values come from?

You can't change the world (usually) or the universe, you can only change you, the way you think about things.

Are you going to hide from the truth like Hitler? Or are you going to face your fears, your insecurities, your doubts, like a thinking human? A blade of grass knows nothing of neutron stars. A grazing cow could care less about carbon and sugar and energy transformation. You know, some people are like blades of grass. Some people are like grazing cows. Some people are ignorant and want to stay ignorant— it's more comfortable that way.

You are different though, can you feel it? Life is not intended to be easy. Life is not always comfortable, to advance takes some doing. And that's okay, since you can't change the world or your atomic structure, you might as well use them to your advantage. Stars are born, they live, and they die. But they get to live again—in an even better form. We are the evolution of mass, and mass is the evolution of energy. *(And energy... could it be the evolution of thought? I 'think' and this book becomes built, it's conjured from my thoughts. My life has been more energized ever since I've tackled this task of thinking and creating.)*

Finally, I can welcome you to the well-house with open arms. The hidden world of atoms and energy has been revealed to you. Helen Keller grew older and had a patient and kind teacher showing her the hidden patterns of the world, helping her to make sense of the physical chaos that surrounded her. Now Helen could do more, could see more *(with her mind, not her broken eyes)*, she could be more. I was once like you and a younger, more naïve, Helen. But I grew, too. Now I do more, now I see more, now I am more.

Is your mind getting blown? Is it uncomfortable to see that we are the wispy and altered remnants of mysterious Big Bang energy? We like knowing things with certainty, and there is something very uncertain and very un-solid about this view of the Cosmos. What is reality then? Reality is what you make it. You have more control than you know.

Your problems—are they 'real'? Sure, they seem real, if you ignore your mortgage payments they don't go away, but you determine their connection to you, how awful or joyous your personal world is. Your problems are relative. Can you see? Can you hear? If a blind-deaf girl who had so much less than you can find joy and serenity, how big are your problems really? Can you overcome them and move on to happier times? I think so. You think so too, it's one reason why you're reading this.

Things seem pretty hectic and important to you right now. They can be less hectic. Things that cause you grief, they can cause you less grief. Your unhappy life, well, that can be turned around too. Step back. See your Stone Age behavior. See the wonder of nature and of energy that surrounds and infuses you. What's important to you? Why is this so important? It's time for you to make better decisions, better judgments. And now you can. You know more now, and your journey, while scary at times, is built by you. Be a better builder. This could be a motto for the human race, but it could be your credo too.

Your duality has hit the extremes. You are nothing, you are empty space. But you are also something, a great organized something, a thinking being made of mostly nothing that can ponder it all. How can you be both? You are. You are a lot of things, if you would just give yourself some credit. I didn't understand Plato when I was younger, now he makes a lot more sense—it's so easy for us to mistake appearance for reality, we believe too readily in what we can see and feel. We are surrounded by illusion and embrace its comforting cloak. See past the shadows. It's time for you to leave the cave and walk toward the well-house, follow the heat of the sun and the scent of honeysuckle blossoms...

Then think what would happen to them if they were released from their bonds and cured of their delusions. Suppose one of them were let

loose, and suddenly compelled to stand up and turn his head and look and walk towards the fire; all (of his) actions would be painful and he would be too dazzled to see properly the objects of which he used to see (only) the shadows. So if he was told that what he used to see was mere illusion, and that he was now nearer reality and seeing more correctly, because he was turned towards objects that were more real, and if on top of that he were compelled to say what each of the passing objects was when it was pointed out to him, don't you think he would be at a loss, and think that what he used to see was more real than the objects now being pointed out to him?

— Plato

The Allegory of the Cave

from ***The Republic***

What you see is what you get

When was the last time that you found yourself in the middle of a slice of forest, alone? Many of you reading this book may not have had this experience. You stand there, surrounded by trees, and you close your eyes. You listen. All around you, things are moving, that's how sound gets made. The babbling brook, the sighing leaves, the distant rat-a-tat-tat of a pileated woodpecker doing her thing—they are all waves of energy moving through the air in all directions. The sounds approach and move past you, also in all directions, getting weaker as their energy is absorbed by the ever present atoms wiggling around. The sound softens until it seems to disappear. *(You can heat up a cup of coffee by yelling at it—Muddy Coffee!!! Why do you make me love you so??!! AAAAaaaaahhhh!!!—Prepare to scream for a few years though, it's not the most efficient way to transfer energy.)*

A storm is coming, the wind is picking up. Different air is moving in, with a different density. Energy travels differently when the molecules change their relative position and the humidity rises. Sounds don't sound the same to your ear now, you detect the difference—they come slightly faster and louder, crisper. Are your eyes still closed? Are you still listening?

We depend so much on our eyes, too much perhaps. You most likely aren't in the forest now, but close your eyes *(unless this is a book-tape and you are driving of course)* and listen to your world. Every sound you hear is because of motion. Because of energy.

Now close your ears as well as your eyes. Okay, maybe that's not possible at the moment, but you can imagine it. With your eyes closed, imagine that all the sounds just went away. Are you brave enough to do it?

Your world would be reduced, reduced to touching and tasting and smelling. You are down to three bodily senses, but the world would still be there, waiting for you to explore it.

It really is difficult to imagine such a limited exposure to the world, and yet some people are forced into this predicament *(Helen Keller was born 'normal', but a childhood illness robbed her of her eyes and ears).* We appreciate hearing and sight and rightly so, but we assume so much validity from our senses. If all of your senses were gone, you would still have your brain, you would still think. Entire worlds could be created within the convolutions of your mind. Think about that—in your mind you could create a movie so real, so detailed, so alive that it *does* seem real. This is a dream. The dream is filled with details from your senses—*you can see the clouds float by, you can hear the water waves lapping at the ocean's shore, you can taste the salt in the air, smell the hot dogs sizzling on the hibachi, feel the sand between your toes...* You can imagine it, can't you, this movie inside your head? It all looks so real and feels so real, and to a part of your Stone Age brain, it is.

For hundreds of millions of years animals have relied on their senses for their very survival. And out of that struggle for food and sex evolved an intelligent being who could manipulate nature, who knew how to analyze, predict, and plan. Humans could 'see' themselves achieving success inside their mind's eye. And then, with language, we could share our visions, *here, think about this for a while...* Allow me to illustrate—can you see them, the puffy white clouds floating by? Can you hear the cry of gulls and the rolling waves crashing at the beach? You can, can't you?

And for most of animal history on this planet, most critters couldn't do this trick of description. For most organisms, what you see is what you get, which is why visual camouflage became important to both predator and prey—a leopard's spots or a rattlesnake's diamond back, you can tilt nature to your advantage, you're allowed to change and improve, to fool the watcher. The two large eye-spots on a butterfly's wings are not there to entice an insect mate sexually, they are meant to mimic the wide eyes of an owl, a fierce predator that smaller birds *(who would want to eat a protein filled butterfly)* usually avoid at first sight.

On a vegetable note, the Passion Flower Vine has developed fake spots as well, 'butterfly egg spots'. These dark little spots on the vine's leaves resemble the package a pregnant butterfly will deposit on some unlucky plant. The Heliconius butterfly will not lay her eggs *(with their promise of leaf-eating caterpillar carnage to come)* on a plant that already has some eggs laid upon it, why submit your future offspring to greater competition? *It's better to find your own plant...* The Passion Flower Vine has fooled the insect, using its own evolutional instincts against it. The 'beautiful but deadly' butterfly flies away.

Evolution has toyed with your brain, upgrading it over several million years—it's investing a whopping **20%** of daily food calorie energy just to think, to function, to take in your surroundings and solve important living and social problems. *(That's **5x** the amount of energy used by most mammal brains. Your brain is like the peacock's tail—the tail takes more invested energy to produce and maintain, it's 'different and sexy' to peahens. Well, the human brain is big and expensive too, but apparently intelligence is sexy... just like a colorful derriere. Intelligence, I think, represents potential—the world throws different problems at you all the time, a clever and intelligent person has the ability to think up new solutions to make survival easier no matter what happens.)* Your brain is constantly filtering information from the senses, trying to make sense of the world. And as the extreme manipulators on this planet endowed with extra brainpower, we can synthetically fool watching eyes the way the dappled leopard does naturally—we can paint patterns on the world. We can take colored pigments and a brush and a canvas and dab on darkened splotches in just the right way... Did I say canvas? I meant a cave wall in southern France about 30,000 years ago... Deep inside the dim recesses we painted animals, animals in motion, animals being hunted by us, and the pictures became real.

By looking at the pictures a protein powered human mind had conjured from memory, your Stone Age brain relived the joy of the successful hunt; you were there again. And in your brain, you are there. Yours is an animal brain, it's used to seeing things for real—the occipital lobe that dominates much of your brain's sight function has evolved to decode the signals of light, *just what is it you are seeing out there?* If there's light, everything you see is seen because they are radiating or reflecting different amounts of Electro-Magnetic energy *(colors are not created equal—blue light is more energetic than red, green light trumps yellow. The rainbow's colors are choreographed into stripes of changing energy).* Objects have colors and are located in different positions, locations, and some things are even moving around—there's a lot to see and think about, and most of this thought is done automatically, at the subconscious level. It all has to be analyzed. And a big, primitive part of your Stone Age brain thinks that whatever it sees, everything, is real.

●   ●

Want to see something disappear before your very eyes? There are two 'dots' on this page. Try this. Cover your Left eye with your hand, but with your Right eye focus on the 'leftmost' dot. You'll still be able to 'see' the 'rightmost' dot using your peripheral vision, but don't look directly at it. Now, while you are still looking at the 'leftmost' dot move closer or farther away from the page (12 inches does it for me)—the 'rightmost' dot should 'disappear'...

This happens because of your optic nerve—it has to connect to the back side of your eyeball, the retina, somehow, and where this nerve is connected there are no sight receptor cells—when both of your eyes are open they each compensate for this 'missing' Electro-Magnetic light energy, but when you close one eye you can do 'magic'... Cover you right eye, but look at the 'rightmost' dot with your left eye, and the other dot will disappear...

We graduated from the popular cave paintings to scratching pictures on harvested whale's teeth *(an art form called 'scrimshaw'—Ivory is more fun to carve than red ochre during long nights at sea).* On sheets of tightly woven fibers, a canvas, we created masterpieces of impressionistic depth, portraits and landscapes, that came alive before our eyes. Even the surreal painted dreams of Salvador Dali looked like you could walk right through the picture frame. *(I think that Salvador would smile at the concept that the atoms of colored paint are made of mostly nothing and don't really touch the canvas—they float above it held in place by electric forces. In his 1954 painting,* **Corpus Hypercubus (Crucifixion),** *there is an image of Christ 'floating' in front of a cross—and the cross itself is 'floating' above the ground. His imagery sometimes goes beyond the third dimension, what goes through your mind when you view a Dali masterpiece? Are you there? Go on, get lost inside a Dali for a while...)*

And this is not the end, we continue on, feeding our brain false images of reality, pictures, and we are enthralled. We can make physical pictures, representations, of anything our imagination wants, and when we do onlookers make that picture come alive in their mind. They are standing among the melted clocks. Images aren't really real, but what's a brain to do when it has only been exposed to reality for most of its evolution? What it sees becomes real because what it sees *is* real—you can't change the way your brain evolved, it's still in the Stone Age after all, plus this brain-sight connection is far older than the mind of Man—it's inherited from our animal ancestors.

Go beyond the static canvas. Making the picture move, a 'movie', is not so farfetched. The animals in M.C. Escher's famous woodcarving prints are frozen in motion, swimming or flying or crawling; to make them move would take lots of still pictures. An image-horse can gallop if you show several drawings of the horse in a special way, but each hand-crafted picture is of the horse at a different moment in time, each picture shows the hoof and the rippling muscles at a slightly different location.

If you put them in order, one behind the next, and 'flip through them', the picture of the horse will start to gallop. Flip slowly and there really is no motion, just a series of still pictures, but flip faster and something magical happens, the drawing comes alive... The hooves appear to move... *(An early attempt at motion photography by Eadweard ['Edward'] Muybridge had a series of 24 closely spaced cameras with thin trip-wires that a galloping horse would snap/trigger as he ran. It was ventured that a horse always keeps at least one foot on the ground, but no one knew for sure—Leland Stanford, the future Governor of California and namesake to Stanford University who was born not in the Golden State but in New York's Mohawk Valley, supposedly placed a wager on the issue and commissioned Muybridge to settle the matter. The time-lapsed series of still photos, of 'snapped' shots, showed that surprisingly yes, a horse **does** become 'airborne' when running... And when you put all of those pictures together and flip through them in just the right way, the horse on command again does its dance of muscular motion. Hey brain, look over here with those baby blues, see the galloping horse before your very eyes...)*

And what if each drawing is a photograph instead, a picture constructed by using super-thin light-sensitive layers of chemicals (*films* if you will) and paper and made with the aid of a lens that mimics the way your own eye works with light's energy. *('Photography' literally means 'to write with light'. Greek is your friend too...)* Now the pictures are perfect, they are just what you would see if you were standing there yourself. Your brain looks at a picture of the Grand Canyon, even though you have never been there, and your breath is taken away—you *are* there. *(Amateur pilots in flight simulators would tend to agree, you learn to fly the plane without ever leaving the ground. To your hands, eyes, and brain, you're airborne... I can vouch for the '**Back to the Future**' flying DeLorean-ride at Universal Studios, Orlando. I also hear great things about Disney World's '**Mission: SPACE**', where you supposedly blast off for Mars—sounds like fun!)*

But let's take perfect pictures with movie cameras, devices that take many, many pictures in a row, each one slightly different from the last. And if you 'flip through them' fast enough, those pictures will come alive, they will appear to move for real. How fast does this flipping need to be to fool your brain? Sixteen picture frames per second, that's how fast. Your television or movie theatre projector might flash them faster *(twenty-four frames per second is the industry standard)*, but it won't matter to your brain. Your brain processes the images at the same rate regardless; it's not speed that we are working on now, it's image quality, we are trying to make it even more real for you.

Plasma screen TV's, digital movie projectors, 3-D virtual-reality goggles, George Lucas' **Industrial Light and Magic** special effects studio—our Stone Age brains are being enveloped by an imagery of reality that's getting ever better. Our dreams are being fed to us from the lighted screen. *(Why Hollywood at all? Thomas Alva Edison had invented the 'moving picture' and was ruthlessly trying to control all aspects of the fledgling industry—as he tried to do with electric light. Independent film-makers, like a young*

Cecil DeMille, wanted out from under Edison's east coast yoke—the distant west coast called. Hollywood was far enough away from oppressive New Jersey, true, but it was also listed meteorologically as the sunniest place in America. You need light and good weather to shoot photographic film; middle-of-nowhere Hollywood seemed perfect, great light and far from egotistic Edison. DeMille completed the world's first feature length film lasting 80 minutes, **The Squaw Man***, at the corner of Sunset and Vine; now the location of a boring bank. He released it in 1914—without any credits. Edison's company, The Motion Pictures Patents Trust, was known for being rather brutal [intimidation through destruction of property and physical violence—think of Edison as '***The Godfather***', not Brando] toward those he thought were trying to steal from him... DeMille did okay as you know, and even today L.A. has more sunny days than any large city in America, even more than Phoenix. Why Hollywood? The sun's light was best there, the most consistent. It's all about the energy.)*

And just how real are these images to us? You might be surprised. With the advent of Functional MRI and other similar technologies *(Magnetic Resonance Imaging—your body is subjected to an extremely strong and vibrating magnetic field, and moving charged particles inside your body, like electrons and ions, are affected by this field and contribute their own magnetic effects. They reveal their position, we know where the energy in your body is),* we can take pictures of your brain while it is working. We can see what parts of the brain 'light up' when you are thinking or doing or seeing something. When you 'see' something has been compared against when you actually 'do' something. Guess what? The same parts light up.

Try solving a **Rubik's Cube**, humanity's most successful game, while lying in an MRI chamber—the scan would show certain areas of your brain activating as you gazed at the puzzle and worked the problem with your fingers. Now take the cube away, now just think about solving the puzzle, you see it using your mind, you imagine it in your hands... The same areas light up. This phenomenon has been dubbed '*mirror neurons*'—parts of the brain can't tell the difference between what is real and what is not real. There's not much difference between what you do and what you see. *(For more information, research the pioneering work of V.S. Ramachandran. A Medical Doctor best known for his work in neurology and visual perception, he currently teaches psychology and neuroscience as a Professor at the University of California, San Diego.)*

This came in handy during our Stone Age days. Let's say that you did not know how to make this new stone tool that's been all the rage recently. But you sit and watch a neighbor who has mastered the art, you sit and watch him work with his hands and materials. As you watch him, your brain gets busy firing its neurotransmitters across the synaptic gaps—it lights up. To your Stone Age brain, it is your hand that grasps a chunk of flint, it is your arm that moves, working and shaping the stone.

Scientists studying distantly spaced archeological remains have documented the relative quick speed at which new advancements of tool making spread through the primitive Stone Age world. We're learning machines. Mirror neurons go a long way in justifying this rapidity in skill dissemination—we learn quickly for a reason, all we have to do is watch. *(Okay students, keep your attention focused on your teachers, watch what they are doing if you want to learn and earn a good grade...)*

To see mirror neurons in a frenzy, go to a city's sports stadium (regular size) and watch the fans, not the players. See them jump and scream, shout in anger and cry in joy. True fans, men and women, are aligning their brains with the players on the field. The emotion of winning is a chemical one that's reinforced by our social upbringing—not only do we become the players on the field, their win or loss is our win or loss, but we are surrounded socially by tens of thousands of like-minded fans, all whose brains are firing the same way ours is.   *(Acelino Freitas, the most popular boxer in Brazil, beat up reigning WBA world champion Joel Casamayor on Jan. 12, 2002. Approximately 50 million Brazilians tuned in to watch the fight live on TV, but what makes this statistic really stand out is the fact that the fight was on at **3:00 AM** local time... The fight 'went the distance' and apparently so did 50 million fans from a world away.)*

Sporting events tap into this vicarious human condition, we are a 'mirror nation'—even if we are home watching the game, it's as if we are there in person. We may be sitting solitarily on the sofa, but in our mind it's a different world. You are the star. And you are also among friends, lots and lots of other people, an invisible legion of fans who feel like you do, it's comforting. Your social group is strong. You are strong—until your team chokes during the big one... *(Go Bills! I grew up south of Buffalo—I hope they win 'it' in my lifetime... When Scott Norwood missed that kick in the Super Bowl I went painfully catatonic, like a lot of other Bills fans I'm quite sure. Be like me, don't blame Scottie, he gave it his all, blame defensive coordinator Walt Corey instead... Bad tackling, don't get me started...)*

But what about good old regular TV or the movies? Are they so different? Think about your favorite movie stars or television icons. They are revered like sports stars. They sometimes even make more money than those modern-day gladiators sweating it out on the field *(or the golf course)*, we pay our stars millions of dollars to be in a film or on a show *(or in a commercial)*—and why? Why do they get millions of dollars? The people who pay them can do so because of the rest of us.

We are the 'non-rich', who may be relatively poor, but our number is Legion—we will turn out in droves to watch. Jim Carrey *(The Twenty Million Dollar Man, the first comedic actor to earn this paycheck)* is not in my living room, but with my TV or DVD he is. Or I can go on down to the movie theatre with its even bigger screen and subject my brain to the imagery, the light and sound, that is Jim Carrey. When you watch Jim Carrey you become Jim Carrey. It's also one of the reasons that bio-pics do so well. When Reese Witherspoon and Joaquin Phoenix play June and Johnny Cash, it's as if you become the famous characters. You feel their joys and triumph, their sadness. *(How many people, women **and** men, cried during 'Beaches'?)* As the celluloid dreams flash across the silver screen, they take on a life inside your head. The director has put his dream inside you, and you embrace the reality, you can't help it. *(Pass the hankies please...)*

You might be tempted to say that we are smarter, more intelligent than this, we know when we are looking at an image. We know that we are not Jim Kelly *(or Steve Tasker)* or Meryl Streep or Bette Midler—but that's the real world, and part of your brain doesn't care what's real. Are memories real? Ever get back your vacation pictures a week after you return from your trip and then take another trip 'in your head' when you view them? To your brain, are those remembered images any less potent than the actual images? What were those things you saw but the Electro-Magnetic light striking the sensitive retina in your eyeball's derriere anyway? What you see is what you get, and who doesn't want the life of a character in an awesome movie? *(Hmmm, I wonder why pornography is so popular...)*

We pay our movie stars millions of dollars for being social icons, for being the best pretenders. Yes, actors pretend to be other people, and they do it so well they convince us *(about halfway through 'Ray' I realized that I had forgotten I was watching actor Jamie Foxx, not the real Ray Charles)*—we don't see the written script, when the words come out of their mouths it's as if they were real, as if they were being thought up on the spot, it's like your own life. You make your own life up as you go along, but the brain sees this new other life, this choreographed and well-lit filmed variation of life—and to your brain it is real, and pleasurable. It's worth the ten bucks at the theatre, or the extra cash to get HBO each month. Can you imagine not having a television? What would the rest of America think of you?

For a rollicking good time poking fun at celebrities, politics, and human culture in general, stay up late with your TV like me (or set your DVR or TiVo® for 12:30 weeknights on CBS) to watch *The Late Late Show starring Craig Ferguson*. When I tune in to his monologue, or celebrity interviews, I often snort with laughter—and that's good. *There, I said it, Craig you're so funny that you make me snort—keep up the good work, you magnificent bastard—you, Sir, are incorrigible... and I like that...* You're funny and a tad bit naughty Craigers (insert 'whip-crack' noise here), and America loves you, with or without your Citizenship. Dave Letterman, your boss, will retire soon *("It's a great day for America everybody, and I'll tell you why...")*—why should he work so hard when he could be spending time with his young son and family? *(I know you have a young son too, Craig, but then you aren't making 'Letterman money' yet, are you? I think you should, too bad I'm not your boss, eh?)* And I want to go on record saying that you, Craig buddy, will slide into that 11:30 National time-slot with much fanfare rather than talented funny-man Jon Stewart, and when you do, I'd like to be your first guest... After all, I have to respect a guy who looks directly at the camera and says with a smile:

It's the magic of show-business, the whole thing runs on crap and sunshine.

*(And I also have to agree with Denis Leary, who, on Craig's show, plugged the film **The Pledge** directed by Sean Penn and starring Jack Nicholson. Denis wasn't in this movie, he*

just really liked it a lot. I saw this movie too, before his recommendation—I see a LOT of movies, go figure—and I have to say that if you have not seen **The Pledge** *then you are missing one of the most finely crafted movies ever made. Says me. And Denis. Go ahead, prove us wrong. I know good art when I see it.)*

The television is the greatest social connector ever invented—you can spend your life traveling all over the world, being all kinds of interesting and beautiful people *(**Beverly Hills, 90210** or **Dallas** or **Dynasty**, anyone?)*, and all without leaving the safety of your couch. But then there is that nasty suppressed realization that you are not the movie star or television celebrity living the high life. Recognize Hollywood for what it's worth, the 'biggest' social club on the planet, and it's sort of small and exclusive.

And when you are in this special *IN*-crowd, you get paid much more than compliments and appreciative glances, you get paid millions of dollars. All because of your social appeal to the masses. Not that there's anything wrong with that, it's what we all want all the time, social approval. Your face becomes recognizable, now lots of people can picture you in their own minds, even when you are not around. *(When I say the name 'Jack Nicholson', what mental image comes forth on your command? Ask a hundred different people and get a hundred different answers.)* We only know so many people after all, there are our family, friends, and neighbors—and then there are the celebrities. Think about this, we may actually know more of the intimate daily life-details of them than our neighbors across the street. *Even though we have never met you Jennifer Aniston in person, we feel we know you quite well. We come up to you in restaurants, on the street, or at the park in a freaky familiar way—"I love you, you are so great..."*

But that adoration works best on a national scale. Ponder over Natalie Portman, a celebrated young actress who gained worldwide fame playing Queen Amidala, the future-wife of *Star Wars'* Darth Vader, in the last three installments of George Lucas' 'double trilogy'. Millions worldwide saw her, now she's even more famous and is getting other acting parts because of her beauty and fame.

Now Natalie is a fine and talented actress *(and brave, she recently let her head be shaved bald for her most recent movie, V for Vendetta)*, but there were other talented and beautiful actresses that could have played that *Star Wars* part. They would now be enjoying this exposure and fame, but they were passed over. It's not only about being good, it's about being seen. Who are we going to get to pretend to be the future-bride of one of cinema's most intriguing villains? Who's going to look the best on-screen?

Natalie has expressed the opinion that without a doubt physical attractiveness helps you to find work in Hollywood—it's imagery that's being sold and we value beauty *(cosmetics giant Revlon 'discovered' her and asked her to model as a child)*. Her movie career has made her popular the world over, but it wasn't always this way. There is her first movie to consider.

She was an unknown when she was cast as the city-wise little American girl who befriends a foreign-born hitman (played masterfully by French actor Jean Reno) in *The Professional*, directed by Luc Besson. She was 12-years-old by the time film-shooting in Paris had wrapped, and when Natalie returned home to her small, private parochial classes back in New York she received a cold welcome.

Her pre-teen classmates were not impressed. Socially, they could have been, they could have reveled in her foreign adventures, but instead what they saw was a girl who thought she was better than them. She was different, she got to cut class and make a big budget movie— *hmmm... privileged, like an aristocrat perhaps... a reason for resentment... And who's Natalie 'Portman'? Before the big movie came along we had classes with Natalie 'Hershlag'...* As Natalie tells it, her entire small class ganged up on her, taunted her. She eventually had to leave this private school because it was such an unhappy experience for her *(she transferred to a public school).* Of course times have changed, now Natalie is all grown up. Now her classroom is the world and she is getting plenty of social acceptance. She's physically attractive, she pretends really well, and her name and face are known by hundreds of millions of social humans. I wonder if those taunting 12-year-olds, now grown up like Natalie, speak with selfish pride to their current circle of acquaintances, *"I used to go to school with Natalie Portman when I was younger, she was great..."*

Now I didn't have Natalie Portman as a student in one of my classes *(I've taught at both public and private schools in and near New York City)*, but I have experienced a little of what it is to be connected to the Hollywood fame machine while attempting to live a 'normal' life. And it's hard to live a 'normal' life when your life really isn't so normal. When millions of people see your face in magazines, in the entertainment news, in movies, on talk shows, during commercials—people tend to treat you differently. Fame can work against you. There is a social price that has to be paid, and sometimes that cost is passed to your children.

I mentioned my experience with Hollywood; it is an odd one. I have taught science, mostly physics, astronomy, meteorology, geology and environmental science, to the children of Hollywood royalty. Sometimes the mother was famous, sometimes the father, sometimes both; you hope that star power wouldn't get in the way of the lives of your children, but it does. You're famous, people want to see you. They've seen you so many other times, now, when they get to see you in the flesh, they get a bit flushed, they act a bit weird in your presence. You're famous, your name is famous, and now your children are famous by association. They get the weird treatment, too. *(I saw this recent headline on a 2006 tabloid—Chelsea Clinton binge eats, she's gained 22 lbs! Hmmm... someone seems to think that we should care, I wonder why? Not really.)*

Here's an interesting predicament. You're a Hollywood actress with a famous name *(Academy Award®️ nominated)* whose child from a previous marriage bears your ex-husband's last name, a name even more famous than yours *(he's taken home a few of those golden statues himself)*. It's parent-teacher night here at the private school. I give my welcome speech and science-course details in a group setting, afterwards parents come up to me and introduce themselves. There are several 'big names' in attendance, but most of my students have their tuition paid through means other than Hollywood gold. This famous woman steps up, I recognize her, she plays a supporting role in one of my favorite television shows, **Alias**. It's Amy Irving. She was married to Steven Spielberg. And their son, my student, bears the stigma of his father's name.

Do a billion people on the planet know the name Spielberg? Is there an American who doesn't? *(In Spike Lee's bio-documentary of Cleveland football legend, **Jim Brown: All American**, the Hall-of-Famer admits that he made a mistake. If he could have lived his life over, he would not have named his son Jim Brown, Jr. His boy's life was harder because of a father's pride.)* There is peace in anonymity, but famous people often forfeit this peace. When you're famous, you seem familiar, people come up to you unbidden when you're a celebrity. *(But you can always move to a remote place in France like Johnny Depp did. He values highly his separate peace.)* People do treat you differently— and a movie-star mother is still a mother, she was concerned for her son. It's hard to trust someone when you're famous, it's a safe assumption that many folks have ulterior motives *(just ask Billy Joel about how loyal his ex-brother-in-law* *finance manager was, then there was also Billy's ex-lawyer who allegedly stole millions from the artist).* I assured her that my academic motives were pure—I love science, I love teaching science, and her son was there to learn science just like the other students *(who came from less flashy backgrounds).* How much did he learn? Hopefully a lot.

Things are different for me now, I've opted to take my classroom to a bigger stage. I still consider myself a Stone Age man with basic Stone Age motives, but instead of hunting on the plain to bring down a week's worth of meals in a dangerous kill, I'm competing in the social world, I'm writing this book to appeal to you, the social masses. I'm developing tools from my surrounding area to make survival easier. Some of those tools are the famous names I've been associated with. You, the reader, are also human with Stone Age tendencies. I know that because of my limited connection with Hollywood celebrities *(and there were more parental celebrities than Amy Irving and Steven Spielberg, ask me about them sometime—between the Oscars®, the Emmys®, the Tonys® and even the Grammys®, I've counted 40 nominations and 12 nabbed statues—and those were just the ones I knew about),* that this creates another reason to talk about my book, or about me, to your friends and neighbors. In the book world, more people talking about you increases your chances for success. I've never written a book before, but as I spy my social environment and the task in front of me, I have to rely on my own skills and available resources. Knowledge and writing pass for skills, and social *(royal)* connections bump up my social standing, and without all of that nasty foot binding...

I'm just a science teacher *(an effective one given my students' level of success and enthusiasm),* and my teaching and writing skills would remain the same regardless of who my students' parents are—just because Spielberg is one of the greatest directors and storytellers to walk this planet, that doesn't make me any better an educator. But it does give you something to talk about when around the water cooler...

I want people to read this book, to be educated and entertained, to help put their lives in perspective. I know that Hollywood's finest are really just people too. They get paid a lot more for their work *(because you like them, you really like them)*, but all they really are, are artists. They mold in light and sound and social perception, not paint and clay. Actors read words from a script, using their faces and bodies to communicate as well as their mouths; directors have to mold the whole thing—the pace, the lighting, the shadows, the angles, the colors, the background, the foreground, and... *Action!* It's all make-believe, and it's worth hundreds of millions of dollars when it's done right, because then you line up to see it, millions and millions of you paying those hundreds of millions of dollars—ten to fifteen dollars at a time.

Regardless of who I know though, what shines through should be the art, my art. I'd like this book to stand on its own merits; it will only sell if people like it as judged in the court of Public Opinion. When Steven filmed the 1971 'made for TV' movie, ***Duel***, for ABC starring Dennis Weaver sparring with a malevolent 18-wheeler, it looked and felt like a big budget Hollywood movie—it was something special. And it still is. *(Not only can you rent this 'old' movie on VCR or DVD, you should!)* Spielberg's art shines through in so many ways. *(And besides, I have a thing for words—'Duel' sounds an awful lot like 'Dual'... Isn't it funny that the word about 'two things' has a twin of its own?)*

But some folks get their start not through art, but by word of mouth. Look at Johnny Knoxville, he's been in some very large Hollywood movies with huge, huge multi-million dollar budgets. ***The Dukes of Hazzard*** *(playing the 'dark-haired heart-throb' Luke Duke)*, ***Men in Black II*** *(playing a two-headed alien)*, ***Walking Tall*** *(the 2004 remake starring* *former wrestler-turned-movie-icon Duane 'The Rock' Johnson; Johnny Knoxville played a smaller supporting role, he pocketed a cool $5,000,000 for his talents—Tom Cruise only got $75,000 for* **Risky Business**, *that doesn't seem fair, does it?)*—and he's a decent actor, don't get me wrong, but he's not classically trained on the stage *(unless you count the time he spent at The American Academy for Performing Arts in Pasadena, California, as a student).* His name gained fame through his wild MTV show, **Jackass**, where he and his cohorts would do rather derogatory and painful things to themselves and their friends. This makes sense to publicity seekers; MTV provides exposure of your face and name to millions of viewers. *(Hey! Look at me!!)* Johnny Knoxville, a musical-sounding un-known name, is now a very well-known name. Having him, and his famous name, in a movie couldn't hurt, especially if he can act, pretend on cue, which he can. But what most people don't know, or haven't seen, is the 'audition' tape that got him onto MTV to begin with.

While writing for a skateboarding magazine, Johnny 'tested safety equipment' on himself while a friend filmed it. It was humorous, and he took this concept to the extreme; he had himself 'hosed down' with pepper-spray, he also had himself shot with a 'Tazer'—the non-lethal *(but it hurts like hell)* electric stun-gun used by police. He didn't stop there, that was shocking and crazy, true, but he could do better. During the 1998 school year I watched a videotape that one of my students brought in and showed me after class. I don't know where he got it, but I think it clearly established Johnny 'performing' on camera. Years later I saw this same video on television, after some ensuing fame of course made it relevant, but part of the performance piece was missing.

The original video footage I saw in '98 ended with Johnny Knoxville being shot with a real gun, the kind that carry real bullets—while wearing a bulletproof vest for protection. *(This hurts like hell as well. Kids, do NOT try this at home, or anyplace else, ever. That goes for you adults also. There is precedent for this though—the inventor of the soft Kevlar® bulletproof vest, Richard Davis, demonstrated the same technique on himself in front of assembled skeptical police officers. They didn't believe that 'flimsy' fabric could stop a bullet—but it does. Not without painful injury though, there is 'soft tissue damage'; all of that energy has to go somewhere. How much does it hurt? Stand on home plate with a bull's-eye painted on your torso and let a major league pitcher whack you with his fastball. Needless to say, a fastball in the gut is better than a bullet in your belly. The inventor got his contract.)* I assume that the folks who aired this early footage a few years later on television wanted to shock you too, but TV has more moral responsibility than some 'highly motivated' guy making an independent shock-film. The self-gun-shooting was wisely edited out, otherwise it might have triggered *(pun intended)* plenty of calls against 'indecency and violence', possibly generating some federal fines along the way. This is an incredibly dangerous thing to do, purposefully shooting yourself, and some would also say incredibly stupid, but look at where he is now. He took a huge risk, his goal was to make a name for himself, Johnny Knoxville, and the best way to do this, for him, was to shock you. It worked. People were shocked. His name is famous. He's in big movies, he's a movie star. You don't have to be that talented to be known worldwide. You just have to be seen.

Consider Paris Hilton. She can't act convincingly, but she is sexy. There are lots of sexier women out there, but they don't have the name 'Hilton' attached to their bodies. She cashed in on her famous name and love of sex—two things that we social humans fall for. Say what you will about young Paris, she's primping and posing, and you're watching. It makes her feel powerful, and she is, because you, the Stone Age public, made her that way. A book about Paris Hilton, that's not that intriguing. But pictures of her scantily clad, those seem to sell quite well.

One man who didn't sell out his famous name is Nicolas Cage, another talented Academy Award® winner *(I've never met the man, but I loved his performance in* **Leaving Las Vegas***)*. The famous name in question is not 'Cage'—he changed his real name to that. No, the famous name that he didn't sell out that I am referring to is his *original/real* famous name, his birth name, Coppola... Nicolas Cage is really Nicholas Coppola. His uncle is the talented and famous Francis Ford Coppola, the legendary director of **The Godfather** and **Apocalypse Now**, among many other works.

Nicolas wanted to be an actor, a good actor, one who is taken seriously for his skills, not just for his name. A famous name is a commodity in and of itself, it opens doors, but at a price. Someone helped you to do it, you didn't accomplish this all on your own, it was a recent descendant who moved and shook the world to create the fame. *(George W. Bush anyone?)* If Nicolas really wanted to get work based on his skills alone, he would have to ditch his famous name. Say goodbye to Nicholas Coppola, say hello to Nicolas Cage. And it all happened for him. His art has earned the accolades he has strived and worked so hard to achieve.

And where did the Cage name come from? It came from the comic books, the adventure and art he so admired when he was an adolescent boy. *(Awesome imagery, eh?— part of your brain thinks that you are the superhero, and super-human power is so seductive to a teenage boy...)* There was a black superhero named Luke Cage that he gravitated toward. Nic adopted the name as his own. Then he took on the world in his own way—and won. In one way you could say Nic Cage is like a superhero—he has a secret identity, a mild-mannered alter-ego... *(It looks like the comic book has come full circle for Nicolas—by the time this book gets printed his new movie,* **Ghost Rider***, a big-budget version of another comic book superhero, should be coming soon to theatres or a DVD store near you. Also, in an even fuller* *circle, acclaimed director John Singleton has been tapped to helm the big Hollywood version of '**Luke Cage**', but as far as I know, Nicolas 'Coppola' is not in it, not yet anyway. Personally, I think he should be, don't you? Come on Nic, use some of that fame.)*

It's fair to say that Nic is an artist, he creates performances that are caught on film, and artists want to be known for their work, for what they conceive and fabricate—it's real currency in the social world, this recognition by everyone else, including your peers. This goes for all kinds of artwork, from film to this book. It all gets created and judged in the court of Popular *(Public)* Opinion, but the world isn't fair. A famous name can skew things both for you and against you.

A not-nearly-so-famous (but getting there) singer-songwriter by the name of Dan Bern (www.danbern.com) has penned a poignant tune about the fictional son of a most famous painter and the problems that his famous name prompts. Listen in on the life of 'Joe' Van Gogh...

Joe Van Gogh is a friend of mine
He's the son of Vincent Van Gogh, you know
Joe has more friends than you do
And Joe Van Gogh is a painter too

I've shared a room with Joe Van Gogh
And all night long he grinds his teeth
It could be genetic, it could be the heat
It's pressure to paint that's my belief

This I'll tell you 'cause this I know
I'm a valuable friend to Joe Van Gogh
I'm the only painter Joe Van Gogh knows
That wasn't first friends with Vincent Van Gogh

Joe Van Gogh is a very good painter
Some sunflowers sure but other stuff, too
But how good a painter we'll never know
'til he gets away from Vincent Van Gogh

An umbilical cord of red Day-Glo
Runs from one to the other though
Through the streets of Amsterdam they go
Joe on the shoulders of Vincent Van Gogh

Joe Van Gogh has a second floor window
With a scene of Amsterdam below
He sits at a canvas with a Marlboro
In his mind, *Van Gogh, Van Gogh, Van Gogh!*

Vincent Van Gogh is good to Joe
He gave his son his ear you know
But it can't be easy being Joe Van Gogh
Trying to paint when your dad is Vincent Van Gogh

People write songs about Vincent Van Gogh
Like Starry Starry Night and other ones, too
And it don't exactly even the score I know
But here's one song about Joe Van Gogh...

If you'd like to hear some more of this talented artist *(he paints and draws too, but his music is what blows me away)* go to his website or see him live in concert. He tours a lot, either solo or with his back-up band, ***The International Jewish Banking Conspiracy***, affectionately known as the ***IJBC***. Musically, they all know their stuff and put together one great and entertaining show—I've seen them switch instruments at The Bowery Ballroom in NYC *during* an encore while playing The Monkees' *'(I'm Not Your) Steppin' Stone'*.

Dan Bern knows the value of 'celebrity' too—Van Gogh isn't on the cover of many magazines, but Tiger Woods has been. Dan has a song titled *'**Tiger Woods**'. (A parody* *of course, the lyrics embrace the benefits of 'big balls'...)* Dan doesn't solely focus on the famous though, he has plenty of other catchy songs, some about himself, but he is *VERY* creative in weaving pop culture throughout his art. Listen and you'll hear tales of: Madonna, Keith Richards, Prince, Pete Rose, Bart Giamatti, Eminem, Bob Dylan, Bruce Springsteen, Monica Seles, Marilyn Monroe, Britney Spears, PJ Harvey, Ani DiFranco, Woody Guthrie, Pee Wee Herman, Adolph Hitler, Charles Darwin, Charlie (Krautmeyer) Manson, God, and the ever popular Jesus Christ. *(It sounds like a party, and you're invited!)* There are plenty more, but you get the idea; he's so creative. Enjoy his art, I do.

He doesn't have a song including Tom Cruise, and that's a good thing—the media and rumor mill and social posturing have turned Tom Cruise into headline gold, but at his expense *(and benefit—people stay interested in him even if it is a wrongly placed interest)*. Who among us is perfect? And while we go to his movies *(he is the only movie star to headline five consecutive films grossing over $100,000,000 each)*, we also love to know about his private life, his trials and tribulations—we live vicariously through our celebrities, but again, they are just artists, just people with a passion like a lot of us. Why do we care so? Now you know. We assign them their importance, and we watch closely, too closely at times. We nit-pick at Thomas Cruise Mapother *[MAY-pah-thur]*.

Luckily Tom is used to it. When he was younger, not only was he fighting the learning disorder dyslexia, but his nomadic and sometimes splintered family traveled around from town to town and school to school. Tom was used to being picked on for being the new kid, for being different. *(Remember Chapter 6—Welcome to the Dark Side? Tom learned at an early age to ignore small comments from small minds.)* It's no wonder that he grew especially close to his mother and three sisters—they had to rely on each other.

When he was younger, an older male relative offered to pay to send him to a private parochial school, but his sisters were offered nothing. Tom's mentality can hardly be described as 'boys are better than girls'. How could it when his formative years found him surrounded by so many loving and supportive women?

An actor wants to please people—it's their job. They want their art to be judged and found worthy. In essence, an artist gives of themselves, and you decide whether or not it's worth the giving. What is there of value to this effort?

Tom isn't any different. *(Are you?)* I suppose that he liked to please his family, and his early forays onto the stage allowed him to take on another persona, to act, and his performance was judged as pleasing. Plus, with his drifting circumstances, it must have been nice to be noticed for something other than just being 'the new kid in town'.

There's one thing that you can say about Tom Cruise, he is passionate about life. Life isn't perfect, but it should be experienced with gusto, eaten for its flavors. Tom has become a student of life, and out of his experience he builds his own life, as well as creating the lives of his on-screen characters.

When performing, he doesn't discount anything that the character would say or do, including things distasteful even to himself. *(It was his idea, not Spielberg's, in **Minority Report**, that his character be responsible for and emotionally shattered by the abduction of his son.)* His allegiance is to the acting, the performance, the art—and he's playing a person. This may be a fictional person, but to Tom this person has a background, has yearnings, has flaws, and he plays that character many different ways sometimes, exploring the nuances—all of them with passion, spontaneity, integrity, and an insight into humanity. Look at the other stars who have fed off his energy and raised their own acting and art even higher *(Paul Newman, anyone? Martin Scorsese's **The Color of Money** was also an*

acting tour de force. **Doom,** *The '#1 video-game of all time'*
[GameSpy 2001] took its name from a Tom Cruise line in
this movie—while entering a pool hall someone asked what
he was carrying in his case; it was a custom pool cue, but his
arrogant and unlikable character, Vincent, responded,
"Doom..."); the list is long, but I really loved hearing about
that scene with Dustin Hoffman at the end of **Rain Man**
when the brothers have to part ways.

It was tender, with Raymond gently putting his head
on Charlie's shoulder, and Tom Cruise, as Charlie Babbitt,
responded also with silent touching emotion and a sense of
wonder and surprise at his own level of connection.   The
scene was powerful and tender—and unscripted. *Hmmm...*
These might be good words to describe Tom's life now.

Tom could retire today, he doesn't need the money.
He learned where the real money is in Hollywood; when you
control the production you assume the risks, and the
rewards. *(Lucas and Spielberg learned this first, they're*
both worth billions.) But when you surround yourself with
talented and loyal people and have an already-established
world-wide social following, it's safe to say that the risks
have been minimized and the rewards quite maximized.
Tom, as producer and star *(and stunt man),* took home over
$70 million dollars for each **Mission: Impossible** movie,
both 1 and 2—and number 3 will no doubt be just as
lucrative. *(Paramount Pictures is a little miffed at how*
much money Tom is getting, but that's the deal they made.)
Even when he's not doing the producing he still pockets $20-
30 million at a clip, or more.

He has millions of dollars, he loves to fly and owns a
WWII P-51 Mustang named *Montana Miss;* Tom can pretty
much do anything Tom wants. So what does he want to do?
What does he find enjoyable?

Being with your family and kids, that goes without
saying. But Tom finds other things enjoyable. There's his
art. He loves the art of making movies. Sure they earn tons

of money, but he loves the art aspect, too. When he was younger, he read about the Samurai code of honor and bravery, the Bushido *[buh-SHE-doe]*, and years later he got to explore that facet of his youth while making **The Last Samurai**.

He is doing more than making a movie for you, he is making the movie for himself. In making it, he learns, he grows, he laughs and smiles at a job well done. And in the end, when the movie makes a ton of money, he gets to give a lot of that money away, he gets to support a lot of the things that he believes in. It's his money and his prerogative.

Tom Cruise is powerful—his fame and fortune have made him so. Tom is also tender, he cares about people in general. He sees that people, based on his experience, are suffering—and it's in his nature to help. *(He spent a year at an Ohio seminary, studying to become a priest, answering a call to serve; he's thought about religion and the human condition deeply. I, too, was active in my church and entertained thoughts of becoming a priest as a boy, but while this calling may have been strong, my love of science and girls—not necessarily in that order—was somewhat stronger. I took a pass on the priesthood.)* Tom's life is also unscripted. It is filled with future adventure that even he has no inkling of.

And what about your life? You should live life like Tomas Cruise Mapother IV. Not with his riches and fame *(though you can try, see how well you do)*, but with his outlook. It's one designed and refined with happiness in mind. Your life is filled with future adventure, too. *(Think of yourself as the producer, director, and star of an independent film,* **My Life**, *one with only a bare-bones script, you'll need to improvise along the way... And... Action!)* Whatever it is that you do in this world for a living, either for monetary gain, your job, or anything you do to define yourself, invest more of yourself, be more passionate about it all. Invest energy, invest pride. No one has to notice you doing it, but you'll know it. You do it for yourself. And soon others will notice something has changed about you even if they don't quite know just what it is. You'll carry yourself differently, you'll believe more in your own self-worth as a human with a purpose. You've discovered a passion. It's in you—you possess the passion, the lust for life. Invest in your family and invest in your work. If you have a hobby, an art form that turns you on, from belly-dancing to snowmobiling, invest in that too.

From an actor who makes his living manipulating light comes a call to action. Learn to live life. I have to agree. I am living and learning, and then living some more. To see Tom revel in his passion, check out any of his movies, but especially **Born on the Fourth of July**, directed by Oliver Stone. You may wind up appreciating the depth of the acting, of Tom's on-screen art, but his passionate portrayal of disabled Vietnam war veteran, Ron Kovic, may also move you to appreciate what you take for granted in life, like walking.

You've been given a gift, but you've also been thrust into a world that your brain was not born into. Take advantage of this world, but beware the imagery designed to take your breath away. There is magic and manipulation in the image, imagine that. Put down the magazine, turn off the TV, walk away from the theatre; if you are blessed with two working eyes, use them to gaze in real time upon that which matters to you, your world. See life as it happens to you, witness your own insanely wide vista—whether from a city sidewalk or a canyon's viewing platform, it doesn't really matter. Go live once in a while, it's the Stone Age way. And your brain likes it this way, look around, won't you?

Now it's your turn to define beauty and grandeur. How lucky is that?

The Bigger Picture

or

David in a block of Stone

Humanity suffers from what I call 'New York City Syndrome'. It goes a little something like this. A long time ago there were deer and turkey roaming Manhattan island, before the Europeans came. The Dutch settled New York, displacing the Native Americans already there, and began calling it 'New Amsterdam'. ('Old' York is in merry old England; more recent landlords would eventually change the name. And who gets to be the landlords? The ones who can take it by force, of course. When English colonists moved in the Dutch couldn't stop them. After the Revolutionary War the British wanted New York, and all the rest, back from those upstart Colonial Americans, and in 1812 they went to war to take what they wanted. They were repelled. You don't always get what you want.)

The Dutch were sailors extraordinaire (Henry Hudson was English, but he was also 'for hire')—New York harbor is an extension of the Hudson River, a wide navigable waterway that boats could easily traverse to the settlements of Albany and Troy. And then it was possible to travel even further into the state's interior via the Mohawk River nestled in its picturesque valley. Eventually the Erie Canal would be constructed, a man-made river with adjustable 'locks' that connected this natural river system to the Great Lakes, meaning ships from the ocean could now reach Buffalo, Cleveland, Detroit, Chicago and other major 'water cities' (interior access via the St. Lawrence River from the ocean was blocked by Niagara Falls)—all this access to water meant that much of the country, and its economy, was accessible to New York. The city grew and prospered accordingly. *(Tiny Portville, south of Buffalo where I grew up, lies on the shores of the Allegany River—this waterway flows southward, to Pittsburgh, where it combines with the Monongahela River to form the Ohio River. This in turn joins the mighty Mississippi River. From little Portville, in western New York State, you can reach New Orleans and the Gulf of Mexico by boat, and then anyplace else the ocean touches... First Portville, next stop—The World)*

The rivers surrounding New York City generated its wealth. You can build boats and float your goods on the water—there is little friction. You can paddle your canoe full of beaver skins and move downstream, or raise sail on your warship and travel upstream to the U.S. Military Academy at West Point, or maybe even load up the steam-powered paddleboat full of tourists for a quick circle-cruise around Manhattan island—*up the Hudson, over into the Harlem River, down the East River, back into the harbor...*

Look at NYC now; is it any wonder that she's the biggest city in the U.S.? With over eight million souls living there (and I used to be one of them), I can tell you what really drives city dwellers crazy. It's the traffic.

America's largest and most commercial city is centered on an island. By definition, it's surrounded by water. This used to be a good thing. We populated the Big Apple when there used to be wild apple trees growing where they will. This was a time before cars, before railroads, before petroleum and electricity. This was the era of the whaling ship. The Navy was King of the Ocean. Water, and floating on it, was a Stone Age technology that served us well for millennia. It took us across the oceans and up and down our rivers. *(After America won its independence, our thoughts turned to the Navy and our own future protection. Military engineers proposed building ships made of steel— but early government politicians of the day were farmers, not* engineers. *They balked at first because they didn't understand the science of density and floating. "Are you crazy? Metal ships will sink, it's wood that floats—you scientists are silly." As it turns out, the scientists weren't so foolish...)* Access to water meant wealth in monetary goods and an increase in the standard of living. Think of this period of initial growth as 'Stone Age New York'—then things changed.

The modern Industrial Revolution transformed the city. Water transport can only take you so far, you're limited to the coasts *(unless you have a handy river or canal—and New York had it all).* But railroads and highways are made by men, not nature, they can connect interior cities that used to be isolated. *Water was so Stone Age, pavement is the new wave...* Fossil fuels, along with roads and wheels, can transform the unbridled environment into one that's more modern, more metal and plastic, more constructed and paved.

So now we build bridges and tunnels to connect New York with the mainland. *('Metro'NY, to include bits of New Jersey and Connecticut, is home to twenty-one million Americans and foreigners.)* Look at a map of the entire United States. At a glance, look and see where the greatest nexus of major highways is located—and there you'll find New York. The Erie Canal as King no longer exists, it's been usurped by upstart I-90; take the Interstate, it's faster... *(Of all these United States, New York, the Empire State, has the most Interstate highways: 29)*

New York City Syndrome. The city was founded in the 'Stone Age', but now it lives in 'modern times' *(reminds me of you)*, and things have changed. Water used to be valued economically, now it causes traffic snarls and works against economy *(of New York's five boroughs, only two touch, Queens and Brooklyn, and yet the social and monetary economy still grow thanks to human perseverance, the overcoming of adversity)*. The bridges and tunnels of

New York are a place that you do not want to be during 'rush' hour, though I think this time-period should more accurately be called 'crush' hour with its trucks and cars all crammed together. *(The Long Island Expressway is often referred to as the 'Long Island Parking Lot'...)*

New Yorkers are forced to deal with their water-generated limitations—it's tough, but what choice do you have if you're tied to this place in its modern times? *(Mayor Michael Bloomberg is 'stepping back in time' to help solve NYC's growing traffic problem—only now it's air traffic he's concerned about, LaGuardia and JFK airports are already 'maxxed-out'. His solution? Seaplanes. Use the waterways as runways. Short commuter flights land in the harbor and then taxi into downtown Manhattan docks.)* New York has a lot of bridges and tunnels to try and ease congestion, but they are not enough—imagine the ease of moving around *if there were no rivers* around New York... But modern New Yorkers do not have that luxury. *(Wouldn't it be nice if, on the human landscape, **there were no racist people**? But modern humans do not have that luxury.)* They have to deal, and some deal better than others with the modern problems that ensue from a city formed with Stone Age values.

Look at yourself.   Your body and brain were developed, honed, in an earlier time, one before science and machines. But things change. The brain goes from dealing with living in a small group, to living with several million strangers in the city *(several hundred million on a national scale, several billion on the planetary)*. There used to be might-makes-right, now there is government and law protecting the weak and victimized. We used to worry about food and shelter for the winter, now we stress over mortgages and weddings, tuition and gasoline. The human brain is suffering from social and scientific advancement the same way New York is.   Sure there are modern conveniences and 'civilized' society, but there are also growing pains, the new ways clash with the old thinking. Listen closely and you'll hear the crunch of fender-benders, or gunshots, when things get really crossed.

Like NYC, the brain was formed in a more primitive time but has been thrust inside the glare of a modern electric spotlight. Our Stone Age desires and sexual posturing have not left us, nor have our animal emotions or bodily functions. Our chemistry is basically constant, from the Stone Age and earlier, but look at how the world has changed. We are stuck the way New Yorkers are stuck, you can't make the rivers go away, and neither can you banish your Stone Age background. You are forced to deal with the cards that are dealt.

Nature produced you, but you interpret nature with your evolved, animal, Stone Age senses, and your brain. Don't think of a forest or meadow or ocean devoid of humans as representing nature; nature is the city, too. You are nature—and forms tend to repeat, only on different scales. You are a city unto yourself.

Food, power, and water are shipped in, the wastes are sent out. There are museums and libraries filled with memories, new buildings are going up *(marrow becomes bone)*, old buildings are going down *(sloughing off of skin cells)*. There are systems in the city, and in you. Both evolved ways to treat the injured, to protect the populous from outside attackers intent on taking and destroying. The roads supporting and feeding the cities are called arteries, and the big ones branch off into local highways, then city streets, then even smaller residential roads. Cars are like red corpuscles; some eventually travel single file along a capillary in search of an address. The blood-platelet and the car deliver their package of energy and potential to the cell or a home, which are also similar—both have protective outer walls, they have nutrients and waste actively and passively passing to an fro. *(Glucose in one case, groceries in the other.)*

There is a smaller picture. There is a bigger picture. What you see and what you feel, as Helen Keller would readily tell you, can be expanded beyond your wildest dreams. I said 'can' be expanded; if you want happiness you are in luck, it can be built—but only by you.

Knowing how people and nature work, this can make you wise in the world's eyes *(I've felt the gaze)*, but knowing about yourself fosters enlightenment. And with enlightenment comes serenity, happiness, peace, and hopefully love.

So how do you build happiness? You build it the way you build anything else, you focus on it. I believe that I gave the *'Do you know Chinese?'* speech since the first year I started teaching. This was an 'opening day' motivational address meant to ease the fears of many students who regarded science as 'tough', difficult to learn. *(It's prejudice, it's Stereotype Vulnerability—How can I succeed when it's so difficult?)* My response is that you can learn science, and you can also learn the Chinese language. "Do you know Chinese?" I would ask, "Can you speak it?" Most of us cannot, and we find the grasping of its musical prose and varied pictograms extremely daunting, or in using my students' vernacular; *that sounds 'hard'*. But there is hope. With a reason, and with determination, you can learn any foreign language. You have that power inside you, just waiting to be released. *(And besides, 'hard' is good—we learn more when things are challenging, and upon accomplishment we will smile even wider. As President John F. Kennedy once said, getting to the moon won't be easy, but it's the challenge, the 'hardness', that will inspire us.)*

It wouldn't be easy at first, the Chinese language is foreign and unfamiliar after all to many of us, but you can sit and focus your attention. You could read English-to-Chinese dictionaries, look at textbooks, listen to a teacher recite the words and then try to recite them back. *(Ecouter et répété... Ou est la bibliothèque? Sorry, three years of le Français coming to bear.)* "You can learn the Chinese language if you want to," I would say to my science students. "All it takes is time, effort, and focus." If students wanted to learn and earn a good grade in my science class *(or any class, I told them)*, all they needed to contribute was their time, their energy, and their focused attention. Want to build a giant pyramid? Whether located in the Egyptian or Nevada desert the demands remain the same—time, effort, and focus produced those puppies. Want some happiness in your life? Time, effort, and human focus are here to assist you.

To read this book takes the aforementioned time, effort, and focus—as did writing it. Never have I put so much of those three things into any endeavor of my life as I have in producing these words, and by investing in myself I have built some happiness, my friends and family would say that I've built quite a bit. They've noticed a change in me for the better.

In a way I'm a little like Tom Cruise. I'm writing this book for you, with hope that it inspires you to tell others, that it will sell well enough to help me monetarily support my family—but I also build this book for me. I've been thinking about writing a book for over ten years, and I've dallied a bit on the side, honing my skills while keeping my day job, but never have I applied such focus, such relentless pressure to achieve a vision. I hope you like it, but if you don't, in the very least I built it for me, and it still makes me smile. I'm lucky. Artists who paint often strive to sell their sweat equity to a single wealthy patron. I, on the other hand, get to share my labor with the world at a much reduced price.

I am a scientist and artist surrounded and enraptured by beauty and grandeur—I've tried to infuse these pages with their energy, to have them somehow resonate, but words were all I had to build with. But I built it anyway, flawed though I am, chip by chip, word by word, and page by page. One printed page is not a lot, but the pages do add up *(try ripping a phone book made of 'flimsy' paper)*. You build your life a day at a time, and one day is not a lot, but the days do add up... Your life is a work of art *(the smaller picture and the bigger picture combine at the same time—Live and in living color, AND in 4D!)* that's a work-in-progress, and it takes time to create, but take an active role, won't you? Apply your focus. What part needs molding?

I've heard an interesting story concerning the one and only Michelangelo and his great marble masterpiece, **David**. At first, there was no statue, just the potential. From the mountainous hillsides a large block of stone was delivered and set up; a 26-year-old Michelangelo was commissioned to create order, to produce a thing of beauty and grandeur out of a 40-year-old flawed block of marble.

On the day he received his official contract, so the story goes, Michelangelo arrived in the morning and looked at the stone until the Italian sun set. The next day the sun rose, and Michelangelo also appeared where he once again spent the naturally illuminated hours just looking at the stone. For thirty days this act repeated, this staring at the stone block, and nervous benefactors and onlookers would wonder if the man had finally lost it. At month's end someone cracked and asked the question that they were all feeling.

"Michelangelo, what are you doing, coming in here day after day but only looking? When are you going to work?"

His response was simple, *"I am working."* David was in the block of stone, just waiting to be released, and it took some time to sit back and think about the options, time to try some variations in your brain before you grabbed your trusty hammer and chisel. And as he saw it in his mind, Michelangelo's mirror neurons fired away; his hands worked the stone many times before they actually touched and chipped the rock. At the end of the month he stood ready. David's path was clear; all he need do was to release the statue that was already there.

This book has been inside me, and it took some time of looking at myself and others before it could be envisioned and created, released from within. What can you build that would make you happier? Think about it. Art readily works as a focus, whether you draw or paint or write or play music; when you invest in the physical human skills that make you happy, you amplify that happiness, so why not invest some more? *(I learned to juggle when I was in college, what a riot—I juggle alone, I smile, I juggle for others, I smile. Juggling, even when I drop the ball, is enough to make me smile.)*

You can invest in love, in another person or spouse. Love is built, as some say, on trust, so I say trust that person you profess to love. If you are in a committed relationship, tell your man, tell your woman, how much they mean to you. Give your gift of time and focus to something you find beautiful, something that you find grand. You won't be disappointed.

Your salaried job may not be about beauty and grandeur, but it is about focus, time, and effort. If you work for someone else, then they are paying you for these things, and you might want to be someplace else—but remember why you are there. The job represents more than a paycheck, it's a way for you to turn your time, focus, and effort into other things. Money is a tool, remember?

You might have a dream of working for yourself, I did. Look to Michelangelo as a guide; spend some time thinking about how you can do that. Put some time, focus, and energy into the project and who knows, some ideas may come to mind. It's possible, maybe pursuing your dream will make you happy, and with continued time, focus and energy, you will be successful. Want to learn Chinese? You can, if

that will make you happy. Think about it. Make a plan.
Write it down. Think about it some more. Make some
changes to the plan, write those down too. Then get started.
(Here is my personal credo in simpler terms: **Think,
Understand, Think, Decide, Do)**

Here's an interesting perspective when it comes to
building anything, it applies to *The David*, and it applies to
your life. No one really knows how a creation is exactly
going to turn out.

Michelangelo would spend days looking and planning,
he would create inside his head, and then he picked up his
tools and got to work. You have ideas for your life, how you
want to build it, shape it; there are themes, areas of
importance. And so the Grand Master chips away at his
project, and your constructed life also takes form with each
rising sun; each are constructions guided by a human mind.

But the details are missing, they are unplanned—but
they happen anyway. Michelangelo didn't see every little
detail when he thought about what he wanted. He wasn't
obsessed with the third knuckle of the left hand, he wasn't
overly concerned about the thickness of an earlobe—and yet
these things were attended to when the time came. He just
went ahead and built them using knowledge and skill.
Sometimes the art is in the details, and the details remain
hidden even to the artist, until they are created in a moment
of focus and effort. There is beauty in the overall statue, but
there is beauty in the details, that's where it gets built after
all. There is grandeur in the human construction. Your day
is filled with tiny details, with a thousand little decisions
that chip away at time like a thousand hammer blows on a
hard block of stone. *(Human life is not static like a statue
though, it is 'kinetic' art.)*

So get started on constructing your life, but take a
clue from Michelangelo and other artists on the value of
looking. I wouldn't be surprised to learn that the stories
about the pensive Italian artist turned out to be true. A

science experiment was performed that studied the painting techniques of both professional and amateur painters. Both types were given the task of creating an image in colored oils of the still-life in front of them. Both artists started, both looked at the objects in question, and then both began dabbing bits of paint on their canvas.

While working, they would both naturally and periodically look back at what they were painting. Some would say that the professional has an advantage, that he or she has innate talent that trumps our untrained amateur. This may be true, but the professional artist does something else, often without even noticing, that the amateur does not. They look more during the mission. Little did our subjects know that their eyes were being followed, and before the pro applies their pigment, they looked back and forth, back and forth, back and forth—much more often than our amateur did. For every artist there are three pictures—the one they see with their eyes, the one in their mind, and the one that's brushed into life. All are important.

Our professional creates a picture in their mind, a picture with details about light and shadow, about color and composition. From the senses to the mind, from the mind to the canvas, and soon a picture will emerge. And when it's done, then someone else can look upon it with senses of their own, they will see the artist's interpretation of light and shadow, color and composition—this will go inside their own brain for analysis, some of it in that automatic Stone Age way we already know about, making it real for themselves.

Creating art can make a person happy, but experiencing art, in any form, can make a person happy too. I love music, both listening and playing/singing *(I used to be a baritone in the Barbershop Quartet)*. I bought my first guitar at age 34 off of **Ebay**, 'America's Garage Sale'; it was a used Ovation acoustic/electric guitar similar to the one Paul Simon made famous. Then I learned how to play it. *(You guessed it, time, energy, and focus was all it took—*

mostly during the commercials, I drafted my downtime into service. I used to watch a lot of TV when I was younger, can you tell? By the way, Paul met his wife, Edie Brickell, while hosting Saturday Night Live one evening—but she was the musical guest, not Paul. Music changed both of their lives. Billy Joel has also confessed that learning how to play the piano turned out to be an excellent way to meet girls...)

Now that I've invested time, energy and focus, I love music even more. And I can relate to Billy—I once had a profile on Match.com to help in attracting a potential mate, and when I changed my primary photo to one of me smiling and playing my guitar, my responses tripled the next day. Guys, you might not be able to change how tall you are or your lack of a chin dimple, but you can learn to play the musical instrument of your choice, and the ladies seem to like it when you sing to them—be you a bullfrog or a whippoorwill, music is a good thing. Invest in yourself, artistically, musically, socially, or otherwise. It pays dividends elsewhere.

So to build happiness you have to look at yourself, find out about what makes you happy and why. Who you are and how you got here—these influence where you are headed. It won't always be easy, but push forward and focus on what's right. You might have to go against your genetics and animal desires at times, but knowing the bigger picture should give you some strength and motivation. Learn to turn obstacles to your advantage.

Here is a good example. Fear of death scares us. And yet I ride a motorcycle. My 65-year-old mother lives in fear of the future accidents that might happen to me. Last summer I rode my motorcycle 2,500 miles in a round-trip between New York and Florida to visit my ailing mother _(her back surgery was not healing at the rate that she was originally led to expect—the pain was excruciating)_. She told me **not** to come to Florida if I was riding the motorcycle. But I couldn't afford to fly or drive at the time, plus I was also looking forward to the adventure, my biggest to date in two-wheel traveling. Despite my mother's fears, I rode my bike down anyway—and loved it.

My mother lives in fear, and that's sad. Her big, smart, inherited brain has not brought her happiness. Instead, it has brought her images of things that might go wrong. Scene after scene roll through her private mental screening room, and her big brain analyzes what it 'sees' and concludes, "it's real, my boy is in trouble". Well, it is not real. What *might happen* is not what *always happens*. Sure there is risk, but that's life. Here are the pictures that my brain sees when I think of a long motorcycle trip. It sees a blue sky with white clouds. It sees a curving strip of asphalt meandering through an American panorama. It sees other bikers passing by in the opposite direction; they are strangers in name only, these anonymous men and women smile and wave at me as they ride by—we have a brotherhood of the road. It makes me feel special and accepted.

Of course it rains sometimes when you are on the road. Of course the bike can have a mechanical problem that strands you. *(Robert Pirsig's **Zen and the Art of Motorcycle Maintenance**, anyone?)* There are lots of things that can go wrong, but that's not why you ride, that's not why you smile. But what can you do if you want to go on a long trip? You have to deal with the rain just as you would the sunshine, and in the end the rain helps you to appreciate the sunshine even more.

Fear of death does not keep me from my motorcycle. Happiness is my goal, and riding through nature, whether along a mountain road or stopped at a light in midtown Manhattan, stimulates my life. If I get caught in the rain, I'll curse, but then I'll smile. There will be sunny days as well.

You have to play the cards you are dealt, and the big brain that you've inherited can play tricks on you, can undermine what it is that you really want. You can't defend against the tricks though if you are just blowing in the wind—you need direction, a purpose. Hopefully, this book has given you some perspective.

Is death the end? Regardless of the existence of the 'afterlife', I know for a fact there exists a 'livinglife'—I'm living it right now. Fear of death isn't a happy thought, but I use it to my advantage all the time. I am blessed with an unknown number of days, as are you, and the same goes for Steven Spielberg and the richest people on the planet. But the end comes to us all, and a billion dollars will not buy anyone another day. From this perspective it's easy to see what it is you really possess that's of true value. Time.

Animals live for the moment. Their tiny brains can't fathom the concept of 'five years from now'. You're an animal too, but one with a big brain. As an animal you live in the moment, but unlike the other animals you possess a big brain that also lets you know with certainty that you are mortal; there is a shapeless danger of death that looms somewhere ahead. We naturally try to avoid danger, but we cannot avoid death, and this is cause for plenty of stress. We don't think about this unpleasant outlook too often when we are younger, maybe that's why we try to look older. And then when we are older and wiser, that's when we try to look younger—we emulate an earlier day when life was happier and more carefree. Do we ever get it 'just right'?

I say be happier now. See more. Do more. Be more. Do this everyday. Do it for little things. Do it for big things. Focus on serenity and progress. Close your eyes, what do you see? Play some movies inside your head—now change the movie. Don't wait for Hollywood, do it yourself. Now open your eyes. Many of us would appreciate our eyes or ears a lot more if they were taken away for a while and then returned. Some people have come close to death, and when they return to the world of the living they have a new appreciation for life. ***Do you have to be out of time to appreciate the time that you have now?***

The greatest asset you have, is time. It's hard to do a lot of different things at the same time—I can't teach the basics of physics in a classroom and be riding down the highway at the same moment *(it would be fun to try—pay attention students as I lean into a tight curve).* Ours is a serial existence, minute by minute, hour by hour, day by day, one moment bleeds into the next—where do you spend your time? When you work overtime at the job, what else could you be doing with that time? Watching TV? Reading a book? Listening to music? Holding your daughter's hand? Calling a friend or a family member on the phone to hear about their day? You can't do these things when you are working—you trade your time for money, and you have to in today's modern economy. Whoever said 'time is money' knew what they were talking about, but money is also time. It's that duality again, people forget that, but it's also not exactly a one-to-one relationship. We chase after money, because money can be made, it can be multiplied. Time cannot be made. Time cannot be multiplied. When the day is done you can't get it back. We work for money, and you need money for things, but what things do you need? Do you need some things because of social pressures? Because of advertising? Because of fear?

Open your eyes. What's important? What ***should*** be important? You can spend time and you can spend money—is time more valuable than money? Who decides your values? I have had friends that died young—some while in their teens, twenties, or their thirties. My life has been enhanced by having these people as my friends, and in their forced absence they have enhanced my life even more. They missed out on many years of their lives, and each would give much to see a sunset or hear a child's laughter or to hold someone's hand. But we are here, left behind to live. My deceased friends and family would want me to smile, to laugh, to appreciate the time that has been given to me. And so I live my remaining days knowing about nature, about knowing how humanity is sometimes blind to the beauty and grandeur that surrounds us and infuses us. I am not blind, my eyes have been opened even when they are closed. I see more. I do more. I am more. And I appreciate life more.

Your senses are a gift. Your life is a gift. Nature and the Cosmos are also gifts. So why get bent out of shape over something someone else said in anger? Why get bent out of shape when the weather turns? Why get bent out of shape over what might have been? People who commit suicide don't do so because they are happy, they are angry and sad, they don't see a bright future, they focus on the past pain and the continuance of anguish. Fight it. Fight the conditioning, the genetic and social programming. All is not lost, there is actually a lot to gain. The future is unwritten.

You may have heard about the mysterious mass-beachings of whales onto dangerous shorelines. These large creatures are sometimes pushed back into the sea by concerned humans, but the whales often swim back onto the sand where they eventually die. Why do they do it? Are they unhappy with life? We can't ask the whales, we can only speculate, but one logical theory believes that whales do this because of social and genetic conditioning. Whales are social mammals, there is a leader to their 'pod', and they are conditioned to 'follow the leader' through millions of years of social living. But what happens when that leader becomes flawed? Maybe the leader develops a brain disorder that screws up their navigation or normal desires. When the leader beaches itself they can't help it, there is something wrong, and the rest of the whales *(who have led a rather slow-moving and unchallenged life)* do what they have always done, they follow the leader without thinking, assuming that their leader is always correct. Whales are not as advanced as humans *(but some humans still behave like whales, yes?)*, they have trouble with analyzing things that are not usual; they think about the moment, they think like animals, and there is great animal pressure to be social, to do what's expected, even if those actions go against what should be right.

Humans are animals, too—are we so different? Look at Hitler (kill all those who don't conform). Look at Jim Jones and his followers in Guyana (kill your children then kill yourselves). Look at 'murder' bombings in the name of God. These are popularly called '*suicide*' bombings as a person who 'gives up their life' for a cause or an ideal does so supposedly selflessly. *(A dog can be taught and trained to kill, to be conditioned, but that doesn't make a dog evil. Consider the source, many foreign terrorists were raised as children in an environment of hate; they are vicious human 'Pit Bulls'. No human is immune to this disease; think of American children raised by 'loving' white-supremacist parents, they are also taught to despise, to deride, to hate. And why? Because of social differences, because of fear, because of group dynamics. It's the Stone Age way, it's uncivilized and selfish, and it's also natural. People can learn, and so can dogs; Pit Bulls may have earned a bad rap, but I've encountered plenty who were raised as loving and happy canines, even around strangers. Does anybody remember 'Spuds MacKenzie'?)* Giving up your life, or your 'time', can be seen as a wonderful gift—but the bomber has taken other lives, has taken time, has taken happiness, all in a bid to hurt others—they *murder* in the name of malice, not God.

We know about hurting, we know about violence, we know about fear, we know about these things because they got us here, they built us up in an earlier time. But this is not where we have to go. During the Cold War *(the 80's)*, when Carl Sagan was working tirelessly (and I say successfully) to inform the world population about the folly of all-out Nuclear War, Sting *(lead singer of **The Police**)* penned an interesting song titled **Russians**. The premise was that our 'Russian enemy' with their communistic diatribe were loving parents too, just like us. We focus on our differences because that's what's normal, it's the Stone Age 'acting out'. But books like this one show that we are learning, we are realizing, we are understanding each other (and ourselves) better than ever before. Sting was right, we spend too much time focusing on ideology and disagreements, when we should be more concerned with biology and the similarities that join us together—we all love our children, right?

In Spike Lee's entertaining and challenging 1989 movie, **Do The Right Thing**, there is a call to 'wake up'; is social rage justifiable? To me rage is normal, it's Stone Age, it served its purpose. But Spike is trying, like myself and Carl Sagan, to get the point across: *What do we ultimately gain when we act on our animal rage?* We three thinkers are putting you to task—do you see who we actually are? Do you see how we aren't that civilized yet? But we are making progress, some of us hear the logical message: **Focus on the Bigger Picture—choose happiness, not derision.** Things can change, they can evolve for the better, for you as a person and for humanity as a whole. People do listen to logic; they've listened to Spike Lee, they've listened to Dr. Sagan, and now it's my turn to carry that banner high.

You can make a difference in your life, even if the social group as a whole is still caught up in Stone Age madness. I believe that the terrorist and murder-bomber would act differently if they knew just how closely related we all are, if they knew how connected everything is, if they knew how precious life should be. Why don't they know these things? Because they haven't been taught these things, they have leaders that guide them along other— more limited and skewed—paths of thought. With Islam, as with any religion, you can focus on peace, if you want to, but hatred of outsiders is also easy. *(And it's natural—but you can fight this programming when the landscape changes, and the social landscape has changed. Just look at the 'recent' developments of law and government. We can't keep you from hating others, but we can punish you for acting on those selfish and destructive impulses. Set your malice aside, find the reason why you hate; have you been conditioned like a dog? Does everything have to be your way or else? We are a complex and primitive people who are prone to disagreements, violence, and social posturing. Time to start thinking, to begin understanding. It's time to rise above your genetics. Open your eyes, use your gift.)*

Who are your leaders? Why do you think the thoughts that you do? Have you tried to understand other people? Why do we have stereotypes? Why do we have animosity? Why do we spend so much of our time worrying?

Be like Michelangelo. Look long and hard on the block of stone that is to become your life. Sure, your past wasn't perfect, and your future won't be either, but perfection is not your goal. Your goal is serenity, peace and happiness in your world, and you can have it. Your future is built by you, learn to be a better builder. Learn about new tools, learn new skills—go ahead, make some mistakes, you'll learn from those too. Learn to be passionate and happy. Be sincere and honest with yourself; understand how this world works and what you do with that knowledge while you are here. Knowing about nature and humanity can help you be happier. Will it? Good luck with that, I'm pulling for you.

My name is David Gardner—Today is Tuesday, May 23rd, 2006. It's 2:33 in the afternoon. It's unseasonably cold here in the Adirondack Mountains for the month of May, and life is very good. I have finally finished what I set out to do, writing this book. And now for the next book... After some time spent celebrating the completion of this one of course. It's not every day that you think, understand, think some more, decide, and then do. But you should. Every day. And so should I. It's easier said than done, but persevere and do it anyway—learn to shine, to give off energy even as you absorb it. Be a beacon. Be yourself— only better. Some leaders do have your best interests in mind: Follow my example, create your own passion, find out what value there is in living. Grab your skills, your senses, and your brain—it's time for you to leave the well-house on an adventure. You're lucky, there's a lot to be excited about.

It's Sunday, June 25th, and it has been a tough month of traveling and editing. Still, I'm quite pleased with the flow of words, the art continues to help me smile. I'm so close now, not long now... But I also fear my own version of OCD, of thinking like Tolstoy, that my words will never be perfect... And that's 'O.K.', I've come to grips with my flaws, and this book is a reflection of me. If there are errors or mistakes, I'll 'roll with the punches'. I know that those *faux pas* were made in the light of sincerity, honesty, and truth. I can live with imperfection, I'll have to, right? And since May 23rd, I've heard some new information (new to me anyway) on the connection between stress in our lives and the accelerated physical aging of our bodies. I'm encouraged. This book is all about happiness, about seeing past the stress of your life to focus on the important and beneficial parts of existence. I practice what I preach, and I'm happy to say that my move from the city to the mountains has produced the desired result. I value a mountain's splendor—the jagged horizon line is a living work of art created by the Earth. I'm a work of art that came from the Earth, too. A kinetic, vital, and happy person I am. Fellow Citizen, won't you join me?

No pessimist ever discovered the secrets of the stars, or sailed to an uncharted land, or opened a new heaven to the human spirit.

– Helen Keller

Bibliography, Suggested Reading List, and the Best Music that you've never heard

The vast majority of the information contained in this book was learned by me over three-plus decades thanks to curiosity and focus. I listened to my teachers, I studied textbooks, I read scientific journals and magazines, I've seen Hollywood special effects and serious scientific documentaries. As a science teacher I have discussed and taught many of these topics and their implications to all of my students. In many ways, writing this book made sense to me because I have long been immersed in the wonder of mystery, of uncovering my own story, of benefiting from observation and logic and previously discovered knowledge. What happened to me when I was 9-years-old that inspired me to find out even more? I looked up and saw the moon one day and wondered, "How did it get there?" Eventually I would look at myself and ask a similar question. I am a scientist, a teacher, an author, and an artist—but I am also a human.

Some information (scientific experiments and data) in this book have been recalled from memory, so they are suspect. However, my memory and attention to detail is normally very good. For example, on pg. 117 in the '*Invaders from Venus*' chapter, I mention where I once heard of a science experiment showing that women speak almost 3x as many words per day on average when compared to men. I do not recall where I heard/read this, or the exact numbers, I just remembered that it was 'almost 3x as many'. After completion of this book, I happened to view on 9/26/2006 a regular weekly episode of ABC's news magazine, *20/20*, called *[GENDER] it's bigger than [SEX]*. It was here that they basically documented the same information, but this time with accurate numbers. Women speak 20,000 words per day, men speak only 7,000. The reporter did not document on air where the experimental numbers came from, they may have been citing the very experiment that I heard of years ago. Regardless, the numbers on the recent show validate my memory, 20,000 words per day is 'almost 3x as many' words compared to 7,000. This situation of cerebral recall is also similar to my claim (on pg. 117 as well) that 'physically unattractive men' need to earn $155,000 more per year to get the same response as 'hot male models' in certain Internet 'love match' services. This figure is also from my memory and was first heard when watching either 20/20 or a show similar to it (*60 minutes* or *Primetime* perhaps, I don't recall the show, just the data, my apologies) sometime in 2006. The show in question did not document the study on air, and made no reference to the actual numbers used, just 'the difference' of $155,000, which stuck in my memory. After completion of this book, I still wondered about this number. Why $155,000? After some logical thought I came to the conclusion that $155,000 is the difference between $45,000 and $200,000. It makes sense to me that these were the numbers used. The experiment works by making the 'hot male model' less economically attractive, so let's put him in the 'makes under 50K category'. The stereotypical geek, by saying he is earning 200K a year, puts him in the 'makes 200K or more' category. Again, I do not know the actual numbers used, this is just logical conjecture on my part. My memory and logic may not be perfect, but they are the tools I use get about in this world as I try to make sense of it all.

One of the major goals of Copyright Law is to advance the growth of knowledge. I have used short passages and quotes in this book in order to facilitate understanding and knowledge; this can be done legally without obtaining written permission if it is done according to established guidelines. This book is all about social commentary, and I've sincerely tried to use all excerpts from other authors in a 'transformative' sense, meaning that I've used their original intent to illustrate a related concept as it applies to my book's (or chapter's) theme. As such, this type of use is protected, especially in non-fiction works of social commentary, by the *fair use doctrine*. In addition, my use of previously copyrighted material has been done in such a way as to enhance the author's words, to expose my readers to published works that they may have never considered or even heard of. If anything, I would hope that if this book becomes successful and widely read, that new sales of the other mentioned books (fiction and non-fiction), and other works from mentioned authors as well, will also increase. I did however ask for written permission from musician Dan Bern to use his entire song, *Joe Van Gogh*, and he graciously granted it.

Bakker, Robert T., *Raptor Red*, New York: Bantam Books, 1995

Brown, Dan, *Angels & Demons*, New York: Simon & Schuster, 2000

Buck, Pearl S., *The Good Earth*, New York: John Day, 1931

Charles, Ray, and David Ritz, *Brother Ray*, New York: Dial Press, 1978

Darwin, Charles, *On The Origin of Species*, London: John Murray, 1859

Gore, Al, *An Inconvenient Truth*, New York: Rodale Press, 2006

Gray, John, *Men are From Mars, Women are From Venus*, New York: Harper Collins, 1992

Hawking, Stephen, *A Brief History of Time*, New York: Bantam, 1988

Jackson, Beverley, *Splendid Slippers: A Thousand Years of an Erotic Tradition*, Berkeley, CA: Ten Speed Press, 1998

Keller, Helen, *The Story of My Life*, New York: Doubleday, Page & Company, 1905

King, Stephen, *Skeleton Crew*, New York: G.P. Putnam's Sons, 1985

King, Stephen (Richard Bachman), *Thinner*, New York: NAL, 1984

Levin, Ira, *The Boys from Brazil*, New York: Random House, 1976

Lowell, Amy, *Robert Frost: The Man and His Work*, New York: Holt, 1923

Martin, Del, *Battered Wives*, Volcano, CA: Volcano Press, 1976

Morris, Desmond, *The Human Zoo*, New York: McGraw-Hill, 1969

Morris, Desmond, *The Naked Ape*, New York: McGraw-Hill, 1967

Pirsig, Robert, *Zen and the Art of Motorcycle Maintenance*, New York: Morrow, 1974

Read, Piers Paul, *Alive*, Philadelphia: Lippincott, 1974

Sagan, Carl and Ann Druyan, *Shadows of Forgotten Ancestors*, New York: Random House, 1992

Tolstoy, Leo, *War and Peace*, Russia: Russki Vestnik, 1865-69 (series)

Trumbo, Dalton, *johnny got his gun*, Philadelphia: Lippincott, 1939

Verne, Jules, *Around the World in Eighty Days*, Paris: Hetzel, 1872

Vonnegut, Kurt, *Galapagos*, New York: Delacorte Press/Seymour Lawrence, 1985

Vonnegut, Kurt, *The Sirens of Titan*, New York: Delacorte Press/Seymour Lawrence, 1959

Wells, Spencer, *The Journey of Man: A Genetic Odyssey*, Princeton, NJ: Princeton University Press, 2002

These other books have also made a significant impact on me:

NON-FICTION

Carl Sagan: *Cosmos, The Dragons of Eden , Broca's Brain, Billions & Billions*
Martin Gardner: *The Relativity Explosion*
Nathan Spielberg, Bryon D. Anderson: *Seven Ideas that Shook the Universe*
Slavomir Rawicz: *The Long Walk*
Og Mandino: *The Greatest Salesman in the World*
Denis Waitley: *The Seeds of Greatness*

FICTION

The best novelist working today (for my money) is Jeffrey Deaver. Read ANY of his books for characters that come alive, action with a breakneck pace, and plot developments that are smart, satisfying, and amazing: the Lincoln Rhyme novels, *The Bone Collector* and *The Empty Chair* for example, also read his techno-thriller, *The Blue Nowhere*, and Hitler-era based thriller, *Garden of Beasts: A Novel of Berlin 1936*

If you've never read any Jack London, what are you waiting for? The *Call of the Wild* and *White Fang* are perennial favorites, and I believe that his haunting short story, *To Build a Fire*, is the best short story ever written. You can read it for free on the web.

Stephen King has been pigeon-holed as a 'horror' writer, but first and foremost he is a talented story teller. Some of my favorites include: *'Salem's Lot, The Shining, Christine, Pet Sematary, The Stand, Misery*, and *The Girl Who Loved Tom Gordon*

If you like Frank Herbert's *Dune* series, check out his earlier (even better) novels: *The Dragon in the Sea, Soul Catcher*, and *Hellstrom's Hive*

Piers Anthony is an imaginative and prolific fantasy and science fiction author with dozens and dozens of novels to his credit. Some of my favorites include his **Xanth** and **Incarnations of Immortality** series, but there are many others. Piers is the hardest working writer I know.

Read Isaac Asimov's tour-de-force novels of **The Foundation Trilogy**, these books are legendary giants of the Golden Age of science fiction.

Orson Scott Card is a multi-award winning best-selling science fiction and fantasy novelist: the **Ender** saga and the **Alvin Maker** series are both excellent displays his talent.

The Best Music that you've never heard

Are you like me? Are you a fan of talented musicians (singers, songwriters, instrumental geniuses) regardless of the musical style? Yes, talent cannot be denied, do yourself a favor and check out these fine artists.

Martin Sexton – (martinsexton.com) – What would you get if you could somehow cross Roy Orbison with Jim Morrison? I have to laugh when the Grammys announce 'best male vocalist' – Marty blows them all away. On his version of **Hard Times**, he sings better than Ray Charles and plays better guitar than Eric Clapton. Every song is a winner *(he has been The National Academy of Songwriters "Artist of the Year")*. I don't get to as many concerts as I would like, but I've seen Marty live almost 30 times now. Check out his amazing catalog of albums: **Black Sheep**, **In the Journey**, **The American**, **Wonderbar**, and **Live Wide Open**

Dan Bern – (danbern.com) – Dan is simply amazing for his witty lyrics and changing style. I wouldn't be surprised at all if he gets inducted into the songwriting Hall of Fame. He is prolific and talented, and has been sometimes labeled as a cross between Woody Guthrie and Elvis Costello. Don't believe me? You should. Listen to: **Dan Bern**, **Fifty Eggs**, **Smartie Mine** (economically priced double album), **New American Language**, and **Fleeting Days**

Chaz DePaolo – (chazdepaolo.com) – If you're a big fan of Stevie Ray Vaughn and Jimi Hendrix, then Chaz is the man for you. He is in love with guitar-based blues, all kinds. Buy **Flirtin' with the Blues** today!

Strunz & Farah – (strunzandfarah.com) – These two men are arguably the best guitarists in the world, and they've been playing together since 1979. Jorge Strunz is from Costa Rica, Adeshir Farah is from Iran, and together they weave Latin and Middle Eastern rhythms like you've never experienced. Think of the best guitar players that you've ever heard, and then add these two to the top of your list. Flow, soul, speed, precision, fret-board acrobatics (yes, they play OFF the fret-board at times), they have their own music label, **Selva**. Mostly instrumental, I would listen to their songs endlessly while grading exams or science labs. They make me happy. I particularly like *The Best of Strunz & Farah*, *Strunz & Farah LIVE*, *Heat of the Sun* and *Americas*. Trust me, you won't believe your ears. Then hit replay…

Booth and the Bad Angel – This is the name of the strange and hypnotic collaboration between Tim Booth (from England, lead singer of the group *James*) and Angelo Badalamenti, most famous for providing the emotional soundscapes to many David Lynch projects, to include *Twin Peaks* and *Blue Velvet*. Is it dance music? Is it soulful? Is it an amazing amalgam from two different types of musicians? Yes, it is all these things and more. There is only one album, and that's a shame. Find it where you can.

Ozric Tentacles – (ozrics.hopto.org/ozrics/index.html) – Imagine the instrumental marriage of a psychedelic Pink Floyd and a technical Yes album. They're hard to describe, the music is just fantastic. With over 20 albums to their name, check out my personal favorite, *Erpland*.

J.J. Cale – (jjcale.com) – He's an American musical treasure who wrote Clapton's famous *After Midnight* and *Cocaine*, as well as *They Call Me the Breeze*. Blending Country, Jazz, and Blues, you'll be tappin' your toes when you listen to my favorites: *5* (1979) and *To Tulsa and Back* (2004)

The Knoa – (theknoa.com) – Picture an instrumental blend of Radiohead and Dave Matthews. These guys will rock you silly, enjoy.

Roger Sprung and **Hal Wylie** – They are both Bluegrass legends; Roger has also invented a new type of musical genre by applying his talented 5-string banjo stylings to Irish music, a morphing he calls 'Irish Grass'. Roger has also recorded with legend **Doc Watson**. Jerry Garcia once said something like '*I wish I could play banjo like Roger Sprung*'. Me too Jerry, me too.